ENVIRONMENTAL ECONOMICS

ENVIRONMENTAL ECONOMICS

Dr Rohini Prasad

Dr Sukanta Sarkar

GenNext Publication

First Published, 2018

Published by

GenNext Publication
5, Ansari Road
Daryaganj, New Delhi-110002
Phone: 9811692060
E-mail: gennextpublication@hotmail.com

Printed at: G. Print Process, Delhi.

Cataloging in Publication Data—DK
Courtesy: D.K. Agencies (P) Ltd. <docinfo@dkagencies.com>

Prasad, Rohini, 1960- author.
Environmental economics / by Dr. Rohini Prasad, Dr. Sukanta Sarkar.
pages cm
Includes bibliographical references.
ISBN 9789380223261

1. Environmental economics. 2. Environmental economics—India. 3. Human ecology—Study and teaching. 4. Human ecology—Study and teaching—India. I. Sarkar, Sukanta, author. II. Title.

HC79.E5P73 2018 DDC 338.927 23

Contents

Part - II
Economics of Social Sector

Foreword

I am glad to know that Professor Rohini Prasad and Dr Sukanta Sarkar have prepared manuscript of a book entitled "Environmental Economics" and the book is going to be published by the Gyan Publishing House, New Delhi, India. Eleven chapters have concluded in this book. By reading the manuscript, I think most of the contemporary topics of environmental economics have been included in it. I am confident that this book will be very useful to the students and researchers of Environmental Studies Economics, Rural development etc.

I wish academic endeavour of the authors of this book shall be fruitful and it will satisfy the academic queries of the readers.

With best wishes.

Date: 12/10/2017

Professor M A Rahman,
PhD (USA)
Director, Centre for Global Environmental Culture (CGEC)
Coordinator, RCE Greater Dhaka and WWOOF Bangladesh
International University of Business Agriculture and Technology
Uttara Model Town, Dhaka, Bangladesh

Preface

Environmental problems are the result of our pursuit of affluence. The economic analysis of environmental issues can be approached from two different perspectives: environmental economics and ecological economics. Environmental economics applies insights from traditional economics to environmental issues. It is a sub-field of economics that is concerned with environmental issues. It is related to ecological economics but there are differences. Most environmental economists have been trained as economists. In recent years there has been growing concern about degradation and pollution of environment and climate change as they impact on future development of both the developing and developed countries. It is concerned with the impact of economic activities on the environment, the significance of ecosystem to the economy, and suggests the appropriate ways of regulating economic activity, so that cosmic balance is achieved in the society.

We desire to express our heartiest thank to Professor B.K. Panda, Department of Economics, Berhampur University, Odisha who despite his busy schedule and hectic academic engagements, all the time encouraged and supported us. We have also beholden to Dr N.G. Pendse, Department of Economics, Rani Durgabati University, Jabalpur who's erudite and scholarly tidbits for preparing such a vast work are still fresh in our mind. We also thanks to Dr Pradeep Kumar Pandey, Centre of Judicial Studies, Dibrugarh University, Assam; Dr Rakesh Joshi, Department of Economics, Saurashtra University, Gujarat; Dr D. Pulla Rao, Department of Economics, Andhra University; Dr Vibhuti Patel, Professor cum Director, Centre for Study of Social Exclusion and Inclusive Policy, SNDT Women's University, Mumbai; Dr WakarAmin, Department of Social Work, University of Kashmir, J & K.; Dr Shazia Manzoor, Assistant Professor Department of Social Work, University of Kashmir, J & K; Dr Pallab Kanti Ghoshal, Department of Commerce, BBM. College, Udaipur, for their valuable suggestions and moral support.

We are heartily grateful to Dr Suman Kalan Chaudhury, Department of Business Administration, Berhampur University, Odisha; who always encouraged us to carry on this constructive work. Further, we express our heartily thankfulness to each and every person who directly/indirectly helped us in preparing this work.

It is hoped that this book will be very useful for society in general and students of economics/environmental studies in particular. Comments and suggestions are most welcomed.

Prof Rohini Prasad
Dr Sukanta Sarkar

Acknowledgement

Environmental problems are the result of our pursuit of affluence. The economic analysis of environmental issues can be approached from two different perspectives, environmental economics and ecological economics. Environmental economics applies insights from traditional economics to environmental issues. It is a sub-field of economics that is concerned with environmental issues. It is related to ecological economics but there are differences. We desire to express our heartiest thank to Professor B.K. Panda, Department of Economics, Berhampur University, Odisha who despite his busy schedule and hectic academic engagements, all the time encouraged and supported us.

We have also beholden to Dr N.G. Pendse, Department of Economics, Rani Durgabati University, Jabalpur who's erudite and scholarly tidbits for preparing such a vast work are still fresh in our mind. We also thanks to Dr. Pradeep Kumar Pandey, Centre of Judicial Studies, Dibrugarh University, Assam; Dr Rakesh Joshi, Department of Economics, Saurashtra University, Gujarat; Dr D. Pulla Rao, Department of Economics, Andhra University; Dr Vibhuti Patel, Professor cum Director, Centre for Study of Social Exclusion and Inclusive Policy, SNDT Women's University, Mumbai; Dr Wakar Amin, Department of Social Work, University of Kashmir, J and K.; Dr Shazia Manzoor, Assistant professor Department of Social Work, University of Kashmir, J and K; Dr Pallab Kanti Ghoshal, Department of Commerce, BBM. College, Udaipur, for their valuable suggestions and moral support.

We are heartily grateful to Dr Suman Kalan Chaudhury, Department of Business Administration, Berhampur University, Odisha; who always encouraged us to carry on this constructive work. Further, we express our heartily thankfulness to each and every person who directly/indirectly helped us in preparing this work. It is hoped that this book will be very useful society in general and students of economics/environmental studies in particular. Comments and suggestions are most welcomed.

Professor Rohini Prasad

Dr Sukanta Sarkar

Abbreviations

AAQMS : Ambient Air Quality Monitoring Stations
ADB: : Asian Development Bank
CBCS : Choice Based Credit Systems
CBI : Central Bureau of Investigation
CFCs : Chlorofluorocarbons
CPCB : Central Pollution Control Board
CTE : Committee on Trade and Environment
CTE : Committee on Trade and Environment
CTS : Central Tibetan Schools
DPEP : District Primary Education Programme
EA : Environment Agency
EFA : Education for All
EoGM : Empowered Group of Ministers
EPI : Environmental Policy Integration
EU : European Union
FAO : Food and Agriculture Organisation
FCA : Forest Conservation Act
GATS : General Agreement on Trade in Services
GEI : Gender Empowerment Index
GHGs : Green House Gases
HDI : Human Development Index
HFCs : Hydro- Fluorocarbons
HVAC : Heating, Ventilation and Air Conditioning
HYV : High Yielding Varieties
ICIMOD : International Centre for Integrated Mountain Development
IDFC : Infrastructure Development Finance Corporation
IDMI : Infrastructure Development in Minority Institutions
IEA : International Energy Agency
IFC : International Finance Corporation
IPCC : Intergovernmental Panel on Climate Change
IRAHE : Independent Regulatory Authority for Higher Education
IRR : Internal Rate of Return

IWPA	:	Indian Wind Power Association
IWTMA	:	Indian Wind Turbine Manufacturers Association
KGBVS	:	Kasturba Gandhi Balika Vidyalaya Scheme
LIL	:	Low and Intermediate Level
MCED	:	Ministerial Conference on Environment and Development
MCI	:	Medical Council of India
MCPFE	:	Ministerial Conference on the Protection of Forests in Europe
MDGs	:	Millennium Development Goals
MDPS	:	Mid-Day Meal Scheme
MLL	:	Minimum Levels of Learning
MNRE	:	Ministry of New and Renewable Energy
MoEF	:	Ministry of Environment and Forests
MoEFCC	:	Ministry of Environment, Forests and Climate Change
MOSPI	:	Ministry of Statistics and Programme Implementation
MPCB	:	Maharashtra Pollution Control Board
MRTS	:	Marginal Rates of Technical Substitutions
MSC	:	Marginal Social Cost
MPC	:	Marginal Private Cost
MEC	:	Marginal External Cost
NDA	:	National Democratic Alliance
NEEPCO	:	Northeast Electric Power Company
NELP	:	New Exploration Licensing Policy
NFP	:	National Forest Policy
NHPC	:	National Hydroelectric Power Corporation
NIOS	:	National Institute of Open Schooling
NLM	:	National Library of Medicine
NPDES	:	National Pollutant Discharge Elimination System
NPV	:	Net Present Value
NVs	:	Navodaya Vidyalayas
ODL	:	Open and Distance Learning
ONGC	:	Oil and Natural Gas Commission
PPP	:	Public–Private Partnership
RLW	:	Radioactive Liquid Waste
RMSA	:	Rashtriya Madhyamik Shiksha Abhiyan
ROI	:	Return on Investment
SAP	:	Special Action Plan
SFM	:	Sustainable Forest Management
SJVNL	:	Satluj Jal Vidyut Nigam
SPCBs	:	State Pollution Control Boards

SSA	:	Sarva Shiksha Abhiyan
TEHIP	:	Toxicology and Environmental Health Information Programme
UAE	:	United Arab Emirates
UEE	:	Universalisation of Elementary Education
UGC	:	University Grants Commission
UNCED	:	United Nations Conference on Environment and Development
UNCSD	:	United Nations Conference on Sustainable Development
UNEP	:	United Nations Environment Programme
UNFCCC	:	United Nations Framework Convention on Climate Change
VOCs	:	Volatile Organic Compounds
WCCB	:	Wildlife Crime Control Bureau
WSSD	:	World Summit on Sustainable Development
WTO	:	World Trade Organisation

Introduction

Economics is the study of the allocation of scarce resources, including how markets function and how incentives affect people's, businesses' and institutions' behaviour. Specifically, economists may analyse issues such as consumer demand and sales to help a company maximize its profits. Economists work for research firms and think tanks, where they study and analyse a variety of economic issues.Environmental policy is the commitment of an organization to the laws, regulations, and other policy mechanisms concerning environmental issues.Neoclassical economics is an approach to economics that relates supply and demand to an individual's rationality and his ability to maximize utility or profit.

Economics is conventionally considered to be a social science that examines the allocation of scarce resources among various potential uses that are in competition with each other. As such, economics attempts to predict and understand the patterns of consumption of goods and services by individuals and society. Economic efficiency implies an economic state in which every resource is optimally allocated to serve each individual or entity in the best way while minimizing waste and inefficiency. When an economy is economically efficient, any changes made to assist one entity would harm another.

Neoclassical economics uses mathematical equations to study various aspects of the economy.Economists divide the factors of production into four categories: land, labour, capital, and entrepreneurship. The first factor of production is land, but this includes any natural resource used to produce goods and services.Within this discipline, environmental and natural resource economics is the application of the principles of economics to the study of how environmental and natural resources are developed and managed. It is an area of economics that studies the financial impact of environmental policies.

Environmental economists perform studies to determine the theoretical or empirical effects of environmental policies on the economy. They study the economics of natural resources from both sides - their extraction and use, and the waste products returned to the environment They research the environmental issues such as renewable energy use, construction of new hydroelectric power plants or transnational pipelines, and pollution control measures.

An environmental economist studies and predicts the impact of environmental events on the local, national, and global economic scales. Environmental economics jobs apply field research data to economic incentives and use the resulting models to assess labour, markets, trading, and outcomes. In very broad terms, environmental economics looks at how economic activity and policy affect the environment in which we live. Courses in environmental economics will vary in the emphasis they give to these issues and some may also discuss issues of natural resource scarcity as well. Most will include some microeconomic theory, looking at how firms and individuals behave when production or consumption involves externalities.

Welfare economics is a branch of economics that uses microeconomic techniques to evaluate well-being (welfare) at the aggregate (economy-wide) level. The field of welfare economics is associated with two fundamental theorems. The first states that given certain assumptions, competitive markets produce (Pareto) efficient outcomes; it captures the logic of Adam Smith's invisible hand. The second states that given further restrictions, any Pareto efficient outcome can be supported as a competitive market equilibrium.

The basic argument underpinning environmental economics is that there are environmental costs of economic growth that go unaccounted in the current market model. These negative externalities, like pollution and other kinds of environmental degradation, could then result in market failure.Environmental economists study the economics of natural resources from both sides, their extraction and use, and the waste products returned to the environment. They also study how economic incentives hurt or help the environment, and how they can be used to create sustainable policies and environmental solutions.

In economics, an externality is the cost or benefit that affects a party who did not choose to incur that cost or benefit. Economists often urge governments to adopt policies that "internalize" an externality, so that costs and benefits will affect mainly parties who choose to incur them. Environmental policy is an academic field that focuses on how man's activities impact the natural world and how governments and other organisations develop solutions to negative impacts through law and regulation. Government, private industry and non-profit organizations employ environmental policy majors.Government can play a role in reducing negative externalities by taxing goods when their production generates spill over costs

Environmental externalities refer to the economic concept of uncompensated environmental effects of production and consumption that affect consumer utility and enterprise cost outside the market mechanism. As a consequence of negative externalities, private costs of production tend to be lower than its "social" cost. Coase theorem is a legal and economic theory that affirms that where there are complete competitive markets with no transactions costs, an efficient set of inputs and outputs to and from production-optimal distribution are selected, regardless of how property rights are divided.

Most environmental goods and services, such as clean air and water, and healthy fish and wildlife populations, are not traded in markets. Their economic value -how much people would be willing to pay for them- is not revealed in market prices. Natural resource economics is a transdisciplinary field of academic research within economics that aims to address the connections and interdependence between human economies and natural ecosystems. Its focus is how to operate an economy within the ecological constraints of earth's natural resources. All businesses, whether domestic or international, are affected by the dynamic economic environment conditions prevalent in the market. Among many economic factors affecting business some are; interest rates, demand and supply, recession, inflation, etc.

Coasian bargaining states that if trade in an externality is possible and there are sufficiently low transaction costs, bargaining will lead to a Pareto efficient outcome regardless of the initial allocation of property. Property rights are theoretical socially-enforced constructs in economics for determining how a resource or economic good is used and owned. Environmental law means the laws that regulate the impact of human activities on the environment. Environmental law covers a broad range of activities that affect air, water, land, flora or fauna. It includes laws that relate to: Protection of animals and plants.In environmental law and policy, market-based instruments are policy instruments that use markets, price, and other economic variables to provide incentives for polluters to reduce or eliminate negative environmental externalities.

Environmental factor is any factor, abiotic or biotic, that influences living organisms. Abiotic factors include ambient temperature, amount of sunlight, and pH of the water soil in which an organism lives. Other common external factors fall into several categories, including socio-economic, legal or ethical, political and technological. Socio-economic factors relate to the values, attitudes and concerns of your target customers and their economic abilities to afford your products. There are a number of different types of economic efficiency. The five most relevant ones are: allocative, productive, dynamic, social and X-efficiency. Allocative efficiency occurs when goods and services are distributed according to consumer preferences.

Economic stability refers to an absence of excessive fluctuations in the macro economy. An economy with fairly constant output growth and low and stable inflation would be considered economically stable. A Pigovian tax is a tax levied on any market activity that generates negative externalities (costs not internalised in the market price). The tax is intended to correct an inefficient market outcome, and does so by being set equal to the social cost of the negative externalities.

Pollution is the introduction of contaminants into the natural environment that cause adverse change. Pollution occurs in different forms; air, water, soil, radioactive, noise, heat/ thermal and light. Pollution is often classed as point source or nonpoint source pollution. Air pollution has always accompanied civilisations. Air pollution comes from both natural and human-made (anthropogenic) sources. Smoke from chimneys, factories, vehicles or burning of wood basically occurs due to coal burning; this releases sulphur dioxide into the air making it toxic. The effects of air pollution are evident too. Pollution started from prehistoric times when man created the first fires. The burning of coal and wood, and the presence of many horses in concentrated areas made the cities the primary sources of pollution. It was the industrial revolution that gave birth to environmental pollution as we know it today. Adverse air quality can kill many organisms including humans. Ozone pollution can cause respiratory disease, cardiovascular disease, throat inflammation, chest pain, and congestion. Pollution control is a term used in environmental management. It means the control of emissions and effluents into air, water or soil.

Carbon dioxide, while vital for photosynthesis, is sometimes referred to as pollution, because raised levels of the gas in the atmosphere are affecting the Earth's climate. Water Pollution has taken toll of all the surviving species of the earth. Almost 60 per cent of the species live in water bodies. Water pollution not only harms the aquatic beings but it also contaminates the entire food chain by severely affecting human's dependent on these. Pollution was not a serious problem as long as there was enough space available for each individual or group. However, with the establishment of permanent settlements by great numbers of people, pollution became a problem, and it has remained one ever since.

Part - I

Environmental Studies

Chapter - 1

Economics of Environment

Few people are capable of expressing with equanimity opinions which differ from the prejudices of their social environment. Most people are even incapable of forming such opinions.

—***Albert Einstein***[1]

Economics is the social science that seeks to describe the factors which regulate the manufacture, supply and consumption of goods and services. Economics emphasis on the performance and communication of economic agents and how economies work. Besides the old-fashioned concern in construction, circulation, and consumption in an economy, economic study may be applied throughout humanity, as in professional, business, health care, and government.

Economic development and political expansion are interred linked. Scottish philosopher Adam Smith (1776) defined what was then called political economy as "an inquiry into the nature and causes of the wealth of nations", in particular as: a branch of the science of a statesman or legislator [with the twofold objectives of providing] a plentiful revenue or subsistence for the people ... [and] to supply the state or commonwealth with a revenue for the public services. Alfred Marshall provides a still widely cited definition in his textbook Principles of Economics (1890) that extends analysis beyond wealth and from the societal to the microeconomic level. Economics is a study of man in the ordinary business of life. It enquires how he gets his income and how he uses it. Thus, it is on the one side, the study of wealth and on the other and more important side, a part of the study of man.

Microeconomics examines how entities, forming a market structure, interact within a market to create a market system. It studies individual markets by simplifying the economic system by assuming that activity in the market being analysed does not affect other markets. Macroeconomics examines the economy as a whole to explain broad aggregates and their interactions "top down", that is, using a simplified form of general-equilibrium theory. International trade studies determinants of goods-and-services flows across international boundaries. It also concerns the size and distribution of gains from trade (wikipedia).[2]

Definition of Welfare Economics

Welfare economics is a division of economics that uses microeconomic methods to assess well-being at the combined level. The field of welfare economics is related with two central statements. The first states that given certain assumptions, competitive produce Pareto efficient outcomes. The second fundamental theorem states that given further restrictions, any Pareto efficient outcome can be supported as competitive market stability. It also offers the theoretical foundations for specific tools of public economics, including cost-benefit analysis.[3]

Welfare economics readings the circumstances under which the resolution to the general equilibrium model can be said to be optimal. It scrutinises the situations for economic efficiency in the production of output and in the conversation of produces, and equity in the circulation of revenue. The boosting of society's well-being needs the optimal distribution of commodities among customers.[4]

Welfare economics is subdivision of economics that pursues to appraise economic plans in terms of their effects on the well-being of the society. It became recognised as a well-defined outlet of economic philosophy during the twentieth century.[5] The inter-relationship among numerous portions of the economy means that certain specific alteration in one part of the economy touches resource distribution in all parts of it. Thus, a central problem in welfare economics relates to whether a particular modification in source distribution will rise or reduction social wellbeing.[6]

Criterion of Social Welfare

In welfare economics, a social welfare function is a function that positions social states as less wanted, more wanted, or unresponsive for each likely pair of social states. In a 1938 article, Abram Bergson introduced the social welfare function. A Bergson–Samuelson social welfare function considers welfare for a given set of individual preferences or welfare rankings. An Arrow social welfare function considers welfare across different possible sets of individual preferences or welfare rankings and seemingly reasonable axioms that constrain the function.The object was to state in precise form the value judgments required for the derivation of the conditions of supreme economic welfare set out by earlier writers, including Marshall and Pigou, Pareto and Barone, and Lerner.[7]

Individual welfare is a function of numerous economic and non-economic variables. To Pigou economic welfare was a portion of general welfare which could bring straight or circuitously into relation with the measuring rod of money. Social welfare composed of two words: social and welfare. Social means society. The term welfare refers to the fulfilment of wants. Social welfare refers to the fulfilment of socialised needs. Every adding to the wellbeing of an individual would establish a module of social welfare.[8]

Bergson pointed out that for associating utility levels of various individuals resulting from alterations in economic rule, making relational comparison of utility cannot be avoided. Bergson put forward a social welfare criterion in which he incorporates clearly such association as utility of individual A from Re 1= utility of individual B from Re 0.20 On the basis of such explicit value judgements or relational judgement of utilities he gives ranking to other social states from the perspective of social wellbeing.[9]

Bentham Criteria

Jeremy Bentham was a British philosopher, jurist, and social reformer. He is observed as the originator of modern utilitarianism. He defined as the "fundamental axiom" of his philosophy the principle that "it is the greatest happiness of the greatest number that is the measure of right and wrong". Bentham's students included his secretary and collaborator James Mill, the latter's son, John Stuart Mill, the legal philosopher John Austin, as well as Robert Owen, one of the founders of utopian socialism. He argued against "natural law" theory and thought that the classical theories of Plato and Aristotle as well as notions such as Kant's Categorical Imperative were too outdated, confusing and/or controversial to be of much help with society's ills and a programme of social reform.[10]

Consider the Utilitarian or Benthamite social welfare function which measures social welfare as the total or sum of individual incomes:

$$W = \sum_{i=1}^{n} Y_i$$

where W is social welfare and Y_i is the income of individual i among n individuals in society. In this case, maximising the social welfare means capitalise on the entire revenue of the individuals in the people, without regard to in what way earnings are dispersed in people. It does not differentiate between a revenue transmission from rich to poor and vice versa. If a revenue hand over from the poor to the rich results in a higher rise in the utility of the rich than the decrease in the utility of the poor, the people is expected to accept such a transfer, because the total utility of the society has increased as a whole.[11]

Bentham's ambition in life was to create a "Pannomion", a complete utilitarian code of law. He not only proposed many legal and social reforms, but also expounded an underlying moral principle on which they should be based. Bentham stated that pleasures and pains can be ranked according to their value or "dimension" such as intensity, duration, certainty of a pleasure or a pain. Bentham was an obsessive writer and reviser, but was constitutionally incapable, except on rare occasions, of bringing his work to completion and publication.[12]

Utilitarianism is a normative ethical theory that places the locus of right and wrong solely on the outcomes of choosing one action/policy over other actions/policies. As such, it moves beyond the scope of one's own interests and takes into account the interests of others. Bentham's Principle of Utility: (1) Recognises the fundamental role of pain and pleasure in human life, (2) approves or disapproves of an action on the basis of the amount of pain or pleasure brought about i.e., consequences, (3) equates good with pleasure and evil with pain, and (4) asserts that pleasure and pain are capable of quantification.[13]

Pareto Optimality Criteria

Pareto efficiency or Pareto optimality is a concept in economics with applications in engineering and social sciences. The term is named after Vilfredo Pareto (1848–1923), an Italian economist who used the concept in his studies of economic efficiency and income distribution. In a Pareto efficient economic system, no allocation of given goods can be made without making at least one individual worse off. Pareto rejected the notion of cardinal utility and its additive nature. He detached the welfare economics from the interpersonal comparison of utilities. Pareto's concept of maximum social welfare is based upon ordinal utility and also free from value judgments. Pareto optimum is a position where it is impossible to make anyone better off without making someone worse off by any reallocation of resources or inputs and outputs.

Pareto efficiency is a state of allocation of resources in which it is impossible to make any one individual better off without making at least one individual worse off. It is also known as Pareto optimality. It is a minimal notion of efficiency and does not necessarily result in a socially desirable distribution of resources: it makes no statement about equality, or the overall well-being of a society[14].

Pareto optimality describes a state of affairs in which resources are distributed such that it is not possible to improve a single individual without also causing at least one other individual to become worse off than before the change. A Pareto improvement is said to have taken place if a change is made in the distribution of goods or resources that results in at least one individual being better off than before the change while not making any other individual worse. In addition to economics, the idea of Pareto efficiency has also had a considerable impact in the field of engineering. It is used to describe a range of choices as a Pareto set or a Pareto frontier.[15]

There are three conditions for Pareto efficiency. The first one can be called allocative efficiency. It concerns how a given stock of consumption commodities is allocated to different consumers. This condition requires that the marginal rate of substitution between any pair of goods be equalised across different consumers. The second condition for Pareto efficiency can be called technical efficiency. It concerns how factors of production are transformed into consumption goods. This condition requires that the technical rate of substitution between any pair of productive factors be equalised across different producers. The third condition can be called production- allocative efficiency. It concerns whether the right mix of consumption goods are produced.[16]

Suppose two persons A and B form the society and consume two goods X and Y. The various levels of their pleasure by consuming various mixtures of the two goods have been represented by their respective indifference curves. In Figure 1, O_a and O_b are the origins for the utilities of two persons A and B respectively. I_{a1}, I_{a2}, I_{a3}, I_{a4} and I_{b1}, I_{b2}, I_{b3}, I_{b4} are their successively higher indifference curve. Suppose the initial distribution of goods X and Y between the members of the society, A and B, is represented by point- K in the Edgeworth Box.

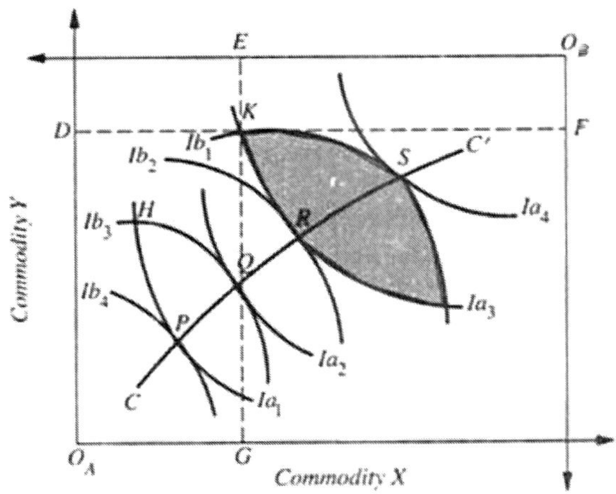

Fig. 1: Pareto Criterion and Pareto Optimality.

Accordingly, individual A consumes O_AG of X + GK of Y and is at the level of satisfaction represented by indifference curve I_{a3}. Similarly, individual B consumes KF of X+ KE of Y and gets the satisfaction represented by indifference curve Ib_1. Thus, the total given volume of goods X and Y is distributed between A and B. In this distribution, it has been found that individual A consumes relatively more quantity of good Y and individual B of good X. Now, with the aid of Pareto's welfare criterion it can shows that a movement from the point K to a point such as S or R or any other point in the shaded region will increase social welfare.

Any changes from K to S through rearrangement of two goods between two individuals increases the level of satisfaction of A without any alteration in the satisfaction of B because as a result of this A will moves to his higher indifference curve I_{a4}, and B remains on his same indifference curve I_{b1} (K and

5 lie on B's same indifference curve I_{b1}). In other words, as a result of the movement from K to S, individual A has become better off whereas individual B is no worse off. Thus, social welfare has increased following the movement from K to S according to Pareto criterion, and therefore it can say that K is not the position of economic optimum.

Similarly, the movement from K to R is also necessary from the point of view of social wellbeing be-cause in this individual B becomes better off without any change-in-the satisfaction of individual A. There-fore, compare to K, both the positions S and R are better. The tangency points of the different indifference curves of the two individuals of the society are the Pareto optimum points and the locus of these points is named 'contract curve'.

In Figure 2, CV is a utility possibility curve which shows the different levels of utilities attained by two individuals A and B of the civilisation resulting from the rearrangement of a fixed bundle of goods and its intake by them.

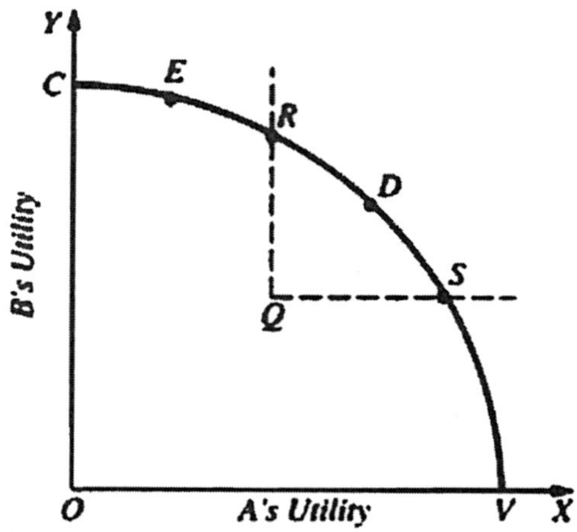

Fig. 2: Pareto Criterion Explained with Utility Possibility Curve.

According to Pareto criterion, a movement from Q to R, or Q to D, or Q to S represents the proliferation in social wellbeing because in such movements the utility of either A or B or both increases. A movement from Q to R suggests that the utility or wellbeing of B increases, while that of A remains the same.

On the other hand, a movement from Q to S suggests that B is no worse off while A has become better off. And a movement from Q to D or any other point on the section between R and S will indicates increase in wellbeing or utility of both the individuals. Thus, points R, D and S are desirable to Q from the point of view of social wellbeing.*

* H.L. Ahuja (2016). Modern Economics, S.chand, New Delhi, pp. 766-768.

But unfortunately Pareto criterion does not help us in assessing the changes in wellbeing if the movement as a result of rearrangement is from the point Q to a point exterior the segment RS; such as point E on the utility possibility curve CV. As a result of the movement from point Q to E, it has been found that the utility of A decreases while that of B increases. In such situations, Pareto criterion cannot express us as to whether social wellbeing increases or decreases.

The utility-possibility frontier demonstrations the different mixtures of utilities received by individuals A and B when the economy is in general equilibrium or Pareto optimum in conversation. It is the locus of supreme utility for one individual for any given level of utility for the other individual. The Grand utility-possibilities frontier is the envelope to the utility-possibilities frontiers at Pareto optimum points of production and exchange. It shows that no recognition of the production-exchange process is thinkable that makes some one better off without, at the same time, making someone else worse-off. To overcome the shortcomings of the Paretocriterion, Kaldor and Hicks introduced the second welfare criterion, which is based on the compensation principle. According to the criterion, an alteration is an enhancement if those who gain from the change can fully compensation the losers and still retain some gain.[17]

Marginal Conditions of Pareto Optimality

Lerner and Hicks derived the marginal conditions which must be fulfilled for the attainment of Pareto optimum. These marginal conditions are based on the following important assumptions:

1. Each individual has his own ordinal utility function and possesses definite amount of each product and factor.
2. Production function of every firm and the state of technology is given and remains constant.
3. Goods are perfectly divisible.
4. A producer tries to produce a given output with the least-cost combination of factors.
5. Every individual wants to maximise his satisfaction.
6. Every individual purchases some quantity of all goods, and
7. All factors of production are perfectly mobile.*

Given the above assumptions various marginal conditions (first-order conditions) required for the attainment of Pareto optimum or supreme social welfare are explained below:

* H.L. Ahuja (2016). Modern Economics, 20th edition, p. 768.

1. The Optimum Distribution of Products among the Consumers: Efficiency in Exchange:

The first condition relates to the optimum distribution of the goods among the many consumers constituting a civilisation at a specific point of period. The condition says: "The marginal rate of substitution between any two goods must be the same for every individual who consumes them both." The marginal rate of substitution of one good for another so as is the amount of one good necessary to reimburse for the damage of a marginal unit of another so as to uphold a similar level of pleasure. So long as the marginal rate of substitution (MRS) between two goods is not equal for any two consumers, they will enter into a conversation which would upturn the pleasure of both or of one without declining the pleasure of the other.

This condition can be better explained with the help of the Edgeworth Box diagram.

In Figure 3, goods X and Y, which are consumed by two individuals A and B composing a society are represented on the X and Taxes respectively. O_A and O_B are origins for A and B respectively. la_1, Ia_2, Ia_3 and Ib_1, Ib_2, lb_3 are the indifference curves showing successively higher and higher satisfaction of consumers A and B respectively. CC is the contract curve passing through various tangency points Q, R, S of the indifference curves of A and B. The marginal rates of substitution between the two goods for individuals A and B are equal on the various points of the contract curve CC'. Any point outside the contract curve does not represent the equality of MRS between the two goods for two individuals A and B of the society.

Let us consider point K where indifference curves I_{a1} and I_{b1} of individuals A and B respectively intersect each other instead of being tangential. Therefore, at point K marginal rate of substitution between two goods X and Y (MRS_{XY})

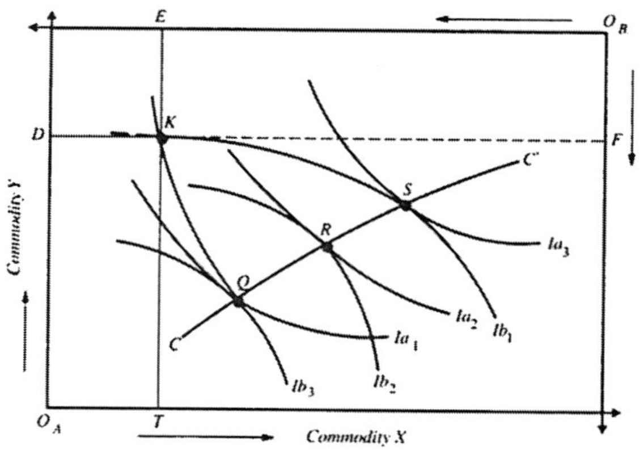

Fig. 3: The Optimum Distribution of Goods.

of individual A is not equal to that of B.With the preliminary sharing of goods as represented by point K, it is likely to rise the pleasure of one individual without any reduction in that of the other or to rise the pleasure of both by rearrangement of the two goods X and Y between them. A movement from K to S rises the pleasure of A without any diminution in B's pleasure.

Similarly, a movement from K to Q growth's B's pleasure without any decline in A's pleasure. The movement from K to R rises the pleasure of both because both move to their higher indifference curves. Thus, movements from K to Q or to S or to any other point on the fragment SQ of the contract curve will, according to Pareto criterion, raise the level of social welfare.

From above it said that movement from any point away from the contract curve to a point on the pertinent section of the contract curve will mean rise in social wellbeing. At any point away from the contract curve in the Edgeworth box, the indifference curves of the two individuals will meet which will mean that MRS_{xy} of two individuals is not the similar. This indicates that through conversation of some units of goods between them, they can move to some point on the contract curve where the social wellbeing will be upper.

Since the slope of an indifference curve signifies the marginal rate of substitution (MRS_{XY}) at any point of the contract curve, which signifies tangency points of the indifference curves, MRS_{XY} of the two individuals are equal. Therefore, points on the contact curve denote the extreme social wellbeing. However, a movement along the contract curve in either way will make one individual better off and the other worse off since it will put one individual on his consecutively higher indifference curves and the other on his consecutively lower indifference curves. Thus, every point on the contract curve represents supreme social wellbeing in the Paretian sense but we cannot say anything about the best of them with the help of Pareto criterion.*

2. The Optimum Allocation of Factors: Pareto Efficiency in Production

The second condition for Pareto optimum entails that the accessible factors of manufacture should be utilised in the making of goods in such a manner that it is difficult to rise the production of open firm without a cut in the production of another or to rise the production of both the goods by any re-allocation of factors of construction.This situation would be attained if the marginal technical rate of substitution between any pair of factors must be the similar for any two firms making two different goods and using both the factors to yield the products.

This condition too can be explained with the help of Edgeworth Box diagram relating to production. This is depicted in Fig. 4. Let us assume two firms A and B producing the similar good by using two factors labour and

* H.L. Ahuja (2016). Modern Economics, 20th edition, pp. 768-769.

capital. The existing quantities of labour and capital are characterised on X and Y axes respectively. O_A and O_B are the origins for firms A and B respectively.

Isoquants I_{a1}, I_{a2}, I_{a3} and I_{b1}, I_{b2}, I_{b3} of firms A and B respectively represent successively higher and higher quantities of output which they can produce by different combinations of labour and capital. The slope of the isoquants, which are convex to the origin, represents the marginal rate of technical substitution (MRTS) between two factors. MRTS of one factor for another is the amount of one factor necessary to compensate for the loss of the marginal unit of another so that the level of output remains the same. So long as the MRTS between two factors for two firms is not equal, total output of a product can be increased by transfer of factors from one firm to another.

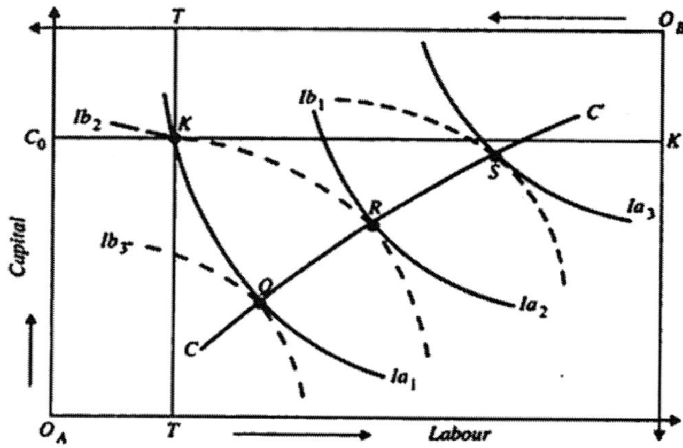

Fig. 4: The Optimum Allocation of Factors.

Any movement from K to S or to Q raises the production of one firm without any decline in the production of the other. The total production of the two firm's rises when through reallocation of factors between the two firms, a movement is made from the point K to the point Q or S on the contract curve. A glimpse at Figure 4 will disclose that movement from point K outside the contract curve to the point R on the contract curve will increase the production of both the firms alone as well as jointly. Therefore, it follows that consistent to a point outside the contract curve there will be some points on the contract curve production at which will ensure greater total output of the two firms.

As the contract curve is the locus of the tangency points of the isoquants of two firms, the marginal rate of substitution of the two firms is the similar at every point of the contract curve CC. It follows that on the contract curve at every point of which MRTS between the two factors of two firms is the sum, the distribution of factors between the two firms is optimal.When the distribution of factors between the two firms is such that they are constructing at a point on the contract curve, then no re-allocation of factors will rise the total production of the two firms taken jointly.

There are several points on the contract curve and each of them signifies the best distribution of labour and capital as between the two firms. But which one of them is best cannot be said on the basis of Pareto criterion because movement along the contract curve in either way signifies such factor rearrangement which rises the production of one and diminishes the production of other firm.*

3. Optimum Direction of Production: Efficiency in Product Mix

This condition relates to the pattern of manufacture. The fulfillment of this condition defines the optimum quantities of diverse goods to be produced with the given factor endowments. This condition states that "the marginal rate of substitution between any pair of products for any person consuming both must be the same as the marginal rate of transformation (for the community) between them." According to this condition, for the attainment of maximum social welfare goods should be produced in accordance with consumer's preferences. Let us explain this with the help of Fig. 5.

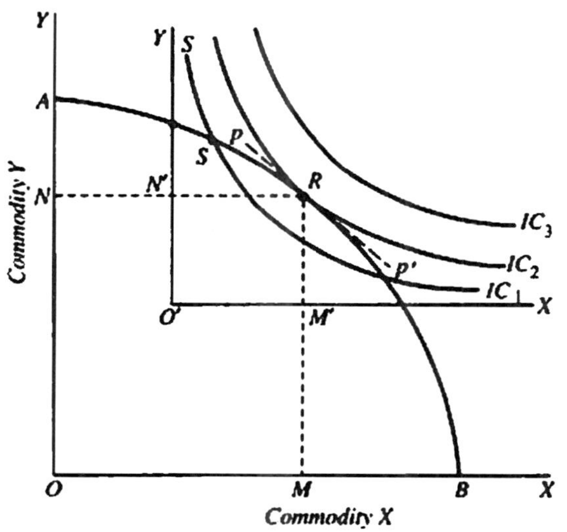

Fig. 5: Optimum Direction of Production Optimum Product Mix.

In Fig. 5 goods X and Y have been denoted on the X and Y axes respectively. AB is a community's alteration curve between any pair of goods X and Y. This curve signifies the maximum amount of X that can be manufactured for any amount of Y, given the amounts of other goods that are

* H.L. Ahuja (2016). Modern Economics, 2015 edition, pp. 770-771.

created and fixed supplies of existing resources. IC_1 and IC_2 are the indifference curves of a consumer the slope of which at a point represents the marginal rate of substitution between the two goods of the consumer. The MRT of the community and MRS of the consumer are equal to each other at point R at which the community's alteration curve is tangent to the indifference curve IC_2 of a representative consumer, Point R symbolizes best composition of production in which goods X and Y are being made and consumed in OM and ON quantities.

This is because of all the points on the community's transformation curve, point R lies at the uppermost possible indifference curve IC_2 of the consumer. For instance, if a combination of goods X and Y embodied by S is being made and taken, the consumer would be at a lesser level of wellbeing because S lies on his subordinate indifference curve IC_1 which intersects the community's transformation curve instead of being tangential to it.

As a result, at point S, MRS_{XY} of the consumer is not equal to the MRT_{XY} of the community. With the situation at S there is a possibility of moving the consumers to a higher indifference curve by changing the way of manufacture i.e. by increasing the manufacture of X and dropping the production of Y. Thus, where community's transformation curve is tangent to the indifference curve of a consumer in the society the optimum direction of production is established at point R.

The Second-Order and Total Conditions of Pareto Optimality

The marginal or the first order conditions are 'necessary' but not sufficient for the attainment of maximum social welfare because the marginal conditions by themselves do not guarantee maximum welfare.The marginal conditions can be fulfilled even at the level of minimum welfare. To attain the maximum social welfare position second-order conditions together with the marginal conditions must be satisfied. The second order conditions require that all indifference curves must be convex to the origin and all transformation curves concave to it in the neighbourhood of any portion where marginal conditions are satisfied.

But even the satisfaction of both (first and second order conditions) does not ensure the largest maximum welfare because even when marginal conditions (first and second order) are fulfilled, it may still be possible to move to a position where social welfare is greater. To attain the maximum social welfare, another set of conditions which are called by J.R. Hicks as the 'total conditions' must also be satisfied.The total conditions state, "That if welfare is to be a maximum, it must be impossible to increase welfare by producing a product not otherwise produced or by using a factor not otherwise used." If it is possible to increase welfare by such activities the optimum position is not determined by marginal conditions alone. Therefore, welfare will be really maximum if the marginal as well as total conditions are satisfied. But such a social optimum too is Hot a unique one. It is one of a large number of optima. The whole analysis of conditions of Pareto optimality assumes a given distribution of income.*

Kaldor-Hicks Compensation Criterion

Kaldor–Hicks criterion is a way of judging economic re-allocations of resources among people that captures some of the intuitive appeal of Pareto improvements. Using the criterion for Kaldor–Hicks improvement, an outcome is an improvement if those that are made better off could in principle compensate those that are made worse off, so that a Pareto improving outcome could be achieved. The Kaldor–Hicks methods are typically used as tests of potential improvements rather than as efficiency goals themselves. They are used to determine whether an activity moves the economy toward Pareto efficiency. It is widely applied in welfare economics and managerial economics.[18]

Economists like Kaldor, Hicks and Scitovsky have made efforts to evaluate the changes in social welfare resulting from any economic reorganisation which harms somebody and benefits the others. The 'compensation principle' is based on the following assumptions:[19]

1. The satisfaction of an individual is independent of the others and he is the best judge of his welfare.
2. There exist no externalities of consumption and production.
3. The tastes of the individuals remain constant.
4. Utility can be measured ordinally and interpersonal comparisons of utilities are not possible.[20]

Nicolas Kaldor was the first economist to give a welfare criterion based on compensating payments. According to him, if a certain change in economic organisation or policy makes some people better off and others worse off, then that change will increase social welfare if those who gain from the change could compensate the losers and still be better off than before. Prof. J.R. Hicks supported Kaldor for employing compensation principle to evaluate the change in social welfare resulting from any economic reorganisation that benefits some people and harms the others.[21]

Pareto efficiency occurs when one party benefits from a decision, but others are not made worse off. In other words, no one loses out. Kaldor Hicks states that a decision can be more efficient as long as in theory, everyone can be compensated to offset any potential costs. Under Kaldor Hicks, the key principle is the idea that in theory people could be compensated. This compensation does not actually have to occur. Whereas under pareto efficiency, this compensation would have to occur through voluntary agreements between two parties. Kaldor-Hicks criteria may be used to judge the effectiveness of a Cost-Benefit Analysis scheme.[22]

* H.L. Ahuja (2016). Modern Economics, 2015 edition, pp. 77[illegible]-772.

Kaldor-Hicks criterion can be explained with the help of the utility possibility curve. In Fig. 6 ordinal utility of two individuals A and B is shown on X and Y axis respectively. DE is the utility possibility curve which represents the numerous mixtures of utilities gained by individuals A and B. As we move downward on the curve DE, utility of A rises while that of B decreases. On the other hand, if we move up on the utility curve ED, utility of B rises while that of A decreases.

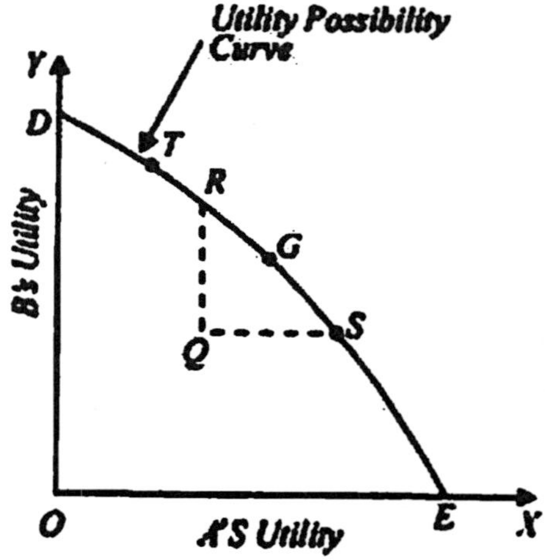

Fig. 6: Kaldor-Hicks Criterion Explained with Utility Possibility Curve.

Suppose the utilities obtained by A and B from the distribution of revenue or production between them is represented by point Q inside the utility possibility curve DE. It assumes that as a result of some change in economic policy, the two individuals move from point Q to point T on the utility possibility curve DE. As a result of this movement, utility of individual B has improved while the utility of A has dropped, that is, B has been become better off and A has become worse off than before. This movement from point Q to point T cannot be evaluated by means of Pareto criterion. Of course, points such as R, G, S or any other point on the segment RS of utility-possibility curve DE are socially preferable to point Q on the basis of Pareto criterion.

The compensation principle propounded by Kaldor-Hicks allows to say whether or not social welfare has greater than before as a result of movement from Q to T. According to Kaldor-Hicks criterion, it will see whether the individual A who benefited with the movement from position Q to position T could reimburse the individual A who is loser and still be better off than before.Now, it will be seen from Figure 6 that utility possibility curve DE passes through points R, G and S. This means that by mere relocation of revenue between the two individuals, that is, if individual B gives some compensation to individual A for the loss suffered, they can move from position T to the position R.

It is marked from the figure that at position R Individual A is as well off as at the position Q but individual B is still better off as compared to the position Q. It means due to a policy change and consequent movement from position Q to position T, the gainer (individual B) could compensate the loser (individual A) and is still better off than at Q.Therefore, according to Kaldor-Hicks criterion, social welfare increases with the movement from position Q to position T, because from T they could move to the position R through mere rearrangement of revenue (i.e. reimbursement).

According to Kaldor-Hicks criterion, compensation may not be actually paid to judge whether or not social welfare has increased. If it is possible for the gainer to compensate the loser and still be better off, the economists can say that social welfare has increased. Gainer can compensate the losers and still be better off only when the change in economic policy leads to the increase in output or real income.

Now, the implications of Kaldor-Hicks criterion become more clear if through redistribution the position of the two individual changes from T to G (see Fig. 6). It is quite apparent that at position G both the individuals A and B are better off than at the position Q. The position T to which the two individuals moved as a result of a certain change in economic policy is superior to the initial position Q from the viewpoint of social welfare, since from position T movement can be made merely through redistribution of income to position G where both are better off as compared to the position Q.

Now let us see what happens to social welfare if as a result of the adoption of a certain economic policy the utility possibility curve moves outward and the two individuals move from a point on a lower utility possibility curve to a point on a higher utility possibility curve. According to Kaldor-Hicks criterion, such a movement causes an improvement in social welfare. Consider Figure 7. UV is the original utility possibility curve and Q represents the position at which the two individuals are initially placed. Now, suppose utility possibility curve shifts outward to the new position, UV, and the two individuals are placed at point R on it.

In movement from Q on the utility possibility curve UV to point R on the utility possibility curve U 'V' the utility of A has improved and that of B has deteriorated. But position R denotes greater social welfare on the basis of Kaldor's criterion when compared to the position Q on the original utility possibility curve UV because with UV as the utility possibility curve it is possible to move through mere redistribution of income from position R to position S where the individual B has been fully compensated for his loss of utility, the individual A is still better off as compared to position Q. Social welfare increases for any change in the economy that moves the individuals from a position on a lower utility possibility curve to a position on a higher utility possibility curve.*

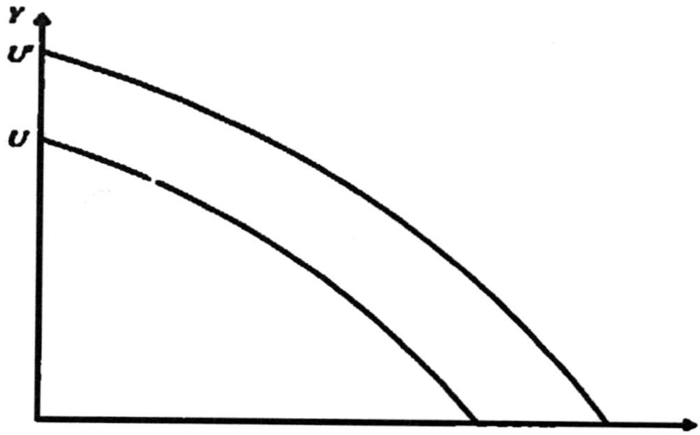

Fig. 7: Kaldor-Hicks Welfare Criterion.

Scitovsky Paradox

Scitovsky pointed out an important limitation of Kaldor-Hicks criterion that it might lead to contradictory results. He showed that, if in some situation, position B is shown to be an improvement over position A on Kaldor-Hicks criterion, it may be possible that position A is also shown to be an improvement over B on the basis of the same criterion. For getting consistent results when position B has been revealed to be preferred to position A on the basis of a welfare criterion, then position A must not be preferred to position B on the same criterion. According to Scitovsky, Kaldor- Hicks criterion involves such contradictory and inconsistent results. Since Scitovsky was the first to point out this paradoxical result in Kaldor-Hicks criterion, it is known as 'Scitovsky Paradox'.

Figure 8 shows how Kaldor-Hicks criterion may lead to contradictory results in some situation. In this figure JK and GH are the two utility possibility curves which intersect each other. Now suppose that the initial position is at point C on JK.

Further suppose that due to a certain policy change, utility possibility curve changes and takes the position GH and the two individuals find themselves at position D. Position D is superior to position C on the basis of Kaldor-Hicks criterion because from position D movement can be made through

* H.L. Ahuja (2016). Modern Economics, 2015, pp. 793-775.

mere redistribution to position F at which individual B has been fully compensated but individual A is still better off as compared to the original position C. Thus, movement from position C to position D satisfies Kaldor-Hicks criterion. But, as has been pointed out by Scitovsky, reverse movement from position D on the new utility possibility curve GH to the position C on the old utility possibility curve JK also represents an improvement on Kaldor-Hicks criterion, that is, C is socially better than D on the basis of Kaldor- Hicks criterion.

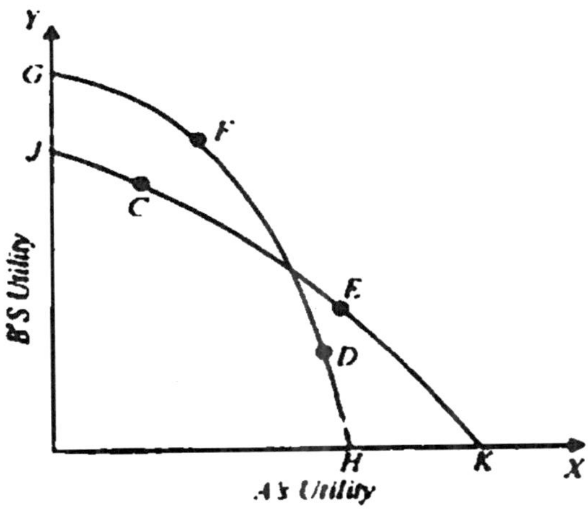

Fig. 8: Scitvosky Paradox.

The movement from position C to the position D due to a policy change is passed by the Kaldor-Hicks criterion and also the movement back from position D to position C is also passed by the Kaldor-Hicks criterion. This implies that D is socially better than C on this criterion and C is also socially better than D on the same criterion. So Kaldor-Hicks criterion leads us to contradictory and inconsistent results. These contradictory results are obtained by Kaldor-Hicks criterion when following a policy change new utility possibility curve intersects the former utility possibility curve. After bringing out the possibility of contradictory results in Kaldor-Hicks criterion Scitovsky formulated his own criterion which is generally known as Scitovsky's Double Criterion.*

Scitovsky's Double Criterion of Welfare

To rule out the possibility of contradictory results in Kaldor-Hicks criterion Scitovsky formulated a double criterion which requires the fulfillment of Kaldor-

* H.L. Ahuja (2016). Modern Economics, 2015 edition, p. 766.

Hicks criterion and also the fulfillment of the reversal test. It means that a change is an improvement if the gainers in the changed situation are able to persuade the losers to accept the change and simultaneously losers are not able to persuade the gainers to remain in the original situation. Scitovsky's double criterion can also be explained with the help of utility possibility curve. In Figure 8, CD and EF are the two utility possibility curves which do not intersect each other at any point. Suppose there is a change from position Q on the utility possibility curve CD to the position G on the utility possibility curve EF as a result of the adoption of a new economic policy.

Such a movement is an improvement on Kaldor-Hicks criterion because G lies on the utility possibility curve EF passing through point R. From the position G, movement can be made to the position R simply by reallocating revenue between the two individuals. And R is better than Q because the utility of both the individuals is greater at R as compared to the position Q. Thus, the Kaldor-Hicks criterion is satisfied and therefore change from Q to G will increase social welfare.

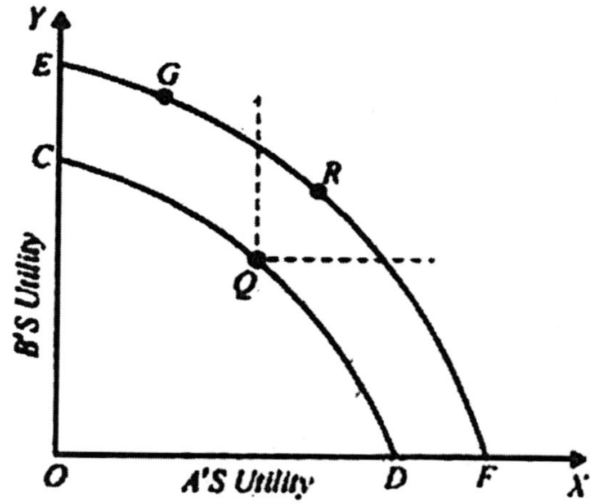

Fig. 8: Scitovsky's Double Criterion.

A movement from the position G back to the original position Q must not be passed by Kaldor-Hicks criterion if Scitovsky's reversal test is to be satisfied. It is marked from Figure 8 that from position R we cannot move to any position on the utility possibility curve CD merely through redistribution of income which is socially better than G. While movement from position Q to G is passed by Kaldor-Hicks criterion, reverse movement from position G to position Q is not passed by Kaldor-Hicks criterion. Hence, the movement from the position Q to G satisfies Scitovsky's criterion. Thus, when the two utility possibility curves are non-intersecting and change involves movement from a position on a lower utility possibility curve to a position on a higher utility possibility curve, the change raises social welfare on the basis of Kaldor-Hicks-Scitovsky criterion.*

The Bergson Criterion

The concept of 'Social Welfare Function' was propounded by A. Bergson in his article 'A Re-formulation of Certain Aspects of Welfare Economics' in 1938. Social welfare function is an ordinal index of society's welfare and is a function of the utility levies of all individuals constituting the society.

Bergson-Samuelson social welfare function can be written in the following manner:

$$W = W(U_1, U_2, U3\ldots\ldots\ldots\ldots, U_n)$$

where W If represents the social welfare U_1, U_2, U_3, ..., U_n represent the ordinal utility indices of different individuals of the society.

Bergson's social welfare function is supposed to be dependent on changes in economic events that have a direct effect on individual welfares. The ordinal utility level of an individual is a function of his own consumption of goods and services and not of others. The social welfare function and its form depend upon the value judgements of the person or institution that the society has authorised to decide.[23]

The Bergson-Samuelson social welfare function is based on explicit value judgements and involves interpersonal comparisons of utility in ordinal terms. Once the social welfare function has been decided upon by value judgements, the maximisation technique is used to obtain the maximum social welfare position at which allocation of resources is Pareto optimum and also the distribution of goods and services is equitable.[24]

The Problem of Second Best

The theory of the second best concerns the situation when one or more optimality conditions cannot be satisfied. The economists Richard Lipsey and Kelvin Lancaster showed in 1956, that if one optimality condition in an economic model cannot be satisfied, it is possible that the next-best solution involves changing other variables away from the values that would otherwise be optimal.[25] The problem of second best poses a nagging and interesting dilemma for antitrust analysis. It has been dismissed as a valid but unworkable criticism of traditional antitrust doctrine.

The problem of second best deals with the question of whether interventions directed at specific market imperfections can improve overall social welfare. According to the theory of second best, correcting specific market imperfections while leaving others untouched will not necessarily

* H.L. Ahuja (2016). Modern Economics, 20th edition, pp. 796-797.

improve social welfare. The theory of second best in general states that in a system where conditions are such that a Pareto optimum exists, if one condition is changed so that it is no longer at its optimum state, then to reach a second best optimum, all the other conditions must be changed from their original first best optimum states.[26]

Arrow's Impossibility theorem

Arrow's impossibility theorem states that, when voters have three or more distinct alternatives, no rank order voting system can convert the ranked preferences of individuals into a community-wide ranking while also meeting a pre-specified set of criteria. This theory is also known as the General Possibility Theorem or Arrow's paradox. The theorem is named after economist Kenneth Arrow, who demonstrated the theorem in his doctoral thesis and popularised it in his 1951 book 'Social Choice and Individual Values'.

Kenneth Arrow's "impossibility" theorem answers a very basic question in the theory of collective decision-making. The technical framework in which Arrow gave the question of social orderings a precise sense and its rigorous answer is now widely used for studying problems in welfare economics. The impossibility theorem itself set much of the agenda for contemporary social choice theory. One of the central issues in the theory of voting is described by Arrow's Impossibility Theorem, which states roughly that no reasonably consistent and fair voting system can result in sensible results. Named after Nobel Prize-winning economist Kenneth Arrow, the theorem starts by establishing a set of reasonable conditions on voting, that is, on the method of aggregating individuals' preferences into group preferences.

Arrow's Theorem states that, when choosing between more than two options, it is impossible in general to implement these four conditions without creating cycling group preferences. Demanding transitive group preferences and the first three conditions implies there will be a dictatorship. In short, the theorem states that no rank-order voting system can be designed that always satisfy these three "fairness" criteria:

(a) If every voter prefers alternative X over alternative Y, then the group prefers X over Y.

(b) If every voter's preference between X and Y remains unchanged, then the group's preference between X and Y will also remain unchanged (even if voters' preferences between other pairs like X and Z, Y and Z, or Z and W change).

(c) There is no "dictator": no single voter possesses the power to always determine the group's preference.

The framework for Arrow's theorem assumes that we need to extract a preference order on a given set of options. Each individual in the society gives a particular order of preferences on the set of outcomes. We are searching for a ranked voting system, called a social welfare function, which transforms the set of preferences into a single global societal preference order.

Arrow assumed that social orderings will be derived, if at all, from information about people's preferences. His point was that even if people do have stronger and weaker preferences, and even if the strengths of their preferences can somehow be measured and made available as a basis for social decisions, nevertheless ordinal information is all that matters because preferences are "interpersonally incomparable". Arrow required aggregation procedures to derive social orderings from more than just a single profile, representing everyone's *actual* preferences. Arrow's rationale for requiring aggregation procedures to handle many profiles was epistemic.

References

1. Brainy Quote, Available at http://www.brainyquote.com/quotes/keywords/environment.html
2. Economics, Available at https://en.wikipedia.org/wiki/Economics
3. Welfare economics, Available at https://en.wikipedia.org/wiki/Welfare_economics
4. Dominick Salvatore, Microeconomics: Theory and applications, p. 587.
5. http://www.britannica.com/topic/welfare-economics
6. H.L Ahuja (2003), Advanced Economic Theory, S. Chand and Company, p.1027.
7. Social welfare function, Available at https://en.wikipedia.org/wiki/Social_welfare_function
8. H.L Ahuja (2003), Advanced Economic Theory, S. Chand and Company, p.1031.
9. Supriya Guru, New Welfare Economics: Compensation Principle, Available at http://www.yourarticlelibrary.com/economics/new-welfare-economics-compensation-principle-with-diagram/37588/
10. http://schoolworkhelper.net/jeremy-bentham-1748-%E2%80%93-1832-the-principle-of-utility/
11. Social welfare function, Available at https://en.wikipedia.org/wiki/Social_welfare_function
12. Jeremy Bentham, Available at https://en.wikipedia.org/wiki/Jeremy_Bentham
13. Online guide to ethics and moral philosophy, Available at http://caae.phil.cmu.edu/Cavalier/80130/part2/sect9.html
14. Pareto efficiency, Available at https://en.wikipedia.org/wiki/Pareto_efficiency
15. http://www.economyprofessor.com/pareto-optimality-1906
16. General equilibrium and Pareto efficiency, Available at http://www.sef.hku.hk/~wsuen/teaching/umicro/sup19.html
17. Dominick Salvatore, Microeconomics: Theory and Applications, p. 593.
18. Kaldor–Hicks improvement, Available at https://en.wikipedia.org/wiki/Kaldor%E2%80%93Hicks_efficiency
19. Supriya Guru, New Welfare Economics: Compensation Principle, Available at http://www.yourarticlelibrary.com/economics/new-welfare-economics-compensation-principle-with-diagram/37588/

20. H.L. Ahuja (2002), Advanced Economic Theory, p. 1059.

21. *Ibid,* p. 1057.

22. http://www.economicshelp.org/blog/glossary/kaldor-hicks/

23. Supriya Guru, The Concept of Social Welfare Propounded by A. Bergson, Available at http://www.yourarticlelibrary.com/economics/the-concept-of-social-welfare-propounded-by-a-bergson/37642/

24. *Ibid.*

25. The theory of second best, Available at https://en.wikipedia.org/wiki/Theory_of_the_second_best

26. Joseph Rebello (2002), The Problem of Second Best: Are Partial Equilibrium and Third-Best Analyses Solutions?, Available at http://home.uchicago.edu/~rposner/rebello2.htm

* Acknowledgement:- Information of the chapter are taken from manuscript of (a) H.L. Ahuja, Modern Economics; (a) M.L. Jhingan, Principle of Economics.

Chapter - 2

Environment and Social Welfare

"Our population and our use of the finite resources of planet Earth are growing exponentially, along with our technical ability to change the environment for good or ill."

— ***Stephen Hawking***[1]

The global economy is now so large that society can no longer safely pretend it operates within a limitless ecosystem. Developing an economy that can be sustained within the finite biosphere requires new ways of thinking. Sustainability is one of those troublesome abstract nouns like justice, truth, and beauty.[2] The Fundamental Theorems of Welfare Economics: The First Theorem: Every Competitive Equilibrium is an Efficient Outcome Under a competitive equilibrium; every consumer faces the same prices. Similarly, each producer faces the same input prices. Second Theorem: If preferences and technology are convex, then every Pareto optimal outcome can be represented as a competitive equilibrium for some pattern of initial endowments and some vector of prices.[3]

Definition of Social Welfare Function

Social welfare function is a function that ranks social states as less desirable, more desirable, or indifferent for every possible pair of social states. Inputs of the function include any variables considered to affect the economic welfare of a society. A social welfare function provides a societal preference based on only individual utility functions, whereas in others it also outputs cardinal measures of social welfare not aggregated from individual utility functions. The form of the social welfare function is intended to express a statement of objectives of a society.[4]

Maximisation of Social Welfare

Professor Bator in his paper "The Simple Analytics of Welfare Maximisation" has presented a more thorough and systematic analysis of the problem of social welfare maximisation." It is a summary of the static long run general equilibrium conditions of a perfectly competitive economy.[5]

The assumptions of maximising welfare are[6]:

1. There are two factors, labour L, and capital K, whose quantities are given (in perfectly inelastic supply). These factors are homogeneous and perfectly divisible.
2. Two products, X and Y, are produced by two firms. Each firm produces only one commodity.
3. Only two homogeneous commodities X and Y are produced in the economy.
4. There is a social welfare function that is based on the positions of A and B in their own preference scale.
5. There are two consumers whose preferences are represented by indifference curves, which are continuous, convex to the origin and do not intersect.
6. The goal of consumers is utility maximisation and the goal of firms is profit maximisation.
7. The production functions are independent. This rule out joint products and external economies and diseconomies in production.
8. The utilities of consumers are independent.[7]

There are fixed amounts of two inputs, labour (L) and Capital (K), available to the economy for the production of two goods, X and Y. The production function for each good is given by smooth isoquants which are characterised by constant returns to scale and diminishing rates of technical substitutions (MRTS). The various points on the contract curve are of efficient locus where an increase in the production of X implies a necessary reduction in the output of Y. From the production contract curve, we can trace the production possibility curve or transformation curve in the output space from the input space. This curve shows the various combinations of X and Y that can be produced with fixed amounts of labour and capital.

The next step is to specify general equilibrium of exchange in the economy consisting of two individuals A and B and two goods X and Y. For this purpose, we derive the grand utility possibility curve from the production possibility curve. The condition for welfare maximisation requires the general equilibrium of exchange and production simultaneously. This condition implies that the marginal rate of substitution of X and Y must equal the marginal rate of transformation between the two. The grand utility possibility curve is the locus of Pareto optimum points of exchange and production. In order to find out which of the Pareto optimum points on the grand utility possibility curve represents the maximum welfare, we have to draw a social welfare function.[8]

Public Goods

It is a good that is both non-excludable and non-rivalrous in that individuals cannot be effectively excluded from use and where use by one individual does not reduce availability to others. Paul A. Samuelson is usually credited as the first economist to develop the theory of public goods. In his classic 1954 paper, "The Pure Theory of Public Expenditure", he defined a public good, or as he called it in the paper a "collective consumption good", as follows: [goods] which all enjoy in common in the sense that each individual's consumption of such a good lead to no subtractions from any other individual's consumption of that good. Public goods that are available everywhere are sometimes referred to as global public goods.

Classical theory of public goods reveals through the works of Adam Smith the following perception on public goods and education: "A man without the proper use of the intellectual faculties of a man is, if possible, more contemptible than even a coward, and seems to be mutilated and deformed in a still more essential part of the character of human nature. Though the state was to derive no advantage from the instruction of the inferior ranks of people, it would still deserve its attention that they should not be altogether uninstructed (...). The state, however, derives no inconsiderable advantage from their instruction".[9]

Public Goods have two distinct characteristics: (a) non-rivalry: several individuals can consume the same goods without diminishing its value, and (b) non-excludability: an individual cannot be prevented from consuming the good.[10] **Impure public goods** are goods that satisfy the two public goods conditions (non-rival and non-excludable) to some extent, but not fully. These are also known as "Quasi-public." An example of an impure public goods would be cable television. **Pure public goods** are goods that are perfectly non-rivalrous in consumption and are non-excludable. Pure public goods are rare because there are few goods that can meet both of these requirements. A classic example of a pure public goods is national defense.[11]

Economists define a public goods as being non rival and non-excludable. The non-rival part of this definition means that my consumption does not affect your consumption of a good. The non-excludable portion of this definition means that I cannot prevent you from consuming a good. Another way of understanding this concept is saying that adding an additional person to the public goods market has a marginal cost of $0. In other words, even those who do not explicitly pay for the good can benefit from the goods.[12]

Optimal amount of public goods is the amount at which the sum of the marginal benefits of all the individuals consuming the goods equals its marginal cost. Graphically, this is given by the point at which the aggregate demand curve for the goods intersects the market supply curve of the goods. A free-rider problem arises because each consumer believes that the public goods will be provided anyway, whether he or she contributes to its payments or not. The problem is that since many individuals behave this way, less than the optimal amount of the public goods will be provided.[13]

There are relatively few examples of pure public goods. Examples include flood control systems, some of the broadcasting services provided by the BBC, public water supplies, street lighting for roads and motorways, lighthouse protection for ships and also national defense services. A quasi-public good is a near-public goods Quasi-public goods are:

1. *Semi-non-rival:* up to a point, extra consumers using a park, beach or road do not reduce the space available for others. Eventually beaches become crowded as do parks and other leisure facilities. Open access Wi-Fi networks become crowded.
2. *Semi-non-excludable:* it is possible but often difficult or expensive to exclude non-paying consumers. E.g. fencing a park or beach and charging an entrance fee; building toll booths to charge for road usage on congested routes.[14]

The classical definition of a public goods is one that is non-excludable and non-rivalrous. Once the goods is produced, it is accessible to all comers, whether or not they pay. Non-buyers cannot be excluded from reaping benefits from the goods. Once the local service club set off the fireworks, it could not prevent spectators in nearby fields from watching[15]. The classic example of a public goods is a lighthouse. Non-excludable because it's not possible to exclude some ships from enjoying the benefits of the lighthouse while at the same time providing the benefits to other ships; and Non-rivalrous because if the lighthouse's benefits are already being provided to some ships, it costs nothing for additional ships to enjoy the benefits as well.[16]

Private Goods

Goods are either rivalrous or non-rivalrous, or either excludable or non-excludable. An alternative definition is that a non-rivalrous goods may be provided to more consumers at a very low marginal cost for each additional consumer. Excludable goods are those for which one can at low cost prevent those who have not paid for the goods from consuming it. Common goods are those which are rivalrous in consumption but non-excludable. A private goods is defined in economics as an item that yields positive benefits to people that is excludable. Unlike public goods, private goods are less likely to have the free rider problem. Assuming a private goods is valued positively by everyone, the efficiency of obtaining the good is obstructed by its rivalry.[17]

According to Encyclopedia Britannica, Private goods, a product or service produced by a privately owned business and purchased to increase the utility, or satisfaction, of the buyer. The majority of the goods and services consumed in a market economy are private goods, and their prices are determined to some degree by the market forces of supply and demand. A number of fairness and justice issues arise with respect to private goods. Pure private goods are both excludable and rivalrous.

Market Failure

Public goods provide a very important example of market failure, in which market-like behaviour of individual gain-seeking does not produce efficient results. The production of public goods results in positive externalities which are not remunerated. If private organisations do not reap all the benefits of a public good which they have produced, their incentives to produce it voluntarily might be insufficient. Consumers can take advantage of public goods without contributing sufficiently to their creation. This is called the free rider problem. The free rider problem depends on a conception of the human being as homo economicus: purely rational and also purely selfish—extremely individualistic, considering only those benefits and costs that directly affect him or her.[18]

Market failure occurs when resources are inefficiently allocated due to imperfections in the market mechanism. There is a clear economic case for government intervention in markets where some form of market failure is taking place. Externalities are common in virtually every area of economic activity. They are defined as third party effects arising from the production and/or consumption of goods and services for which no appropriate compensation is paid. Externalities can cause market failure if the price mechanism does not take into account the full social costs and social benefits of production and consumption. Consumers can create externalities when they purchase and consume goods and services.

In economics, an externality is a cost or benefit from an economic transaction that parties external to the transaction receive or incur. An externality refers to the uncompensated impact of one person's actions on the well-being of a bystander. An externality arises when a person engages in an activity that influences the well-being of a bystander and yet neither pays nor receives any compensation for that effect. Externalities can be either positive or negative, and they can be generated from both the production and the consumption side of a transaction.

When the impact on the bystander is adverse, the externality is called a negative externality. Negative externalities lead markets to produce a larger quantity than is socially desirable. Any form of negative externality results in an over allocation of the goods or service associated with the externality. Society is producing too much of a bad thing. Government might wish to discourage production or consumption of the goods or service through the use of excise taxes, surtaxes, or tariffs.[19]

Positive externalities exist when the marginal social benefit of production and or consumption exceeds the marginal private benefit i.e. production and/or consumption generate external benefits that may go under-valued by the market. Where substantial positive externalities exist, the goods or service may be under consumed or under provided since the free market may fail to take into account their effects. Individuals who consider only their own private costs and private benefits will do too much of any activity that generates negative externalities, and too little of one that generates positive externalities. When externalities are present the individual pursuit of self-interest rarely results in maximum social welfare. When it does not, we have an outcome that is, by definition, inefficient.[20]

According to mainstream economics, efficient resource allocation is outcome of: (a) rational choices/decisions by economic agents; and (b) Free and competitive market structure. Market failure occurs when the market fails to give efficient allocation of resources, due to non-fulfillment of conditions. Government can play a crucial role to improve the inefficient market outcomes.[21]

Many people on the political right believe that free markets are the solution to most any problem. The main market failure in retirement insurance markets is called "moral hazard" – people who will not save for retirement because in they know that a compassionate society will give them enough to survive in any case. There are two important market failures in the healthcare market. The first is moral hazard, and it is much like the moral hazard problem in retirement insurance markets. A second problem, an information problem, is called adverse selection. There are many other market failures in healthcare markets, e.g. patients not knowing enough about treatments to be informed consumers, and all of them can be mostly resolved through government managed healthcare systems such as those adopted in other developed countries.[22]

References

1. Brainy Quote, Available at http://www.brainyquote.com/quotes/keywords/environment.html
2. Ecological Economics and Sustainable Development, Selected Essays of Herman Daly, Available at http://library. uniteddiversity.coop/Measuring_Progress_and_Eco_Footprinting/Ecological_Economics_and_Sustainable_Development-Selected_Essays_of_Herman_Daly.pdf
3. Vani K. Borooah, Market Failure: An Economic Analysis of its Causes and Consequences, p.7.
4. Social welfare function, Available at https://en.wikipedia.org/wiki/Social_welfare_function
5. M.L. Jhingan, Micro economics, p. 671.
6. Trisha, Maximisation of Social Welfare (8 Assumptions), Retrieved from http://www.economicsdiscussion.net/economics-2/maximisation-of-social-welfare-8-assumptions/6024
7. Maximisation of Social Welfare, Available at http://www.tutorsonnet.com/maximisation-of-social-welfare-homework-help.php

8. M.L. Jhingan, Microeconomics, pp. 670-75.
9. Education and the Characteristics of Public Goods- Overlaps and Differences, Available at http://store.ectap.ro/articole/635.pdf
10. http://are.berkeley.edu/~zilber11/EEP101/Lecture-Summary-PDF/lec09-10-Public-Goods.pdf
11. See https://publicecon.wikispaces.com/Public+Goods
12. See http://www.econport.org/content/handbook/Market-Failure/Public-Goods/PRIV-V-PUB.html
13. Dominick Salvatore, Microeconomics-Theory and applications, p. 614.
14. Geoff Riley, Public goods, Available at http://beta.tutor2u.net/economics/reference/public-goods
15. See http://faculty.winthrop.edu/stonebrakerr/book/public_goods.htm
16. Public Goods: Examples, Available at https://en.wikipedia.org/wiki/Public_good
17. See http://www.pitt.edu/~upjecon/MCG/MICRO/GOVT/Pubgood.html
18. Public good, Available at https://en.wikipedia.org/wiki/Public_good
19. See http://macnomics.mscuttle.com/wp-content/uploads/2010/09/Handout-Unit-3-Topic-5-rev.pdf
20. See http://www.revisionguru.co.uk/economics/edexeconunit2.pdf
21. See http://www.hrdiap.gov.in/87fc/study_meterial/economics/Market%20 failure.pdf
22. See http://www.thefiscaltimes.com/Columns/2013/06/18/7-Important-Examples-of-How-Markets-Can-Fail

Chapter - 3

Environmental Economics

"If we're destroying our trees and destroying our environment and hurting animals and hurting one another and all that stuff, there's got to be a very powerful energy to fight that. I think we need more love in the world. We need more kindness, more compassion, more joy, more laughter. I definitely want to contribute to that."

—***Ellen DeGeneres***[1]

Environmental problems are the result of our pursuit of affluence. The economic analysis of environmental issues can be approached from two different perspectives, environmental economics and ecological economics. Environmental economics applies insights from traditional economics to environmental issues. Ecological economics places greater emphasis on sustainability based on ecosystem integrity, stressing that all economic activity occurs within the broader biological and physical systems that support life. Ecological economists are more likely to see the value of nature as something extending beyond any monetary estimates.[2]

Pollution can be classified in terms of its damage mechanism. This has important implications for how pollution targets are set and for the way in which pollution is most appropriately controlled. The distinction here concerns whether damage arises from the flow of the pollutant or from the stock of pollution in the relevant environmental medium. Flow-damage pollution occurs when damage results only from the flow of residuals: that is, the rate at which they are being discharged into the environmental system. Stock-damage pollution describes the case in which damages depend only on the stock of the pollutant in the relevant environmental system at any point in time.[3]

Environmental economics is an emerging area in the realm of economic science. Before 1970s a little attention was paid for the growth and development of this part of the area of knowledge in economics. The first oil stock in 1971 and thereafter the emergence of relatively higher levels of environmental damages at the global level prompted the scholars in this field to apply economic tools to environmental science.[4] Environment, environmentalists, environmentalism etc., are the common words used in our ordinary life in recent years. Environmentalists are those who love and care for environment, which realise that any damage to the environment will affect the life of living things. Environmental concern of environmentalists and fundamental environmentalists are different.[5]

Definition of Environmental Economics

Environmental economics is a sub-field of economics that is concerned with environmental issues. It is related to ecological economics but there are differences. Most environmental economists have been trained as economists. It was a major influence for the theories of natural capitalism and environmental finance, which could be said to be two sub-branches of environmental economics concerned with resource conservation in production, and the value of biodiversity to humans, respectively.[6]

Beneficiation of Environmental Economics

Environmental economics looks at how economic activity and policy affect the environment in which we live. Some production generates pollution - for example, power station emissions can cause acid rain and also contribute to global warming. The central questions in environmental economics concern this tradeoff: (a) If environmental protection is costly, how much should we spend on pollution control?; (b) In making these decisions, how can we compare the benefit of a 'clean' environment with the costs of pollution control?; '(c) Is government intervention in the economy needed to reduce pollution, or can we rely on the market economy to get us to the optimal outcome?; and (d) What form should government policies to cut pollution take? Why does Europe operate a 'cap and trade' emissions trading scheme rather than impose a carbon tax?.[7]

The beneficiation strategy provides a framework that seeks to translate the country's sheer comparative advantage inherited from mineral resources endowment to a national competitive advantage. The strategy is aligned to a national industrialisation programme, which seeks to enhance the quantity and quality of exports, promote creation of decent employment and diversification of the economy, including promotion of the green economy. The strategy presents an intervention that advances the developmental agenda of government.[8] In very broad terms, environmental economics looks at how economic activity and policy affect the environment in which we live. Some production generates pollution for example; power station emissions cause acid rain and also contribute to global warming.[9]

Environmental economics is concerned with the impact of economic activities on the environment, the significance of ecosystem to the economy, and suggests the appropriate ways of regulating economic activity, so that cosmic balance is achieved in the society. Environmental Economics can help us understand why many of the Earth's natural resources are under threat, and what we can do to address these threats. The major in Environmental and Natural Resource Economics provides students with tools to weigh options and make important decisions concerning the protection, restoration, development, and use of our natural resources.[10]

Relation between Environmental Economies and Economics

In recent years there has been growing concern about degradation and pollution of environment and climate change as they impact on future development of both the developing and developed countries. Increases in population cause over-exploitation of natural resources such as forests, water, fisheries and minerals at a rate far greater than their capacity to regenerate. Populations increases cause over-exploitation of land and water resources and loss of biodiversity and forests and will therefore endanger sustainability of agriculture and food security in the country.[11]

The relationship between economic growth and the environment is, and will always remain, controversial.[12] Since the outbreak of the famous industrial revolution in Europe, the enginery-based manufacture has gradually replaced the agriculture-based natural economy. People thought that without the industrial revolution, without its enormous productivity, our society would not have the overstepping progress of society, and the social life would not become so rich and varied. Agricultural pollution combined with industrial contamination's emissions made the four circle seriously damaged. Industrial production and research especially heavy industry will bring invisible pollution to human, including noise pollution, electromagnetic pollution, nuclear radiation pollution and so on, which hang a layer of the terrible shadow over human health and survival.[13]

Environmental economics discuss how resources and environment can help for economic development and growth. Pollution is a threat foe our economy and so it should be decrease. One can easily identify various instruments for controlling pollution if he or she studies Environmental economics.

Ecological Economics

Ecological economics was founded as a modern movement in the works of and interactions between various European and American academics. Among the topics addressed by ecological economics are methodologies, allocation of resources, weak versus strong sustainability, energy economics, energy accounting and balance, environmental services, cost shifting, and modeling. Ecological economics is founded upon the view that the neoclassical economics assumption that environmental and community costs and benefits are mutually canceling "externalities" is not warranted.[14]

Ecological economics is a trans-disciplinary field. It's not trying to be a sub-discipline of economics or a sub-discipline of ecology, but really it's a bridge across not only ecology and economics but also psychology, anthropology, archaeology, and history. It tries to study everything outside the market as well as everything inside the market and bring the two together. It tries to study everything outside the market as well as everything inside the market and bring the two together[15].

Ecological Economics addresses the relationships between ecosystems and economic systems in the broadest sense. These relationships are the locus of many of our most pressing current problemsbut they are not well covered by any existing discipline. Environmental and resource economics, as it is currently practiced, covers only the application of neoclassical economics to environmental and resource problems.[16] It is poised to play a leading role in the ongoing effort to reconcile economic theory and policy with accepted knowledge from other discipline.[17]

Ecological economics takes a broader perspective and recognises that there are more things that contribute to human well-being than just the amount of stuff, such as health and education (human capital), friends and family (social capital) and the contribution of the earth and its biological and physical systems (natural capital). It is a growing transdisciplinary field that aims to improve and expand economic theory to integrate the earth's natural systems, human values and human health and well-being. It is also seeking true economic efficiency.[18]

Resources Economics

Economic resources are the factors used in producing goods or providing services. In other words, they are the inputs that are used to create things or help you provide services. Economic resources can be divided into human resources, such as labour and management, and nonhuman resources, such as land, capital goods, financial resources, and technology.[19] Resource economics does not bother about the environmental impact of production and consumption, but environmental economics deals with these aspects.

There are four fundamental types of economic resources: Land, Labour, Capital, and Entrepreneurship. Land includes all natural physical resources like gold, iron, silver, oil etc. Some countries have very rich natural resources and by utilising these resources they enrich their economy to the peak. The **human** input in the production or manufacturing process is known as labour. Workers have different work capacity. To the **economist,** that money is not investment that someone put into the bank or in a stock market. In fact, in economics, capital is a term that means investment in the capital goods. The **Entrepreneurship** is person or individual who wants to supply the product to the market to make profit.[20]

Important Issues in Environmental Economies

Environmental economics is considered both as positive and normative science. It covers both micro and macro aspects of different pollution problems. It is an application of scientific theories and general application of welfare economics. It deals with economic and managerial aspects of pollution and natural resources. It interacts between human beings and their physical surroundings. It studies the impact of pollution on human beings and suggests national utilisation of resources in a proper way so that there may be an increase in social welfare or minimisation of social costs.[21]

Environmental economics is primarily concerned with the impact of economic activities on environment and its implications for the individual firm, industry and the economy as a whole. The main objective of environmental economics is to maintain a balance between economic development and environmental quality. It has emerged as a discipline to tackle environmental problems from an economic welfare framework. It is inherently a multi-disciplinary subject. It consists of an integration of many varied disciplines such as biology, ecology, physical sciences, ethics and main stream economics.[22]

Macro-Economics Policy and Environmental

Many macroeconomic policies have an indirect and a wide spread impact on the countries 'resources and the environment'. Stabilisation and structural adjustment programmes aim for a stable economy over the long run. Macroeconomic policies may or may not be successful in generating economic growth but these policies have an indirect impact on the environment due to changes in income, taxes, subsidies, public revenue and innovative capacity.[23]

Many of the basic tenets of macroeconomic policy need to be redefined in the context of current global problems. The objectives of macroeconomic policy should include economic stabilisation, distributional equity, broad social goals such as income security, education, and universal healthcare, and the management of economic growth. There is an increasing recognition that the achievement of social goals is essential to environmental sustainability.[24] Environmental economics has traditionally fallen in the domain of microeconomics, but recently approaches from macroeconomics have been applied to studying environmental policy.

Microeconomic theoretical and empirical analysis are usually used to answer questions about the effect of pollution on health, the effect of policy on pollution, or the optimal design of resource policy. There has recently been a growth in research that combines methods from macroeconomics with policy questions related to environmental economic.[25] Development of macroeconomic stability is important to the expectations formed by entrepreneurs and, therefore, for industrial production. In particular, inflation targeting credibility stimulates industrial production, since it increases the confidence of entrepreneurs about the functioning of the economy and their businesses.[26] The link between poverty and environment is often mentioned in the debates on sustainable development" and structural adjustment.[27]

Macroeconomic policy is concerned with the operation of the economy as a whole. In broad terms, the goal of macroeconomic policy is to provide a stable economic environment that is conducive to fostering strong and sustainable economic growth, on which the creation of jobs, wealth and improved living standards depend.[28] In addition to active macroeconomic policies, countries that have achieved sustained economic growth have used a range of supportive policy interventions. They involve a country-specific mix of trade, finance and investment policies, along with active labour market and social policies.[29]

Common Property Resources

Common-pool resource is a type of good consisting of a natural or human-made resource system (e.g. an irrigation system or fishing grounds), whose size or characteristics makes it costly, but not impossible, to exclude potential beneficiaries from obtaining benefits from its use. The use of the term "common property resource" to designate a type of good has been criticised, because common-pool resources are not necessarily governed by common property protocols. It tends to be particularly susceptible to depletion and degradation. This creates problems for sustainable development and for resource stewardship in general since many of the key global resources are common property.[30]

Some classic examples of common-pool resources are fisheries, forests, underwater basins, and irrigation systems. Common-pool resources are susceptible to overuse and are thus prone to "tragedies of the commons," which are present when individual and group interests are in conflict. Fish resources are generally considered common property and open to any user. This, the assumption goes, makes them susceptible to the "tragedy of the commons" in which selfish users are both the villains and the victims. While it is true that wild fish populations cannot readily be privatised, it hardly follows that they are completely open-access. In addition to social controls found in many traditional fishing communities, amply documented by anthropologists, many administrative controls in contemporary fisheries management also create limited property rights over fishery resources.[31]

Common-pool resources may be owned by national, regional or local governments as public goods, by communal groups as common property resources, or by private individuals or corporations as private goods. In economics, open access resources are, for the most part, rivalrous, non-excludable goods. This makes them similar to common goods during times of prosperity. Unlike many common goods, open access goods require little oversight or may be difficult to restrict access.[32] Common Property Resources are usually non-exclusive resources to which rights of use are distributed among a number of co-owners, generally identified by their membership in a community or a village. Common property resources are those resources which are accessible to the whole community or village and to which no individual has exclusive ownership or property rights. The common property resources can be subjected to individual use but no individual can claim ownership over them as it is used by a number of stakeholders who have their own independent right to use.[33]

Common property resource management regimes are defined as a set of institutional arrangements that regulate the use of common pool resources (CPRs, also called the commons). The institutional arrangement or property rights governing CPRs could be no property (open access), private property, government property, and common or communal property CPRs are those natural and human-constructed resources where it is difficult to exclude potential users and the benefits derived from the resource are subtractable. These are called the principles of difficulty of exclusion and subtractability.[34] However, CPR institutions have generally faced an unsupportive policy environment; it is therefore over-simplistic for those in favour of privatisation of property rights to ascribe their erosion to commercial or demographic pressures per se.[35]

Stevenson defines common property as a form of resource ownership with the following characteristics:

- The resource unit has bounds that are well defined by physical, biological, and social parameters.
- There is a well-delineated group of users, who are distinct from persons excluded from resource use.
- Multiple included users participate in resource extraction.
- Explicit or implicit well-understood rules exist among users regarding their rights and their duties to one another about resource extraction.
- Users share joint, nonexclusive entitlement to the in situ or fugitive resource prior to its capture or use.
- Users compete for the resource and thereby impose negative externalities on one another.
- A well-delineated group of rights holders exists, which may or may not coincide with the group of users.[36]

References

1. Brainy Quote, Available at http://www.brainyquote.com/quotes/keywords/environment.html
2. Brian Roach, Jonathan M. Harris and Anne-Marie Codur, Microeconomics and the Environment, See http://www.ase.tufts.edu/gdae/education_materials/modules/microeconomics_and_the_environment.pdf

3. Roger Perman, YueMa, James McGilvray and Michael Common, Natural Resource and Environmental Economics, See http://econdse.org/wp-content/uploads/2014/01/perman_et_al_chapters_6_and_7.pdf
4. Environmental Economics: Meaning, Definition and Importance, Available at http://www.newagepublishers.com/samplechapter/001600.pdf
5. See http://www.newagepublishers.com/samplechapter/001600.pdf
6. Environmental Economics, Available at https://en.wikipedia.org/wiki/Environmental_economics
7. Environmental Economics, Available at http://studyingeconomics.ac.uk/module-options/environmental-economics/
8. Beneficiation economics, Available at http://www.dmr.gov.za/beneficiation-economics.html
9. Environmental economics, Available at http://whystudyeconomics.ac.uk/During-your-study/module-choices/Environmental-economics/
10. See http://www.uri.edu/roadmap/academic_roadmap/schools/uri/programs/enre/
11. Supriya Guru, Relationship between Environment and Economic Growth, Available at http://www.yourarticlelibrary.com/economics/relationship-between-environment-and-economic-growth/38423/
12. See https://ideas.repec.org/h/eee/grochp/1-28.html
13. Hua Liu, Investigation of Relationship between Economy and Environment, http://ccsenet.org/journal/index.php/jgg/article/view/1823/1734
14. Ecological economics, Available at https://en.wikipedia.org/wiki/Ecological_economics
15. See http://insights.som.yale.edu/insights/what-ecological-economics
16. See http://www.uvm.edu/~jfarley/EEseminar/readings/What%20is%20 eco logical %20economics.pdf
17. John Gowdy and Jon D. Erickson, The approach of ecological economics, Cambridge Journal of Economics 2005, 29, 207–222.
18. What is Ecological Economics? Available at http://sustainablepath.org/wp-content/uploads/2008/11/what-is-ecological-economics-one-pag-pdf-080123.pdf
19. See http://study.com/academy/lesson/what-are-economic-resources-definition-types-examples.html
20. The Four Economic Resources of every Economic System, Available at https://en.docsity.com/news/economics/economic-resources-economic-system
21. Smriti Chand, Nature and Scope of Environmental Economics, Available at http://www.yourarticlelibrary.com/economics/environmental-economics/nature-and-scope-of-environmental-economics-explained/39401/
22. Smriti Chand, Nature and Scope of Environmental Economics, Available at http://www.yourarticlelibrary.com/economics/environmental-economics/nature-and-scope-of-environmental-economics-explained/39401/
23. Policies and the Environment, Available at http://coe.mse.ac.in/onerview/7.pdf
24. Jonathan Harris, G-DAE Working Paper No. 01-09: "Macroeconomic Policy and Sustainability, Available at http://www.ase.tufts.edu/gdae/publications/working_papers/macroandsust.pdf

25. See http://www.nber.org/papers/w18794.pdf
26. Economic policies, macroeconomic environment and entrepreneurs' expectations, Available at http://www.emeraldinsight.com/doi/abs/10.1108/01443581311283952
27. Harald Fuhr, Katja Roeken, Marcus Schaper and Alexander Wegener, Macroeconomic Policies, Poverty, and the Urban Environment. A Review of the Literature, Available at http://www.uni-potsdam.de/u/ls_intpolitik/WebsiteFuhr04/staff/publicationfuhr/reports/environm.pdf
28. http://www.aph.gov.au/About_Parliament/Parliamentary_Departments/Parliamentary_Library/pubs/BriefingBook44p/MacroeconomicPolicy
29. Thematic Think Piece, Macroeconomic stability, inclusive growth and employment, Available at http://www.un.org/millenniumgoals/pdf/Think%20Pieces/12_macroeconomics.pdf
30. Fikret Berkes (1987). The common property resource problem and the fisheries of Barbados and Jamaica, Volume 11, Issue 2, pp. 225–235.
31. Fikret Berkes (1985). The common property resource problem and the creation of limited property rights, Volume 13, Issue 2, pp. 187–208.
32. Common-pool resource (2017), Retrieved from https://en.wikipedia.org/wiki/Common-pool_resource
33. https://www.lawteacher.net/free-law-essays/property-trusts/common-property-resources-in-indian-context.php
34. Aditi Mukherji, Common Property Resource Management, http://sk.sagepub.com/reference/geography/n195.xml
35. Michael Richards, Common Property Resource Institutions and Forest Management in Latin America, Volume 28, Issue 1, January 1997, pp. 95-117.
36. http://wiki.p2pfoundation.net/Common_Property

Chapter - 4

Theories of Externalities

"In a few decades, the relationship between the environment, resources and conflict may seem almost as obvious as the connection we see today between human rights, democracy and peace."

—*Wangari Maathai*[1]

Historically, the recognition by humans of their impact upon the earth has consistently lagged behind the magnitude of the damage they have imposed. Even today, technological optimists and others ignore the mounting evidence of global environmental degradation until it intrudes more inescapably upon their personal welfare.[2] In economics, an externality is the cost or benefit that affects a party who did not choose to incur that cost or benefit.

Unregulated markets in goods or services with significant externalities generate prices that do not reflect the full social cost or benefit of their transactions; such markets are inefficient. Neoclassical welfare economics asserts that, under plausible conditions, the existence of externalities will result in outcomes that are not socially optimal. Those who suffer from external costs do so involuntarily, whereas those who enjoy external benefits do so at no cost. An external cost may pose an ethical or political problem.[3]

Definition of Externalities

Externalities are common in virtually every area of economic activity. They are defined as third party effects arising from the production and/or consumption of goods and services for which no appropriate compensation is paid. Externalities can cause market failure if the price mechanism does not take into account the full social costs and social benefits of production and consumption.[4]

In Economics, externality describes the cost or benefits of any activity experienced by an unrelated third party. For example, an electronics factory releases harmful chemicals into a river. The river provides water to residents of a nearby town. Even though the town residents are not paying for, or benefiting from the electronics factory, its existence is still affecting their quality of life. Externality may be either positive or negative.[5]

Externalities occur when producing or consuming a good cause an impact on third parties not directly related to the transaction. Positive externalities are benefits that are infeasible to charge to provide; negative externalities are costs that are infeasible to charge to not provide. Economists measure externalities the same way they measure everything else: according to human beings' willingness to pay. Externalities are probably the argument for government intervention that economists most respect.

Positive Externality

Positive externality describes an activity that leaves a positive effect on a third party. For example, a college decides to slash its tuition rates by half. This encourages more people to get educated. A better-educated workforce, in turn, helps businesses produce more. Thus, even though the businesses did not pay for the reduced college tuition, they still reap a positive external benefit from the college's move.

Such externality exists when an individual or firm making a decision does not receive the full benefit of the decision. When a positive externality exists in an unregulated market, consumers pay a lower price and consume less quantity than the socially efficient outcome. In order to get consumers to consume more of a good that has a positive externality, a subsidy can be given to them.

Examples of positive production externalities include: (a) A beekeeper who keeps the bees for their honey. A side effect or externality associated with such activity is the pollination of surrounding crops by the bees; (b) the construction and operation of an airport. This will benefit local businesses, because of the increased accessibility; (c) An industrial company providing first aid classes for employees to increase on the job safety. This may also save lives outside the factory; (d) a foreign firm that demonstrates up-to-date technologies to local firms and improves their productivity.

Examples of positive consumption externalities include: (a) An individual who maintains an attractive house may confer benefits to neighbors in the form of increased market values for their properties; (b) An individual receiving a vaccination for a communicable disease not only decreases the likelihood of the individual's own infection, but also decreases the likelihood of others becoming infected through contact with the individual; (c) Increased education of individuals, as this can lead to broader society benefits in the form of greater economic productivity, a lower unemployment rate, greater household mobility and higher rates of political participation.

The existence of a positive externality means that marginal social benefit is greater than marginal private benefit. For example, in considering the market for education, free markets would supply quantity Q at price P. If the external benefit is included, the socially efficient output rises to quantity Q1.

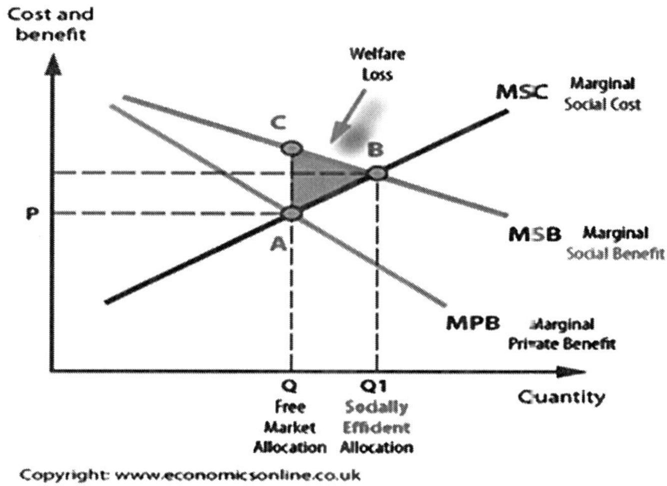

By consuming only quantity Q, marginal social benefit is above marginal social cost, and more of the good should be consumed. At Q, the marginal social cost is A (Q – A), and the private benefit is also A (Q – A) but the marginal social benefit is C (Q – C). Therefore, if only Q is consumed, there is an opportunity cost to society, which is represented by the area of welfare loss, A, C, B. Positive production externalities occur in many situations, most notably with the construction and operation of infrastructure projects, such as a new airport, or motorway.

Negative Externality

Negative externality describes an activity that leaves a negative impact on an unrelated third party. For example, any industrial activity that releases harmful pollutants into the environment can be said to have negative externality. A factory that spews carbon compounds into the atmosphere promotes global warming, which, in turn, affects seasonal cycles, destroys wildlife habitats and causes climate change.

Such externality is a spillover of an economic transaction that negatively impacts a party that is not directly involved in the transaction. The first party bears no costs for their impact on society while the second party receives no benefits from being impacted. This occurs when marginal social cost is greater than marginal private cost (MSC > MPC).There are two types of negative externalities: (a) Negative Production Externality - when a firm's production reduces the well-being of others who are not compensated by the firm. (b) Negative consumption externality - when an individual's consumption reduces the well-being of others who are not compensated by the individual.[6]

A negative externality is a cost that is suffered by a *third party* as a result of an economic transaction. In a transaction, the producer and consumer are the first and second parties, and third parties include any individual, organisation, property owner, or resource that is indirectly affected. Externalities commonly occur in situations where property rights over assets or resources have not been allocated, or are uncertain.[7] It is an economic activity that imposes a negative effect on an unrelated third party. It can arise either during the production or the consumption of a good or service. Many negative externalities are related to the environmental consequences of production and use.

Examples for negative production externalities include: (a) Air pollution from burning fossil fuels. This activity causes damages to crops, (historic) buildings and public health; (b) Water pollution by industries that adds effluent, which harms plants, animals, and humans; (c) Noise pollution during the production process, which may be mentally and psychologically disruptive; (d) the depletion of the stock of fish in the ocean due to overfishing; (e) The depletion of the stock of fish in the ocean due to overfishing. This is an example of a common property resource, which is vulnerable to the "Tragedy of the commons" in the absence of appropriate environmental governance.

Examples of negative consumption externalities include: (a) Sleep deprivation due to a neighbour listening to loud music late at night; (b) Antibiotic resistance, caused by increased usage of antibiotics; (c) Higher congestion costs and increased accident risks when people use public roads;[8] (d) Consumption by one consumer causes prices to rise and therefore makes other consumers worse off, perhaps by reducing their consumption. These effects are sometimes called "pecuniary externalities." There are several general types of solutions to the problem of externalities:

(1) Pigovian taxes or subsidies intended to redress economic injustices or imbalances.
(2) Regulation to limit activity that might cause negative externalities.
(3) Government provision of services with positive externalities.
(4) Lawsuits to compensate affected parties for negative externalities, and
(5) Mediation or negotiation between those affected by externalities and those causing them.[9]

Economies and Diseconomies of Scale

Economies of scale are the cost advantages that enterprises obtain due to size, output, or scale of operation, with cost per unit of output generally decreasing with increasing scale as fixed costs are spread out over more units of output. Economies of scale apply to a variety of organisational and business situations and at various levels, such as a business or manufacturing unit, plant or an entire enterprise. It is a term that refers to the reduction of per-unit costs through an increase in production volume. This idea is also referred to as diminishing marginal cost.

Economies of scale often originate with fixed capital, which is lowered per unit of production as design capacity increases. In his Economic and Philosophic Manuscripts (1844), Karl Marx observes that economies of scale have historically been associated with increasing concentration of private wealth, and have been used to justify such concentration. Marx points out that concentrated private ownership of large-scale economic enterprises is a historically contingent fact, and not essential to the nature of such enterprises.[10]

Costs per unit can decrease as the volume of production increases for different reasons. First, fixed costs of production can be spread over a larger number of units as the volume of units produced increases. Second, people can often save money by obtaining discounts for bulk purchases of raw resources used in production. Finally, costs may be reduced because the increase in volume may justify you acquiring specialised equipment and specialised labour that lead to more efficiency.[11]

Economies of scale can arise in several areas within a large enterprise. While the benefits of this concept in areas such as production and purchasing are obvious, economies of scale can also impact areas like finance. It may reduce variable costs per unit because of operational efficiencies and synergies. Economies of scale can be classified into two main types: (a) *Internal* – arising from within the company; and (b) *External* – arising from extraneous factors such as industry size.[12]

As some firms grow in size their unit costs begin to fall because of: (a) Purchasing economies when large businesses often receive a discount because they are buying in bulk; (b) Marketing economies from spreading the fixed cost of promotion over a larger level of output; (c) Administrative economies from spreading the fixed cost of management staff and IT systems over a larger level of output; and (d) Research and development economies from spreading the fixed costs of developing new or improved products over a larger level of output.[13]

Economies of Scale occur for various reasons. In large scale operations workers can do more specific tasks. With little training they can become very proficient in their task, this enables greater efficiency. If a firm merged it could rationalise its operational centres, e.g. it could have one head office rather than two. Some investments are very expensive and perhaps risky, therefore only a large firm will be able and willing to undertake the necessary investment. A bigger firm can get a better rate of interest than small firms.[14]

There are many merits of large scale production. Internal economies arise within the firm because of the expansion of the size of a particular firm. External economies arise with the expansion of the industry. The large scale production is always associated with more and more division of labour. The large scale production always makes use of machine. With an increase in the size of the firm, the cost of management is reduced. A large business can secure credit facilities at cheaper rates. The production of standardised goods is possible on account of the large-scale production. The large scale production is conducive for the development of technology also.[15]

Diseconomies of scale are the forces that cause larger firms and governments to produce goods and services at increased per-unit costs. The concept is the opposite of economies of scale. Economic theory predicts that a firm may become less efficient if it becomes too large. The additional costs of becoming too large are called diseconomies of scale. Diseconomies of scale result in rising long run average costs which are experienced when a firm expands beyond its optimum scale.[16]

Diseconomies of scale lead the marginal cost of a product to increase as a company grows. This is the opposite of economies of scale which cause the marginal cost for a product to decrease as a result of efficiencies achieved as a company grows and can spread its fixed costs over a larger quantity of products/services offered.[17] Diseconomies of scale can occur for the following reasons: (a) Poor communication in a large firm; (b) Alienation: Working in a highly specialised assembly line can be very boring, if workers become de motivated. In a large firm there is an increased gap between top and bottom e.g. call centres; (c) Lack of control: when there is a large number of workers it is easier to escape with not working very hard because it is more difficult for managers to notice shirking;[18] and (d) Staff can feel remote and unappreciated in a large organisation. When staff productivity begins to fall, unit costs begin to rise.[19]

There are other reasons also, as the business expands communicating between different departments and along the chain of command becomes more difficult. There are more layers in the hierarchy that can distort a message and wider spans of control for managers. Workers can often feel more isolated and less appreciated in a larger business and so their loyalty and motivation may diminish. It is harder for managers to stay in day-to-day contact with workers and build up a good team environment and sense of belonging. It is harder to ensure that all workers are working for the same overall goal as the business grows. It is more difficult for managers to supervise their subordinates and check that everyone is working together effectively.[20]

External Cost

The difference between private costs and total costs to society of a product, service, or activity is called an external cost; pollution is an external cost of many products. External costs are directly associated with producing or delivering a good or service, but they are costs that are not paid directly by the producer. When external costs arise because environmental costs are not paid, market failures and economic inefficiencies at the local, state, national, and even international level may result.

Private Costs + External Costs = Social Costs

External costs are not reflected on firms' income statements or in consumers' decisions. However, external costs remain costs to society, regardless of who pays for them. Society is better off when production and consumption decisions are based on social costs that include external costs, because external costs really do matter in the real world.[21] External costs are costs which affect society on top of those costs the firm has already paid. Examples could include pollution or health costs. These external costs are added to the private cost to give the total social cost.[22]

An external cost occurs when producing or consuming a good or service imposes a cost upon a third party. If there are external costs in consuming a good (negative externalities), the social cost will be greater than the private cost.The existence of external costs can lead to market failure. This is because the free market generally ignores the existence of external costs.[23] An external cost, such as the cost of pollution from industrial production, makes the marginal social cost (MSC) curve higher than the private marginal cost (MPC).

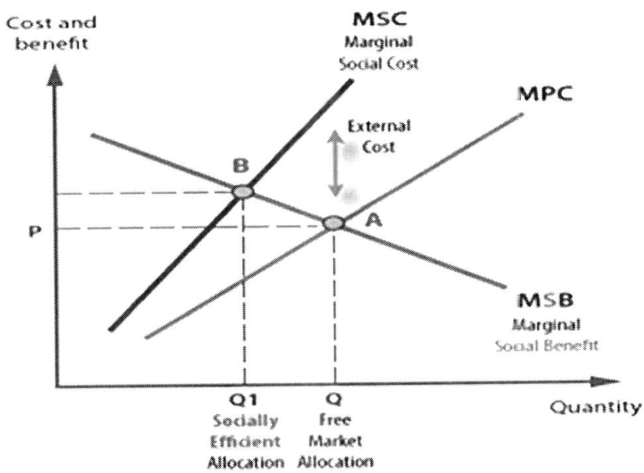

Copyright: www.economicsonline.co.uk

The socially efficient output is where MSC = MSB, at Q1, which is a lower output than the market equilibrium output, at Q.

Net welfare loss can exist in two situations. Firstly, it exists when the marginal cost to society of a particular economic activity, such as manufacturing 200,000 computers, is greater than the marginal benefit to society. Secondly, it can exist when the marginal benefit of a given economic activity, such as producing 50,000 m computers, is greater than the marginal cost.

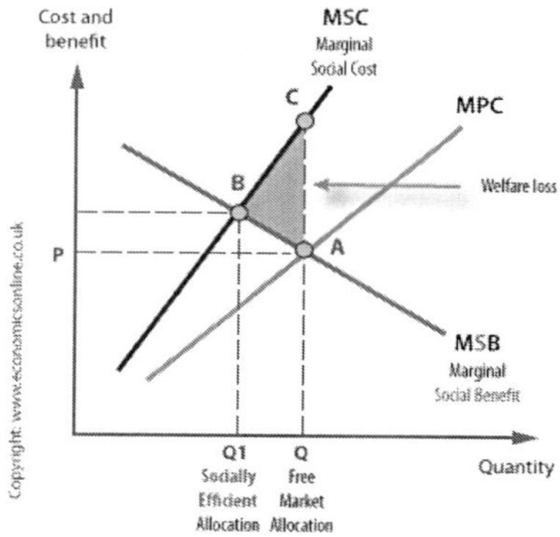

The first situation can occur when the market produces 'too much', and the second when it produces 'too little'.

Marginal Social Cost

In economics, marginal cost is the change in the total cost that arises when the quantity produced is incremented by one unit. That is, it is the cost of producing one more unit of a good. In general terms, marginal cost at each level of production includes any additional costs required to produce the next unit. If the cost function is differentiable joining, the marginal cost is the cost of the next unit produced referring to the basic volume.

$$\text{Marginal Cost } (MC) = \frac{dC}{dQ}$$

If the cost function is not differentiable, the marginal cost can be expressed as follows.[24]

$$MC = \frac{\Delta C}{\Delta Q}$$

Marginal social cost means the total cost to society as a whole for producing one further unit, or taking one further action, in an economy. This total cost of producing one extra unit of something is not simply the direct cost borne by the producer, but also must include the costs to the external environment and other stakeholders.

Calculated as:[25]

MSC=MPC+MEC

Where:

MSC = Marginal Social Cost

MPC = Marginal Private Cost

MEC = Marginal External Cost (Positive)

Marginal social benefit is an important concept in microeconomics that describes the net social value of any product, activity or service.[26]

Marginal Private Cost

Marginal cost incurred by a household (or business) in actually consuming (or producing) a good. Marginal private cost is the change in the producer's total *cost* brought about by the production of an additional unit of a goods or service. It is also known as marginal cost of production. It is the cost of producing an additional unit of a commodity that is paid by those producing the commodity. The marginal private cost curve is the firm's supply curve.[27]

Pigovian Taxes and Subsidies

A Pigovian tax is a tax applied to a market activity that is generating negative externalities. The tax is intended to correct an inefficient market outcome, and does so by being set equal to the social cost of the negative externalities. Pigovian taxes are named after economist Arthur Pigou who also developed the concept of economic externalities. William was instrumental in framing Pigou's work in modern economics.

Pigovian tax is a kind of tax, which is levied to correct a negative cost that is created by the actions of any business firm, but that is not considered in a firm's private costs or profit. Such tax is the difference between marginal social cost and the marginal private cost. When Arthur Pigou first came up with the concept, he laid down a set of assumptions, one of which is a perfectly competitive market. Pigovian tax can be applied to all spheres of production, be it production of a goods (automobile) or service (transportation, banking etc). Baumol and Oates (1975) argue that if Pigovian tax is set equal to the level of marginal damage (external cost) at the Pareto-optimal level of pollution, the industry will move towards its optimal pollution level. Pigovian tax enhances welfare of the society; restricting over-consumption. It also generates additional revenue for the government.[28]

Pigou argues that industrialists seek their own marginal private interest. When the marginal social interest diverges from the marginal private interest, the industrialist has no incentive to internalise the cost of the marginal social cost. To deal with over-production, Pigou recommends a tax placed on the offending producer. If the government can accurately gauge the social cost, the tax could equalise the marginal private cost and the marginal social cost. In more specific terms, the producer would have to pay for the non-pecuniary externality that it created. The Pigovian tax is a method commonly used by governments as it has relatively low transaction costs associated with implementation.[29]

Taxes and subsidies change the price of goods and, as a result, the quantity consumed. Pigovian taxes were theorised to correct negative externalities by imposing an additional marginal cost on a producer. By penalising an unfavourable behaviour, economic policymakers believe that the tax system would discourage or limit the activity which causes the negative externality. Pollution is often cited as a practical example of the potential of

Pigovian taxation. Before the 1970's, Pigovian taxing has met some applicable success in the US, but was soon replaced by a more profitable system of "pollution rights." Policymakers prefer this system because polluters don't lose profits by taxation, and may even earn extra profits by selling their unused pollution rights to a needy polluter.[30]

Pigovian tax is applicable only because market economies often fail to provide a proper incentive to reduce negative externalities. For example, a coal-powered plant may be polluting a nearby river by disposing its harmful byproducts in the river instead of shipping the byproducts to a special facility.[31]

References

1. Brainy Quote, Available at http://www.brainyquote.com/quotes/keywords/environment.html
2. Robert Costanza, John Cumberland, Herman Daly, Robert Goodland, Richard Norgaard, An Introduction to Ecological Economics, Available at http://library.uniteddiversity.coop/Measuring_Progress_and_Eco_Footprinting/An_Introduction_to_Ecological_Economics.pdf
3. Externality, Available at https://en.wikipedia.org/wiki/Externality
4. See http://www.revisionguru.co.uk/economics/edexeconunit2.pdf
5. Kasia Mikoluk, Marginal Social Benefit: Basics of Microeconomics, Available at https://blog.udemy.com/marginal-social-benefit/
6. See http://publicecon.wikispaces.com/Negative+Externalities +and+the+Environment
7. Nagetive externality, Available at http://www.economicsonline.co.uk/Market_failures/Externalities.html
8. Externality, Available at https://en.wikipedia.org/wiki/Externality
9. *Ibid.*
10. Economies of scale, Available at https://en.wikipedia.org/wiki/Economies _of_scale
11. See http://study.com/academy/lesson/economies-of-scale-definition-benefits-examples.html
12. See http://www.investopedia.com/terms/e/economiesofscale.asp
13. Economies of scale, Available at http://www.bbc.co.uk/schools/gcsebitesize/business/production/productioncostsrev1.shtml
14. Definition of Economies of Scale, Available at http://www.economicshelp.org/microessays/costs/economies-scale/
15. Smriti Chand, The Advantages and Disadvantages of Large Scale Production, Available at http://www.yourarticlelibrary.com/economics/the-advantages-and-disadvantages-of-large-scale-production/10901/
16. See http://www.economicsonline.co.uk/Business_economics/Diseconomies _of_scale.html
17. See http://www.investinganswers.com/financial-dictionary/economics/diseconomies-scale-1506

18. Diseconomies of scale, Available at http://www.economicshelp.org/microessays/costs/diseconomies-scale
19. See http://www.bbc.co.uk/schools/gcsebitesize/business/production/productioncostsrev3.shtm
20. See http://www.tutor2u.net/business/gcse/production_diseconomies_of_scale.htm
21. What is the difference between private and social costs, and how do they relate to pollution and production? Available at http://www.frbsf.org/education/publications/doctor-econ/2002/november/private-social-costs-pollution-production
22. See http://www.bized.co.uk/reference/diagrams/Marginal-Private-Cost-and-Marginal-Social-Cost
23. External cost, Available at http://www.economicshelp.org/blog/glossary/external-costs/
24. Marginal cost, Available at https://en.wikipedia.org/wiki/Marginal_cost
25. Marginal social cost, Available at http://www.investopedia.com/terms/m/marginalsocialcost.asp
26. Kasia Mikoluk, Marginal Social Benefit: Basics of Microeconomics, Available at https://blog.udemy.com/marginal-social-benefit/
27. See https://www3.nd.edu/~cwilber/econ504/504book/outln7b.html
28. What is Pigovian Tax Economics Essays, Available at http://www.ukessays.com/essays/economics/what-is-pigovian-tax-economics-essay.php
29. Pigovian tax, Available at https://en.wikipedia.org/wiki/Pigovian_tax
30. Pigovian Taxation as a Means of Reducing Carbon Emissions Available at https://astriddare.wordpress.com/2011/04/05/pigovian-taxes/
31. See http://www.investopedia.com/terms/p/pigoviantax.asp

Chapter - 5

Environmental Value

"Chimpanzees, gorillas, orangutans have been living for hundreds of thousands of years in their forest, living fantastic lives, never overpopulating, never destroying the forest. I would say that they have been in a way more successful than us as far as being in harmony with the environment."

—***Jane Goodall***[1]

Environment is the surrounding things. It includes living things and natural forces. The environment of living things provides conditions for development and growth as well as danger and damage. In biology and ecology, the environment is all of the natural materials and living things, including sunlight. Environment is the events and culture that a person lived in. A person's beliefs and actions are dependent on his environment.[2]

The natural environment encompasses all living and non-living things occurring naturally on Earth or some region thereof. It is an environment that encompasses the interaction of all living species. The atmosphere of the Earth serves as a key factor in sustaining the planetary ecosystem. The thin layer of gases that envelops the Earth is held in place by the planet's gravity. Dry air consists of 78 per cent nitrogen, 21 per cent oxygen, one per cent argon and other inert gases, such as carbon dioxide. Earth's atmosphere can be divided into five main layers. These layers are mainly determined by whether temperature increases or decreases with altitude.[3]

Definition of Environmental Value

Environmental Values is an international peer-reviewed journal that brings together contributions from philosophy, economics, politics, sociology, geography, anthropology, ecology and other disciplines, which relate to the present and future environment of human beings and other species. It brings together contributions from philosophy, economics, politics, sociology, geography, anthropology, ecology and other disciplines, which relate to the present and future environment of human beings and other species.[4]

Environmental Values is concerned with the basis and justification of environmental policy. It aims to bring together contributions from philosophy, law, economics and other disciplines, which relate to the present and future environment of humans and other species; and to clarify the relationship between practical policy issues and more fundamental underlying principles or assumptions.[5] It is often suggested that environmental attitudes and environmental behaviour are related to people's values. Values are typically conceptualised as important life goals or standards that serve as guiding principles in life. Many studies on environmental behaviour have been conducted without carefully defining environmental behaviour. Often environmental behaviour is assumed to be an undifferentiated class of behaviours.[6]

Use Value

Use value or value in use is the utility of consuming a good—the want-satisfying power of a goods or service in classical political economy. The concepts of value, use value, utility, exchange value and price have a very long history in economic and philosophical thought, from Aristotle to Adam Smith, and their meanings evolved. Adam Smith recognised that commodities may have an exchange-value but may satisfy no use-value, such as diamonds, while a commodity with a very high use-value may have a very low exchange-value, such as water. The transformation of a use-value into a social use-value and into a commodity is not automatic or spontaneous, but has technical, social and political preconditions.[7]

Use-value is the qualitative aspect of value, i.e., the concrete way in which a thing meets human needs: "The utility of a thing makes it a use-value. But this utility is not a thing of air. Being limited by the physical properties of the commodity, it has no existence apart from that commodity. A commodity, such as iron, corn, or a diamond, is therefore, so far as it is a material thing, a use-value, something useful.

This property of a commodity is independent of the amount of labour required to appropriate its useful qualities. When treating of use-value, we always assume to be dealing with definite quantities, such as dozens of watches, yards of linen, or tons of iron. The use-values of commodities furnish the material for a special study, that of the commercial knowledge of commodities. Use-values become a reality only by use or consumption: they also constitute the substance of all wealth, whatever may be the social form of that wealth. In the form of society, we are about to consider, they are, in addition, the material depositories of exchange-value."[8]

Option Value and Non Use Value

In cost benefit analysis and social welfare economics, the term option value refers to the value that is placed on private willingness to pay for maintaining or preserving a public asset or service even if there is little or no likelihood of the individual actually ever using it. The term "option value" and its theoretical underpinnings as a non-user benefit were initially developed in 1964 by Burton Weisbrod. It was posited as an element of benefit distinct from the traditional concept of consumer surplus.[9]

In finance, the time value of an option is the premium a rational investor would pay over its current exercise value (intrinsic value), based on the probability it will increase in value before expiry. There are several *options* pricing models that use these parameters to determine the fair market *value* of the *option*. It is important to differentiate between an *option* premium and its theoretical *value*.

Non-use value is the value that people assign to economic goods (including public goods) even if they never have and never will use it. It is distinguished from use value; which people derive from direct use of the goods. The concept is most commonly applied to the value of natural and built resources. Non-use value as a category may include: option value, bequest value, and Existence value.

The term option value refers to the value that is placed on private willingness to pay for maintaining or preserving a public asset or service even if there is little or no likelihood of the individual actually ever using it. Bequest value, in economics, is the value of satisfaction from preserving a natural environment or a historic environment, in other words natural heritage or cultural heritage for future generations. Existence values are an unusual and somewhat controversial class of economic value, reflecting the benefit people receive from knowing that a particular environmental resource, such as Antarctica, the Grand Canyon, endangered species, or any other organism or thing exists.[10]

International Carbon Tax

A carbon tax is a tax levied on the carbon content of fuels. It is a form of carbon pricing. Carbon is present in every hydrocarbon fuel and is released as carbon dioxide when they are burnt. Carbon taxes offer a potentially cost-effective means of reducing greenhouse gas emissions. It can be a regressive tax, in that they may directly or indirectly affect low-income groups disproportionately. Carbon dioxide is one of several heat-trapping greenhouse gases emitted by humans.

A carbon tax is a form of pollution tax. Pollution taxes are often grouped with two other economic policy instruments: tradable pollution permits/credits and subsidies. These three environmental economic policy instruments are built upon a foundation of a command and control regulation. A carbon tax is called a price instrument, since it sets a price for carbon dioxide emissions. A number of policies have been suggested to address concerns over competitive losses due to one country introducing a carbon tax while another country does not. Both energy and carbon taxes have been implemented in responses to commitments under the United Nations Framework Convention on Climate Change.[11]

Carbon tax is a form of pollution tax. It levies a fee on the production, distribution or use of fossil fuels based on how much carbon their combustion emits. The government sets a price per ton on carbon, then translates it into a tax on electricity, natural gas or oil. It is based on the economic principle of negative externalities. Externalities are costs or benefits generated by the production of goods and services.[12] Carbon tax is usually defined as a tax based on greenhouse gas emissions generated from burning fuels. It puts a price on each ton of GHG emitted, sending a price signal that will, over time, elicit a powerful market response across the entire economy, resulting in reduced emissions. It has the advantage of providing an incentive without favouring any one way of reducing emissions over another.[13]

The carbon tax applies to the purchase or use of fuels within the province. The amount of GHGs emitted when a unit of fuel is burned depends fundamentally on the chemical make-up of the fuel, particularly on the amount of carbon in the fuel. That fact allows for a relatively simple administrative process for applying the carbon tax. Administratively, the carbon tax is applied and collected in essentially the same way that motor fuel taxes are currently applied and collected, except natural gas which is collected at the retail level. This minimises the cost of administration to government and the compliance cost to those collecting the tax on government's behalf.[14]

Carbon tax is a fee placed on greenhouse gas pollution mainly from burning fossil fuels. This can be done by placing a surcharge on carbon-based fuels and other sources of pollution such as industrial processes. Under this system, the price to pollute sets the strength of the economic signal and determines the extent to which green choices are encouraged. Many industrialised countries have used carbon taxes to discourage fossil fuel emissions and promote clean energy. In a cap-and-trade system, government puts a firm limit, or cap, on the overall level of carbon pollution from industry and reduces that cap year after year to reach a set pollution target. As the cap decreases each year, it cuts industry's total greenhouse gas emissions to the limit set by regulation, and then forces polluters that exceed their emissions quota to buy unused quota from other companies. Cap-and-trade has been used successfully in the U.S. to reduce emissions of sulphur dioxide and nitrous oxide, two key ingredients responsible for acid rain.[15]

Carbon tax has many advantages, like as (a) Carbon taxes have been suggested as a way to internalise the negative Externality of carbon emissions; (b) Carbon taxes provide an incentive for firms to use and develop more environmentally friendly production processes; and (c) They can also raise money to be spent on environmental initiatives.[16] The production of carbon dioxide is widely held to contribute to social / environmental problems such as global warming. This carbon pollution is a negative externality. It is a cost imposed on the whole of society and not just the individual who consumes a certain product. A higher price of carbon emissions will encourage firms and consumers to develop more efficient engines or alternatives to consuming carbon emissions. The revenue raised from carbon tax could be used to subsidise alternatives such as green electricity or the revenue raised could be used to repair the damage caused by environmental pollution.[17]

There are various disadvantages of a carbon tax: (a) Most politicians hesitate to advocate for a tax: The Clinton administration failed to implement an energy tax, and it is seen as politically risky; (b) Carbon tax: there is no limit on the amount of carbon that can be emitted. The dollar price is known, but the quantity of emissions may not reach the desired, or scientifically imperative, target; (c) Distrust of Federal Spending priorities: based on how Congress has used new revenue sources in the past, CO_2 tax revenues may end up being wasted in special interest spending, or priorities that are only peripheral to climate or sustainability (corn-based ethanol, nuclear, etc).[18]

A carbon pricing scheme in Australia, commonly referred to as the "Carbon tax", was introduced by the Gillard Government and became effective on 1 July 2012, and was in operation until it was repealed by the Australian senate on 17 July 2014. The scheme required entities which emit over 25,000 tonnes per year of Carbon dioxide equivalent greenhouse gases and which were not in the transport or agriculture sectors to obtain emissions permits. The Government is running several major 'Industry Assistance' programmes to reduce the Carbon Tax impact for these 185 affected companies. These have the effect of significantly reducing the actual carbon tax raised. Because the Australian carbon tax does not apply to all fossil fuels usage, it only had an effect on some of the emitters of greenhouse gases. The carbon pricing scheme was intended to improve energy efficiency, convert electricity generation from coal to alternatives and shift economic activity towards a low carbon economy. Because carbon pricing would indirectly flow through to consumers, the Australian government implemented household assistance measures.[19]

The announcement in November 2014 of a U.S.-China agreement to curb greenhouse gas emissions was both a surprise and a potential milestone, shattering, perhaps, the "alliance of denial," as the New York Times once termed it, by which the two nations used each other's inaction as a pretext to postpone action on climate. What are less clear are the policies by which China will actually bend and reduce its burning of carbon fuels, especially coal. This dirtiest fossil fuel is the mainstay of China's energy economy, not only in power generation but in industrial production and even provision of heat.[20] China and the United States are the two largest carbon-emitting countries in the world, currently responsible for more than 40 per cent of the world's carbon emissions. China is not only the top emitter; it also has one of the highest growth rates and will account for half of the projected increase in emissions between 2010 and 2040.

China increased its fuel-consumption tax the first time in five years amid falling global oil prices as part of steps to fight pollution and cut carbon emissions. The nation is seeking fight pollution and improves energy efficiency amid record smog levels in cities including Beijing and Shanghai. The government will use the added revenue to combat pollution, address climate change and improve public health and the environment, according to a separate statement.[21]

The Chinese Government plans to develop emissions trading schemes in seven key cities and provinces from 2013. These schemes will cover around 250 million people. The Chinese Government aims to work towards a nation-wide approach after 2015. Canada does not have a federal carbon tax, but two Canadian provinces have existing carbon taxes (Quebec and British Columbia). Alberta implemented emissions trading in 2006 and Quebec's scheme will start in 2013. A further two provinces, British Columbia and Ontario, are considering emissions trading schemes. The Canadian Federal Government has no immediate plans to implement national emissions trading. The New Zealand Government set up an emissions trading scheme in 2008. The scheme covered forestry initially, and was then expanded in 2010 to cover stationary energy, transport, liquid fossil fuels and industrial processes. The Republic of Korea passed legislation in May 2012 for an emissions trading scheme to start from 1 January 2015.

The European Union emissions trading scheme began in 2005 and now covers the 27 countries of the European Union, and three non-European Union members: Iceland, Liechtenstein, and Norway. Several European countries have enacted a carbon tax. They include: Denmark, Finland, Ireland, the Netherlands, Norway, Slovenia, Sweden, Switzerland, and the UK. Finland introduced the world's first carbon tax in 1990, initially with exemptions for specific sectors. The Netherlands introduced a carbon tax in 1990, which was then replaced by a tax on fuels. In 2007, it introduced a carbon-based tax on packaging, to encourage recycling. In 1991, Sweden enacted a tax on the use of coal, oil, natural gas, petrol and aviation fuel used in domestic travel. In 1991, Norway introduced a tax on carbon. South Africa introduced a carbon tax on new vehicle sales in September 2010. In 1997, Costa Rica enacted a tax on carbon pollution, set at 3.5 per cent of the market value of fossil fuels. In 1993, the UK government introduced a tax on retail petroleum products, to reduce emissions in the transport sector.[22]

The Economic Survey advocates India, which imposes a higher carbon tax on most of fossil fuels, could do more in the case of coal. The report says, "India has moved from a carbon subsidisation regime to one of significant carbon taxation regimes - from a negative price to a positive price on carbon emissions." Since October 2014, the report's authors say, the government has "increased the carbon tax by nearly \$60 per tonne of carbon dioxide in case of petrol and nearly \$42 per tonne in the case of diesel". In the case of coal, the chief economic advisor of the National Democratic Alliance government and his team suggest, if one was to account for health costs and climate change costs of burning the black gold, a tax of $15 per tonne would still ensure that large scale coal power plants continue to break even and yet bring down India's emissions by 358 million tonnes a year - more than the entire emissions of France.[23]

Environment and WTO

The WTO has no specific agreement dealing with the environment. The WTO agreements confirm governments' right to protect the environment, provided certain conditions are met, and a number of them include provisions dealing with environmental concerns. At the end of the Uruguay Round in 1994, trade ministers from participating countries decided to begin a comprehensive work programme on trade and environment in the WTO. They created the Trade and Environment Committee. This has brought environmental and sustainable development issues into the mainstream of WTO work.

The committee's work is based on two important principles: (a) The WTO is only competent to deal with trade. In other words, in environmental issues its only task is to study questions that arise when environmental policies have a significant impact on trade. The WTO is not an environmental agency. Its members do not want it to intervene in national or international environmental policies or to set environmental standards. Other agencies that specialise in environmental issues are better qualified to undertake those tasks; and (b) If the committee does identify problems, its solutions must continue to uphold the principles of the WTO trading system.[24]

The WTO gives great latitude to members to restrict trade to protect the environment. There are two general arguments for "including" environment in the WTO. The first is that the GATT is out of date; when it was drafted, environmentalism was not a public issue. The second is that the environment is of such importance that WTO rules should allow trade restrictions to support protection of the environment. It is true the word "environment" does not appear in the GATT. Sustainable development was added as one of the general objectives of the World Trade Organisation when it was established in 1994. There are several provisions in the WTO agreements dealing with environment. There is a reference to sustainable development as one of the general objectives to be served by the WTO in the Marrakech Agreement which established the WTO. There are provisions in the Agreement on Agriculture and the General Agreement on Trade in Services (GATS).[25]

Allowing for the optimal use of the world's resources in accordance with the objective of sustainable development and seeking to protect and preserve the environment are fundamental to the WTO. These goals, enshrined in the Preamble of the Marrakesh Agreement, go hand in hand with the WTO's objective to reduce trade barriers and eliminate discriminatory treatment in international trade relations. The commitment of WTO members to sustainable development and the environment can be seen in WTO rules. In general terms the rules, with their fundamental principles of non-discrimination, transparency and predictability, help set the framework for members to design and implement measures to address environmental concerns. Since the entry into force of the WTO in 1995, the WTO Dispute Settlement Body has had to deal with a number of disputes concerning environment-related trade measures. The WTO also supports sustainable development and the environment through its specialised committees and bodies. One unique institutional venue is the Committee on Trade and Environment.[26]

The 1994 Ministerial Decision on Trade and Environment created the WTO's Committee on Trade and Environment, which is open to the entire WTO membership, with some international organisations as observers. The committee's mandate is broad, and it has contributed to identifying and understanding the relationship between trade and the environment in order to promote sustainable development.[27] The WTO contributes to protection and preservation of the environment through its objective of trade openness, through its rules and enforcement mechanism, through work in different WTO bodies, and through ongoing efforts under the Doha Development Agenda. The Doha Agenda includes specific negotiations on trade and environment and some tasks assigned to the regular Trade and Environment Committee.[28]

Under WTO rules, as confirmed by WTO jurisprudence, members can adopt trade-related measures aimed at protecting the environment, subject to certain specified conditions. These measures are not necessarily discussed at the WTO. WTO members can adopt trade-related measures to protect the environment and human health and life as long as such measures comply with GATT rules, or fall under the exceptions to these rules. This right has been affirmed by panels and the Appellate Body time and again. Article XX on General Exceptions lays out a number of specific instances in which WTO members may be exempted from GATT rules. Two exceptions are of particular relevance to environmental and human health protection: Articles XX(b) and (g) allow WTO members to justify GATT-inconsistent measures if these are either necessary to protect human, animal or plant life or health, or if the measures relate to the conservation of exhaustible natural resources, respectively.[29]

References

1. Brainy Quote, Available at http://www.brainyquote.com/quotes/keywords/environment.html
2. Environment, Available at https://simple.wikipedia.org/wiki/Environment
3. Natural environment, Available at https://en.wikipedia.org/wiki/Natural_environment
4. See http://journals.sfu.ca/whpres/index.php/ev
5. Environmental values, Available at http://www.cep.unt.edu/values.html
6. Wouter Poortinga, Linda Steg and Charles Vlek (2004), Values, Environmental

concerns and Environmental behavior: A Study into Household Energy Use, Environment and Behaviour, Vol. 36 No. 1, pp.70-93.

7. Use value, Available at https://en.wikipedia.org/wiki/Use_value
8. See https://www.marxists.org/glossary/terms/u/s.htm
9. Option value, Available at https://en.wikipedia.org/wiki/Option_value_(cost _ benefit_analysis)
10. Non-use value, Available at https://en.wikipedia.org/wiki/Non-use_value
11. Carbon tax, Available at https://en.wikipedia.org/wiki/Carbon_tax
12. Sarah Dowdey, How carbon tax works, Available at http://science.howstuffworks.com/environmental/green-science/carbon-tax.htm
13. From official website of British Columbia (http://www.fin.gov.bc.ca/tbs/tp/climate/A1.htm)
14. *Ibid.*
15. From official website of David Suzuki Foundation (http://www.davidsuzuki.org/issues/climate-change/science/climate-solutions/carbon-tax-or-cap-and-trade/)
16. Tejvan Pettinger (2012), Carbon tax- Advantages and disadvantages, Available at http://www.economicshelp.org/blog/glossary/carbon-tax/
17. Tejvan Pettinger (2013), Carbon tax- Pros and Cons, Available at http://www.economicshelp.org/blog/2207/economics/carbon-tax-pros-and-cons/
18. Cap and Trade vs. Carbon Tax, Available at http://www.carbonshare.org/docs/capvscarbontax.pdf
19. Carbon pricing in Australia, Available at https://en.wikipedia.org/wiki/Carbon_pricing_in_Australia
20. http://www.carbontax.org/what-about-china/
21. China to Increase Fuel Tax to Curb Pollution, Carbon Emissions, Available at http://www.bloomberg.com/news/articles/2014-11-28/china-to-increase-fuel-tax-to-curb-pollution-carbon-emissions
22. Factbox: Carbon taxes around the world, Available at http://www.sbs.com.au/news/article/2013/10/29/factbox-carbon-taxes-around-world
23. India's carbon tax already much above global expectations, Available at http://www.business-standard.com/budget/article/india-s-carbon-tax-already-much-above-global-expectations-115022800021_1.html
24. The environment: a specific concern, Available at https://www.wto.org/english/thewto_e/whatis_e/tif_e/bey2_e.htm
25. Alan Oxley, WTO and the Environment, Available at http://www.apec.org.au/docs/oxley2001.pdf
26. An introduction to trade and environment in the WTO, Available at https://www.wto.org/english/tratop_e/envir_e/envt_intro_e.htm
27. The Committee on Trade and Environment, Available at https://www.wto.org/english/tratop_e/envir_e/wrk_committee_e.htm
28. From official website of World Trade Organisation, Available at https://www.wto.org/english/tratop_e/envir_e/envir_e.htm
29. WTO rules and environmental policies: introduction, Available at https://www.wto.org/english/tratop_e/envir_e/envt_rules_intro_e.htm

PART - II

Economics of Social Sector

Chapter - 6

Pollution

"If we each take responsibility in shifting our own behavior, we can trigger the type of change that is necessary to achieve sustainability for our race or this planet. We change our planet, our environment, our humanity every day, every year, every decade, and every millennia."

—***Yehuda Berg***[1]

Basically, our environment is composed of atmosphere, earth, water and space. In absence of pollution, it remains clean and enjoyable. The interaction of the atmosphere, lithosphere, hydrosphere and biosphere is continuing for years together.[2] While modern societies face growing concern about global environmental issues, developing countries are experiencing complex, serious and fast-growing pollution problems of their own. During the period of rapid economic growth after the Second World War, Japan experienced a variety of terrible environmental problems on a scale unprecedented in the world. Environmental pollution is more than just a health issue; it is a wider social issue in that pollution has the potential to destroy homes and communities. Pollution problems are also closely tied to the mode of development in developing countries.[3]

The environmental consequences of rapid industrialisation have resulted in countless incidents of land, air and water resources sites being contaminated with toxic materials and other pollutants, threatening humans and ecosystems with serious health risks. More extensive and intensive use of materials and energy has created cumulative pressures on the quality of local, regional and global ecosystems.

Definition of Pollution

Pollution is the introduction of harmful substances or products into the environment. It is the introduction of contaminants into the natural environment that causes adverse change. It can take the form of chemical substances or energy, such as noise, heat or light. Society as a whole faces many environmental problems, and as a result, environmental awareness tends to be a pressing issue. Every day, people recycle cans, glass bottles, and newspapers. Many people buy bottled water, or own filters for their tap water, as a health precaution from the pollutants in normal everyday drinking water.[4]

Pollution can be defined as the introduction into the natural environment (air, water or land) of substances (pollutants) that are liable to cause harm to human health or to animals, plants and the wider environment. Water pollution occurs when a river, lake or other body of water is adversely affected due to the addition of pollutants.[5] It can be defined as an undesirable change in the physical, chemical or biological characters of land, air or water that may or will affect harmfully the human life, its properties, aesthetics, health and all other such perspectives of civilisation.[6]

Pollution is when something is added to the environment that is harmful or poisonous to living things. A pollutant is a waste material that pollutes air, water or soil. Three factors determine the severity of a pollutant: its chemical nature, the concentration and the persistence. To protect the environment from the adverse effects of pollution, many nations worldwide have enacted legislation to regulate various types of pollution as well as to mitigate the adverse effects of pollution.

Classification of Pollution

Pollution is a challenge in the twenty first century. It is a common fact in more or less every country. Scientists are constantly studying how the different types of pollution affect the environment and how it can be controlled. Much has been done to reduce and control pollution, but there is still more that needs to be done.[7] According to wikipedia, the major forms of pollution is:

(1) Air Pollution

Air pollution is the introduction of particulates, biological molecules, or other harmful materials into Earth's atmosphere, causing disease, death to humans, damage to other living organisms such as food crops, or the natural or built environment. An air pollutant is a substance in the air that can have adverse effects on humans and the ecosystem. The substance can be solid particles, liquid droplets, or gases.

In order to understand the causes of Air pollution, several divisions can be made. Primarily air pollutants can be caused by primary sources or secondary sources. The pollutants that are a direct result of the process can be called primary pollutants. A classic example of a primary pollutant would be the sulphur-dioxide emitted from factories. Secondary pollutants are the ones that are caused by the inter mingling and reactions of primary pollutants. Smog created by the interactions of several primary pollutants is known to be as secondary pollutant.[8]

Automobiles play a major role in urban traffic and have contributed to making our lives more convenient. In exchange for this convenience, they are causing air pollution. Due to loose national emission limits on old diesel vehicles, which have resulted in preventing the popularisation of new diesel vehicles meeting stricter limits and generating chronic traffic congestion, air pollution from automobiles has not improved at all and countermeasures have been lagging for a long time.[9]

Air pollution can harm us when it accumulates in the air in high enough concentrations. Millions of Americans live in areas where urban smog, particle pollution, and toxic pollutants pose serious health concerns[10]. Short-term air pollution can aggravate the medical conditions of individuals with asthma and emphysema. Long-term health effects can include chronic respiratory disease, lung cancer, heart disease, and even damage to the brain, nerves, liver, or kidneys. Like photochemical pollutants, sulphur oxides contribute to the incidence of respiratory diseases. Acid rain, a form of precipitation that contains high levels of sulphuric or nitric acids, can contaminate drinking water and vegetation, damage aquatic life, and erode buildings. When weather condition known as a temperature inversion prevents dispersal of smog, inhabitants of the area, especially children and the elderly and chronically ill, is warned to stay indoors and avoid physical stress.[11]

(2) Light pollution

Light pollution is excessive, misdirected, or obtrusive artificial light. It is the alteration of light levels in the outdoor environment due to man-made sources of light. Indoor light pollution is such alteration of light levels in the indoor environment due to sources of light, which compromises human health. In disrupting ecosystems, light pollution poses a serious threat in particular to nocturnal wildlife, having negative impacts on plant and animal physiology. It can confuse the migratory patterns of animals; alter competitive interactions of animals, change predator-prey relations, and cause physiological harm.[12]

In general, the most common action is that light pollution alters and interferes with the timing of necessary biological activities. In the span of a mere one hundred years, our creation of a never-occurring night is having some real effects on the animals that were here before us. For the same melatonin suppression problems, we have with lights at night, creates similar problems in animals.[13] Light pollution is largely the result of bad lighting design, which allows artificial light to shine outward and upward into the sky, where it's not wanted, instead of focusing it downward, where it is. Ill-designed lighting washes out the darkness of night and radically alters the light levels—and light rhythms—to which many forms of life, including ourselves, have adapted.[14]

It is a growing problem that threatens wildlife, humans, natural habitats, our energy use and the heritage of appreciation for our night sky. Leaving lights on in vacant buildings, outdoor lights pointing up to the sky and unshielded outdoor lights all contribute to light pollution or sky glow. There are four different components of light pollution:[15]According to "The First World Atlas of the Artificial Night Sky Brightness," a report on global light pollution published in volume 328, issue 3 (2001) of the *Monthly Notices of the Royal Astronomical Society*, two-thirds of the U.S. population and more than one-half of the European population have already lost the ability to see the Milky Way with the naked eye.[16]

The larger implications of light pollution extend beyond local ecosystems and physical health. With an estimated two-thirds of Earth's population living under light-polluted skies, over-illumination is an international concern. Disturbing evidence has emerged showing that light pollution exacerbates air pollution. Each night, compounds called nitrate radicals break down polluting chemicals in the air that form smog and ozone.[17]

(3) Water Pollution

Water pollution is the contamination of water bodies. It is a major global problem which requires ongoing evaluation and revision of water resource policy at all levels. It has been suggested that water pollution is the leading worldwide cause of deaths and diseases. There are many specific causes of water pollution, but before we list the toppers, it's important to understand two broad categories of water pollution. Point-source pollution is usually monitored and regulated, at least in Western countries, though political factors may complicate how successful efforts are at true pollution control. Nonpoint sources are much more difficult to monitor and control, and today they account for the majority of contaminants in streams and lakes.[18]

Most water pollutants are eventually carried by rivers into the oceans. Water pollution caused industrial waste products released into lakes, rivers, and other water bodies, has made marine life no longer hospitable. Humans pollute water with large scale disposal of garbage, flowers, ashes and other household waste. In many rural areas one can still find people bathing and cooking in the same water, making it incredibly filthy.[19]

Water pollution is generally induced by humans. It results from actions of humans carried on to better self. These could be treated under the various activities that man engages in, that lead to pollution. The growth of human population, industrial and agricultural practices is the major causes of pollution. Highly polluted rivers have obnoxious smell and contain little or no flora or fauna. Another source of water pollution is the discharge of hot water from cooling engines in the industries. This increases water temperature and lowers the metabolic rate of organisms. This then raises their oxygen demand. The effects of pollution are greater in shallow, enclosed or slow flowing streams.[20]

Water contamination weakens or destroys natural ecosystems that support human health, food production and biodiversity. Water-borne diseases kill millions of people, particularly those under the age of five, world-wide every year. Livelihoods such as agriculture, fishing and animal husbandry are affected by poor water quality. Biodiversity, especially of freshwater ecosystems is under threat due to water pollution. India's 14 major, 55 minor and several hundred small rivers receive millions of litres of sewage, industrial and agricultural wastes. The most polluting source for rivers is the city sewage and industrial waste discharge.[21]

Water-borne diseases are infectious diseases spread primarily through contaminated water. Though these diseases are spread either directly or through flies or filth, water is the chief medium for spread of these diseases and hence they are termed as water-borne diseases. Most intestinal (enteric) diseases are infectious and are transmitted through faecal waste.[22]

(4) Noise Pollution

Noise pollution is the disturbing or excessive noise that may harm the activity or balance of human or animal life. The source of most outdoor noise worldwide is mainly caused by machines and transportation systems, motor vehicles, aircraft, and trains. Indoor noise can be caused by machines, building activities, and music performances, especially in some workplaces. Noise pollution is almost entirely human generated, whether by machine sources or amplified sound of human creation. Approximately ninety per cent of all such intrusive sound arises from such transport devices as motor vehicles, aircraft and rail activities.

By definition, noise pollution takes place when there is either excessive amount of noise or an unpleasant sound that causes temporary disruption in the natural balance. This definition is usually applicable to sounds or noises that are unnatural in either their volume or their production[23] It is measured in the units of decibels and is denoted by the dB. The noise which is more than 115 dB is tolerant. The industrial limit of sound in the industries must be 75 dB according to the world health organisation. A type writer can produce a sound at 60 dB.[24] With sound levels above 85 dB, damage is related to sound pressure (measured in dB) and to time of exposure. The major cause of hearing loss is occupational exposure, although other sources of noise, particularly recreational noise, may produce significant deficits. Studies suggest that children seem to be more vulnerable than adults to noise induced hearing impairment.[25]

Noise pollution affects both health and behaviour. Unwanted sound (noise) can damage psychological health. It can cause hypertension, high stress levels, tinnitus, hearing loss, sleep disturbances, and other harmful effect. Such pollution causes a large array of annoyance effects and behavioural change in humans and animals. These range from decreased learning rates, inducement of hostility, frustration threshold reduction to speech interference and sleep disturbance.[26] There are two types of hearing loss: conductive and sensorineural. In conductive deafness sound-pressure waves never reach the cochlea, most often as a consequence of a ruptured eardrum or a defect in the ossicles of the middle ear. Conductive hearing loss can be minimised, even overcome by use of the familiar hearing aids. The most common is worn over the mastoid bond behind the pinna. It picks up sound waves and transmits them through the skull to the cochlea.[27]

(5) Soil Pollution

In a general sense, soil pollution definition is the presence of toxic chemicals (pollutants or contaminants) in soil in high enough concentrations to be of risk to human health and/or ecosystem[28]. It comprises the pollution of soils with materials, mostly chemicals that are out of place or are present at concentrations higher than normal which may have adverse effects on humans or other organisms.[29] It is caused by the presence of xenobiotic (human-made) chemicals or other alteration in the natural soil environment. It is typically caused by industrial activity, agricultural chemicals, or improper disposal of waste. The main reason why the soil becomes contaminated is due to the presence of man waste. The waste produced from nature itself such as dead plants, carcasses of animals and rotten fruits and vegetables only adds to the fertility of the soil.[30]

The main factors of land pollution are increasing rate of soil erosion caused due to deforestation. Natural factors of soil erosion (like rainfall, wind, topography etc.) are further increased by human activities. In most of the developing countries increasing rate of soil erosion due to deforestation and faulty agricultural practices has degraded land to a large scale because the fertile top soil has been washed out.[31] Main anthropogenic sources of heavy metals exist in various industrial point sources e.g., present and former mining activities, foundries, smelters and diffuse sources such as piping, constituents of products, combustion of by products, traffic, industrial and human activities.[32]

The main reason for soil contamination is due to the presence of anthropogenic activities. These waste products are made of chemicals that are not originally found in nature and hence lead to soil pollution. It is typically caused by industrial activity, chemicals used in agriculture and improper disposal of waste. Soil contamination leads to health risks due to direct and indirect contact with contaminated soil. Such pollution causes huge disturbances in the ecological balance and the health of the organisms is under risk.[33]

There are many different ways that soil can become polluted, such as: (a) Seepage from a landfill; (b) Discharge of industrial waste into the soil; (c) Percolation of contaminated water into the soil; (d) Rupture of underground storage tanks; (e) Excess application of pesticides, herbicides or fertiliser; and (f) Solid waste seepage. The most common chemicals involved in causing soil pollution are: (a) Petroleum hydrocarbons, (b) Heavy metals, (c) Pesticides, and (d) Solvents.[34] Intensification of agricultural production by practices of irrigation, excessive fertilisers, pesticides, insecticides etc. have created the problems of soil pollution. The improper and continuous use of herbicides, pesticides and fungicides to protect the crops from pests, fungi etc. alter the basic composition of the soils and make the soil toxic for plant growth. Organic insecticides like DDT, aldrin, benzenehexachloride etc. are used against soil borne pests.[35]

Contaminated or polluted soil directly affects human health through direct contact with soil or via inhalation of soil contaminants which have vaporised; potentially greater threats are posed by the infiltration of soil contamination into groundwater aquifers used for human consumption, sometimes in areas apparently far removed from any apparent source of above ground contamination. Health consequences from exposure to soil contamination vary greatly depending on pollutant type, pathway of attack and vulnerability of the exposed population. Chronic exposure to chromium, lead and other metals, petroleum, solvents, and many pesticide and herbicide formulations can be carcinogenic, can cause congenital disorders, or can cause other chronic health conditions.

The presence of heavy metals in soil in toxic amounts can cause irreversible developmental damage in children, according to the website Tropical Rainforest Animals. Although lead and mercury may be found naturally in soil, high concentrations of either metal may cause damage to the developing brains of young children, which in turn may lead to neurological problems. Plants that are grown in lightly polluted soil continuously absorb molecules of the pollutants. Since the plants cannot get rid of these molecules, they accumulate in the plant, causing higher amounts of pollution to exist in the plant than in the soil. Animals that eat many of these polluted plants take on all the pollution those plants have accumulated.[36]

(6) Thermal Pollution

Rise in the temperature in the ecosystem due to the release of excessive heat energy into the environment by artificial methods or natural disasters is called Thermal Pollution. It results in a temperature rise which is the main cause for the melting of the polar ice caps, which is in turn leading to a rise in the water levels. It has increased significantly since the eighteen hundred resulting in a hotter earth.[37] It is usually associated with increases of water temperatures in a stream, lake, or ocean due to the discharge of heated water from industrial processes, such as the generation of electricity.[38]

Thermal pollution is the degradation of water quality by any process that changes ambient water temperature. A common cause of thermal pollution is the use of water as a coolant by power plants and industrial manufacturers. When a power plant first opens or shuts down for repair or other causes, fish and other organisms adapted to particular temperature range can be killed by the abrupt change in water temperature known as thermal shock. It is one parameter of the broader subject of water pollution. There can be significant environmental consequences of thermal pollution with respect to surface receiving waters such as rivers and lakes; in particular, decrease in biodiversity and creation of an environment hospitable to alien aquatic species may occur.[39]

Some thermal power plants use coal as fuel. Coal-fired power plants constitute the major source of the thermal pollution. Nuclear power plants emit a large amount of unutilised heat and traces of toxic radio nuclear into nearby water stream. Domestic sewage is often discharged into rivers, lakes, canals or streams without waste treatment. The municipal water sewage normally has a higher temperature than receiving water. Control of thermal pollution is necessary as its detrimental effects on aquatic ecosystem may be detrimental in the future.[40]

Thermal pollution is directly responsible for mortality of aquatic organisms. Increase in temperature of water leads to exhaustion of microorganisms thereby shortening the life span of fish. Above a certain temperature, fish die due to failure of respiratory system and nervous system failure. The rising temperature increases the toxicity of the poison present in water. Abrupt changes in temperature alter the seasonal variation in the type and abundance of lower organisms leading to shortage of right food for fish at the right time.[41]

A large increase in temperature can lead to the denaturing of life-supporting enzymes by breaking down hydrogen- and disulphide bonds within the quaternary structure of the enzymes. Decreased enzyme activity in aquatic organisms can cause problems such as the inability to break down lipids, which leads to malnutrition. Releases of unnaturally cold water from reservoirs can dramatically change the fish and macro invertebrate fauna of rivers, and reduce river productivity.[42] It is known that temperature changes of even one to two degrees Celsius can cause significant changes in organism metabolism and other adverse cellular biology effects.

Thermal pollution may also increase the metabolic rate of aquatic animals, as enzyme activity, resulting in these organisms consuming more food in a shorter time than if their environment were not changed. An increased metabolic rate may result in food source shortages, causing a sharp decrease in a population.[43] Such pollution from power plants and factories is relatively easy to control. Instead of discharging heated water into lakes and streams, power plants and factories can pass the heated water through cooling towers or cooling ponds, where evaporation cools the water before it is discharged. To prevent thermal pollution due to devegetation, the prescription is simple: do not devegetate. Landowners can leave strips of trees and vegetation along streams and shorelines. Grazing livestock can be kept away from stream sides by fencing. All efforts to control erosion also have the effect of keeping water clearer and, thus, cooler.[44]

(7) Plastic Pollution

Plastic is now a regular material that is being used on a daily basis. It is everywhere either in the form of food containers, financial transactions (Debit/ Credit cards, plastic money), storage, baggage, stationary items, electronic and electrical products and every foreseeable item that a human being can think of.[45] Basically, it is a synthetic polymer that consists of many organic and inorganic compounds, and is mostly derived from petrochemicals like olefins. Plastic materials are mainly classified as thermoplastics (polystyrene and polyvinyl chloride) and thermosetting polymers. Ethylene oxide, xylene, and benzene are some of the chemical toxins present in plastic, which can have hazardous effects on the environment. Plastic is a non-biodegradable product, with the potential to cause great harm to the environment.[46]

Plastic pollution involves the accumulation of plastic products in the environment that adversely affects wildlife, wildlife habitat, or humans. The prominence of plastic pollution is correlated with plastics being inexpensive and durable, which lends to high levels of plastics used by humans. According to the trade association Plastics Europe, world plastic production grew from some 1.5 million tons in 1950 to an estimated 275 million tons in 2010; some four million to 12 million tons is discarded into the oceans annually by countries with ocean coastlines. Since the ocean is downstream from nearly every terrestrial location, it is the receiving body for much of the plastic waste generated on land.

In the ocean, plastic pollution can kill marine mammals directly through entanglement in objects such as fishing gear, but it can also kill through ingestion, by being mistaken for food.[47] Plastic pollution affects every waterway, sea and ocean in the world. This pollution also has huge costs for taxpayers and local governments that must clean this trash off of beaches and streets to protect public health, prevent flooding from trash-blocked storm drains, and avoid lost tourism revenue from filthy beaches. The most effective way to stop plastic pollution in our oceans is to make sure it never reaches the water in the first place. Reducing, reusing, and recycling are the best way to stem the tide of plastics into our oceans.[48]

Indian Perspectives

Air pollution in India is quite a serious issue with the major sources being fuel wood and biomass burning, fuel adulteration, vehicle emission and traffic congestion. Fuel wood and biomass burning is the primary reason for near-permanent haze and smoke observed above rural and urban India, and in satellite pictures of the country. As of 2009, majority of Indians still use traditional fuels such as dried cow dung, agricultural waste, and firewood as cooking fuel. India is the world's largest consumer of fuel wood, agricultural waste and biomass for energy purposes. Fuel wood, agricultural waste and biomass cake burning releases over 165 million tons of combustion products into India's indoor and outdoor air every year. A United Nations study finds firewood and biomass stoves can be made more efficient in India.[49]

Of the world's top 20 polluted cities, 13 are in India compared to just three in China. Air pollution slashes life expectancy by 3.2 years for the 660 million Indians who live in cities, including Delhi. In China, the corresponding dip is marginally lower at three years. The Ganga and Yamuna are ranked among the world's 10 most polluted rivers. China has just one. The two nations have seen furious economic growth in the past decade fueling a rapid rise in pollution. China leads the world in carbon emissions and India is in third position. A three-year analysis of the water quality in 290 rivers by the Central Pollution Control Board said about 66 per cent of the stretches monitored had high organic pollution. It means 8,400 km of these rivers are badly polluted and not fit for supporting aquatic life.[50]

Delhi's air pollution levels are among the worst in the world but new research is pointing at something even more worrying. A government agency that recently started monitoring the most dangerous class of particulate pollutants- ultrafine particulate matter or PM_1- found its levels to be quite high even in the low-pollution pre-monsoon season in comparatively cleaner locations of the city such as central Delhi's Lodhi Road. PM_1 is the tiniest class of pollution particles. Currently, no safe standards have been set for PM_1. PM_1 levels remain high even in wet weather because rain doesn't wash away very fine particles. Monitoring of PM_1 levels can help the government address the major source of pollution. The PM_1 particles are so light that now for vehicles with Euro 5 fuel standard, the emission is being counted in number of pollution particles as against the weight of particles.[51]

People living in Mumbai and Navi Mumbai have been breathing polluted air, which falls under the "poor to severe" category for a considerable number of observations throughout 2013-14, found a report on the air quality status of Maharashtra, published by the Maharashtra Pollution Control Board (MPCB). The report was prepared by The Energy and Resources Institute based on air quality data monitored by MPCB. Ambient air quality monitoring stations at Sion and Bandra recorded 'moderate' and 'poor' air quality for 70 to 80 per cent of the recorded observations, while 'poor' or 'moderate' air quality was recorded for more than 35 and 60 per cent of the observations respectively at Navi Mumbai and Panvel.[52]

Kolkata is the most polluted metropolis in the country with its pollution levels recorded highest among eight tropical Asian countries, according to study. Among major metropolis in India, Kolkata was found to be the most polluted city with its pollution levels recorded highest among the eight tropical Asian countries. Several compounds have been identified as hormone disruptors which can alter normal function of endocrine and reproductive systems in humans and wildlife. Cardiovascular disease, cancer, obesity, and diabetes have also been linked to POPs.[53]

Seventy per cent of Kolkata's citizens suffer some form of respiratory disease. Delhi is not far behind at 68 per cent, reports a new study on air pollution by the Chittaranjan National Cancer Institute, West Bengal's department of environment and the Central Pollution Board, Delhi. Kolkata has the highest number of people suffering from lung cancer in the world. This is because it is one of the most polluted cities in the world. Lung cancer cases, as also other air pollution-related health problems including haematological abnormalities, impaired liver function, genetic changes and neurobehavioural problems, were found to be most prevalent amongst those categories of workers exposed to high levels of vehicular emission. These include roadside hawkers, traffic policemen and taxi and auto drivers.[54]

Kanpur is the most polluted city in the country, with high quantities of Respirable Suspended Particulate Matter (RSPM) in the air, according to the results of a survey carried out by the Central Pollution Control Board (CPCB). Chennai is the least polluted city. As per data collected by the CPCB between the months of January and April 2002, RSPM levels varied from 119 micrograms to 257 micrograms per cubic metre in Kanpur, while in Chennai it was found to be within the range of 25-49 mgm/cubic metre as against the standard level of 60 mgm/cubic metre.[55]

Water pollution has many sources. The most polluting of them are the city sewage and industrial waste discharged into the rivers. The facilities to treat waste water are not adequate in any city in India. Presently, only about 10 per cent of the waste water generated is treated; the rest is discharged as it is into water bodies. The main organic materials are food and vegetable waste, plant nutrient come from chemical soaps, washing powders, etc. Domestic sewage is very likely to contain disease-causing microbes. Disposal of domestic waste water is a significant technical problem. Sewage generated from the urban areas in India has multiplied manifold since 1947.[56]

In India soil pollution is mainly due to pollution concentration in urban areas and unplanned development of industries. It has been estimated that the urban population of India produces about 15 million tonnes of solid waste per annum causing pollution. Soil pollution many a time results in agricultural pollution when it refers to liquid and solid waste from farming including run-off from the pesticides, fertilisers, animal carcasses etc.[57]

The accelerated use of chemical fertilisers and biocides in agriculture is the major cause of soil pollution. They are used to increase the yields and to save the crops from insects, pests and unwanted plant growth. The use of biocides gained momentum in India with the commencement of Green Revolution in 1966-67. The introduction of high yielding varieties (HYV) of seeds gave birth to heavy doses of chemical fertilizers and biocides. The overall per hectare consumption of fertilizers rose from a mere 0.55 kg in 1950-51 to 67 kg in 1992-93 and to 89.8 kg in 2003-04. The highest per hectare consumption of N.P.K. fertilizers was in Punjab (189.1), followed by Haryana (167.1), Andhra Pradesh (136.8), Manipur (130.5), Uttar Pradesh (126.7), and

West Bengal (122.4). In Arunachal Pradesh, Nagaland, Mizoram and Sikkim, the consumption of N.P.K. fertilizers was less than 4 kg/hectare.[58]

Control of Pollution

Pollution control is a term used in environmental management. It means the control of emissions and effluents into air, water or soil. Without pollution control, the waste products from consumption, heating, agriculture, mining, manufacturing, transportation and other human activities, whether they accumulate or disperse, will degrade the environment. The Toxicology and Environmental Health Information Programme (TEHIP) at the United States National Library of Medicine (NLM) maintains a comprehensive toxicology and environmental health web site that includes access to resources produced by TEHIP and by other government agencies and organisations.

India provides a compelling setting to explore the effectiveness of environmental regulations in a developing country for several reasons. India's population of nearly 1.2 billion accounts for about 17 per cent of the planet's population. Second, the country is experiencing rapid economic growth of about 6.4 per cent annually over the last two decades, which is placing significant pressure on the environment. India has a relatively extensive set of regulations designed to improve both air and water quality. Its environmental policies have their roots in the Water Act of 1974 and Air Act of 1981. These acts created the Central Pollution Control Board (CPCB) and the State Pollution Control Boards (SPCBs), which are responsible for data collection and policy enforcement, and also developed detailed procedures for environmental compliance. The Ministry of Environment and Forests (MoEF), created in its initial form in 1980, was established largely to set the overall policies that the CPCB and SPCBs were to enforce.[59]

Central Pollution Control Board of India is a statutory organisation under the Ministry of Environment and Forests. It co-ordinate the activities of the State Boards by providing technical assistance and guidance and resolve disputes among them. It is an apex organisation in country in the field of pollution control, as technical wing of MoEF. Board has its head office in New Delhi, with seven zonal offices and five laboratories. It is constituted on 22 September 1974 under Section 3 of the Water (Prevention and Control of Pollution) Act, 1974 with the main function to promote cleanliness of streams and wells in the different areas of the States. Its functions come under both national level and as State Boards for the Union Territories. It under the Water (Prevention and Control of Pollution) Act, 1974, and the Air (Prevention and Control of Pollution) Act, 1981, aims to promote cleanliness of streams and wells in different areas of the States by prevention, control and abatement of water pollution, and to improve the quality of air and to prevent, control or abate air pollution in the country.[60]

As per the policy decision of the Government of India, the CPCB has delegated its powers and functions under the Water (Prevention and Control of Pollution) Act, 1974, the Water (Prevention and Control of Pollution) Cess Act, 1977 and the Air (Prevention and Control of Pollution) Act, 1981 with respect to Union Territories to respective local administrations. CPCB along with its counterparts State Pollution Control Boards (SPCBs) are responsible for implementation of legislations relating to prevention and control of environmental pollution.[61]

The Ministry of Environment, Forests and Climate Change is an Indian government ministry. The ministry is responsible for planning, promoting, coordinating, and overseeing the implementation of environmental and forestry programmes in the country. The main activities undertaken by the ministry include conservation and survey of the flora of India and fauna of India, forests and other wilderness areas; prevention and control of pollution; afforestation, and land degradation mitigation.

The Environment Ministry has proposed to come out with a scheme with an aim to develop at least one city forest on forest land in cities having municipal corporations. The Environment Ministry has proposed an urban forestry scheme namely 'nagar van udyan yojna' on pilot basis. The aim is to develop at least one city forest initially on forest land ranging from 20 ha to 100 ha in cities having municipal corporations. The main objective is to create awareness about environment and help students identify and learn about the various benefits of trees and plants. Under the scheme, 1,000 schools of the country will be selected every year and each will raise at least 1,000 saplings by involving students. Selected schools will receive grant of Rs 25,000 in the first year and Rs 10,000 per year for the subsequent two years[62].

Management of radioactive waste in Indian context includes all types of radioactive wastes generated from the entire nuclear fuel cycle right from mining of uranium, fuel fabrication through reactor operations and subsequent reprocessing of the spent fuel. Since the spent fuel is reprocessed with a view to recover and reuse the U and Pu produced there, the fuel cycle is termed as 'closed', unlike in other countries like USA, Canada, etc. where the spent fuel is stored as waste. Radioactive wastes are also generated from use of radionuclides in medicine, industry and research. Effective management of radioactive wastes involves segregation, characterisation handling, treatment, conditioning and monitoring prior to final storage/disposal. Radioactive wastes arise in different forms viz; solid, liquid and gas with variety of physical and chemical/radiochemical characteristics.

Low and intermediate level liquid wastes are generated in relatively large volumes with low levels of radio-activity. If a particular stream of radioactive liquid waste contains short-lived isotopes, it may be stored for adequate time period to ensure that majority of the radionuclides die down, thus, following the 'delay and decay' principles. High level radioactive liquid waste (HLW) containing most (<99%) of the radioactivity in the entire fuel cycle is produced during reprocessing of spent fuel.

In addition, hull waste i.e., the hollow clad tubes, is generated as solid HLW after the spent fuel is dissolved for the purpose of reprocessing. The management of high level liquid waste in the Indian context encompasses the following three stages. (i) Immobilisation of high level liquid waste into vitrified borosilicate glasses. (ii) Engineered interim storage of the vitrified waste and other high level wastes with passive cooling and surveillance over a period of time, qualifying it for ultimate disposal. (iii) Ultimate storage/disposal of the vitrified waste and other high active solid waste in deep geological repository.[63]

Basically, there are seven Pollution regulations.

1. The Water (Prevention & Control of Pollution) Act, 1974, and its amendments;
2. The Water (Prevention & Control of Pollution) Cess Act, 1974 and its amendments;
3. The Air (Prevention & Control of Pollution) Act, 1981 and its amendments;
4. The Environment (Prevention) Act, 1986 and its amendments, (a) National Environmental Tribunal Act of 1995 and (b) National Environmental Appellate Authority Act of 1997;
5. Hazardous Waste (Management and Handling) Rules, July 1989; and
6. The Public Liability Insurance Act, 1991.

The Public Liability Insurance Act 1991 has been included as the sixth environmental regulation because it is the first regulation which gives some teeth to the other five pollution regulations listed above.[64]

Environment Protection Act, 1986 is an Act of the Parliament of India. In the wake of the Bhopal Tragedy, the Government of India enacted the Environment Protection Act of 1986 under Article 253 of the Constitution. Passed in March 1986, it came into force on 19th November 1986. The purpose of the Act is to implement the decisions of the United Nations Conference on the Human Environments they relate to the protection and improvement of the human environment and the prevention of hazards to human beings, other living creatures, plants and property. The Act is an "umbrella" legislation designed to provide a framework for central government coordination of the activities of various central and state authorities established under previous laws, such as the Water Act and the Air Act. The objectives of the act are:

(a) To co-ordinate the activities of the various regulatory agencies already in existence.

(b) Creation of an authority or authorities with adequate powers for environmental protection.

(c) Regulation of discharge of environmental pollutants and handling of hazardous substance.

(d) Speedy response in the event of accidents threatening environment and punishment to those who endanger human environment, safety and health.[65]

The Ministry of Environment and Forests, Government of India, notified the Hazardous Waste (Management and Handling) Rules on July 28, 1989 under the provisions of the Environment (Protection) Act, 1986, which was further amended in the year 2000 and 2003 and recently The Hazardous Wastes (Management, Handling and Transboundry Movement) Rules, 2008 were notified for effective management of hazardous waste.The Public Liability Insurance Act has been incorporated on 22nd January 1991. This Act has been established to provide immediate insurance for the person who met with an accident while handling hazardous substance and other similar circumstances.This Public Liability-Insurance will help the weaker section of the people who handles such hazardous substances and chemicals from delayed relief or compensation. This Act provides immediate insurance relief to such person with genuine injury occurring through an accident as prescribed in this Act.

All owners of such factory or industry handling hazardous substance shall take several insurance policies in order to provide immediate relief to its own employee during such unforeseen accident or injury or even death while handling such chemicals or substances. In case if any owner fails to take such insurance before this Act, shall take such Insurance for Contract of insurance within a year of Commencement of this Act. No person shall claim for relief in case if such accident occurs due to his own wrong handling or negligent in handling, etc.

Every owner shall renew their insurance policies before the expiry date of such policies in order to meet such unforeseen circumstances throughout the period. Owners should not take insurance policies less than the paid-up-capital of undertaking hazardous chemicals and substances that is owned and controlled. At the same time the amount of insurance policies should not exceed Fifty Crores Rupees. The liability of the insurer for one insurance policy shall be within the amount prescribed in the contract of insurance in that policy.

The owners shall pay not only premium to the insurer but also for a relief fund not more than such premium paid as specified in this Act. The insurer later shall return back the excess amount of Relief Fund to the owners. In case if the insurer fails to returns the money on time, it shall be recoverable as arrears of land revenue or of public fund.The Central Government shall by notifications exempt itself, State Government, any Corporations owned by Central and State Governments and any Local Authority from this Insurance operation except in case where the owners fail to maintain such insurance policies to provide immediate relief to its employees during accident while handling hazardous substances. The Collector immediately after knowing about such accident shall investigate such occurrence and publicity made in such a manner to receive application of Claim for injury, death, etc. either by the same person or his legal representatives or agent of such deceased person.

The Collector shall not appreciate any application that is made any other members other than the members specified in this Act. The Application must be filled with all relevant particulars and should be made within five years of such unforeseen accident caused while handling hazardous substances. The Collector after receiving the application shall fix a date for enquiry through notification to the Owner and Parties after giving an opportunity to hear and pass such award to grant relief to the affected parties that appears to be fit for his quantum of injury incurred.

The copies of the awards shall be given to the parties within fifteen days from the date of award. During the award the insurer are demanded to pay such amount as specified in the award within thirty days from the date of such award and deposit such amount before the Collector. The Collector shall demand for relief fund if any and asked to deposit such amount as specified in the award. The Collector shall also demand for any amount paid by the Owner as specified in the award and is asked to deposit before him. The Collector has the power as specified in Civil Procedure Code, 1908.

The Central Government shall with notification introduce an Environment Relief Fund that is paid with a scheme framed and administered in accordance with this Act. The Central Government shall authorise a person to monitor such place where hazardous substances where carried forward for usage, as and when necessary to see whether any of the provisions of this Act has been violated or to be performed. All expenses incurred by such person for disposal of hazardous substances shall be recovered through arrears of land revenue or of public fund from the Owner.

The Central Government shall pass any directions in pursuance to this Act to any of the Officers or person authorised to do so or Owner or agents, etc. In case if the Central Government through its authorised person comes to know that the Owner is handling such hazardous substances against the provisions of this Act shall be produced before the Magistrate on application by such person.

All expenses incurred on legal proceedings shall be recoverable from the Owner as arrears of land revenue or of public fund. Any person acting in contravention to this Act shall be punished with imprisonment with or without fine as it deems fit. No legal action shall be taken against any activities done in pursuance to this Act. The Central Government shall have enormous powers to make any number of rules in pursuance to this Act. It shall constitute any number of committees as and when necessary. Each rules or schemes framed should be assented by the Houses of Parliaments.[66]

Air Pollution Control

Delhi's poor air quality has rightly made it the centre of media and government attention. However, the Indian government's own air quality monitoring apparatus now shows the focus so far may have remained too narrowly on some pollutants and, as a result, only on some cities. While Delhi and the rest of north India have higher particulate matter levels, cities such as Chennai find high concentrations of other toxic pollutants including Sulphur dioxide and nitrogen dioxide. The government has taken a great first step in setting up a national Index and in making data for 11 cities, for now, public. Data for more cities and monitoring stations need to be brought online. The next step should be for policy-makers to actually look at this data; the government's own website is clearly showing that a number of Indian cities are experiencing what should be health emergencies on a daily basis, going by their AQI levels.[67]

The U.S. Embassy and Consulates General in India maintain an air quality monitoring programme with on-site measuring instruments. The Government of India and state government agencies also provide publicly available air quality information for cities throughout India. The Central Pollution Control Board air pollution monitoring sites cover the areas of Dilshad Garden, ITO, Shadipur, Delhi College of Engineering, and Dwarka. The data is displayed in raw concentrations only and has not been converted to an Air Quality Index. The Indian Meteorological Department air pollution monitoring sites cover the areas of Mathura Road, Aya Nagar (Gurgaon area), IMD Delhi (Jor Bagh area), IGI Airport, IITM Delhi, Noida, Guru Teg Bahadur Hospital (Ghaziabad area), Dhirpur, Delhi University, Pitampura. The data is displayed using IMD's own air quality index, different from that of the U.S. EPA.[68]

The government of Delhi has taken on the National Green Tribunal, contesting that old private vehicles plying in the National Capital Region are not significant contributors. The NGT had earlier ordered a ban on all diesel vehicles over 10 years of age in the Delhi-NCR region and petrol vehicles older than 15 years - commercial or private. But as the government protested, it put the ban on hold, hearing the government out. Using the IIT report, the government has advocated focusing on long-term reforms that would bring improvement to Delhi's air. One of them is improving the quality of fuel used in vehicles. The government insists that regular pollution control checks could suffice to ensure old vehicles are not polluting.[69]

Industry is looking for solutions to the air pollution problem. The best solution would be to stop burning fossil fuels all together but at this time we have no other alternatives. Scientists are trying ways to cut down on pollution. Some of the solutions to help slow the depletion is to use hydro-fluorocarbons (HFCs) instead of CFCs, cutting down on the use of CFCs, and using alternative jet fuel which doesn't release Nitrous gas.[70]

Air (Prevention and Control of Pollution) Act, 1981 is an Act of the Parliament of India to control and prevent air pollution. It was amended in 1987. This is an Act to provide for prevention, control and abatement of air pollution in the country so as to preserve the quality of air. Central and State

Boards constituted u/s 3 & 4 of Water [Prevention and Control of Pollution] Act, 1974 were deemed also as Central and State Boards for prevention and control of air pollution. It is an Act to provide for the prevention, control and abatement of air pollution, for the establishment, with a view to carrying out the aforesaid purposes, of Boards, for conferring on and assigning to such Boards powers and functions relating thereto and for matters connected therewith. The Salient Points of the Act are:

(a) The Act is applicable to whole India.

(b) U/s 19 of the Act, Central / State Govt. in consultation with SPCB is vested with power to declare Air Pollution Control Area in which the provisions of the Act shall be applicable.

(c) As per provisions in section 21 [2], no person can establish or operate any industrial plant without the consent of State Pollution Control Board shall complete the formalities to either grant or refuse consent. During the course of the processing consent application, Board may seek any information about the industry after giving notice in Form-II.

(d) Under section 22, 22(A) operating any industrial plant so as to cause emission of any air pollutant in excess of standard laid down by State Board, is liable for litigation by the Board.[71]

There are various measures to Control Air Pollution:

(1) Activated carbon is one of the most popular forms of air pollution control. This type of control involves the use of a pollution filter, carbon, to reduce the amount of pollutants that are allowed to escape into the air.

(2) Fuel switching based on meteorological conditions or air pollution forecasts have been used to prevent air pollution problem in many areas.

(3) Nuclear power plants are relatively pollution free when compared to the coal fired power plants.

(4) Biofiltration is another effective type of air pollution control. It uses microorganisms, often bacteria and fungi, to dissolve pollutants. Industries that employ biofiltration systems include food and waste plants, pharmaceutical companies, and wastewater management facilities.

(5) Use of low sulphur fuel instead of high sulphur fuel by electric utilities is an example of this method.

(6) Use of oil with low ash content or natural gas for a dryer at an asphalt plant to reduce particulate matter is another example of this method.[72]

(7) Encourage people to use more and more public modes of transportation to reduce pollution.

(8) Switch off fans and lights when you are going out Large amount of fossil fuels are burnt to produce electricity.

(9) Clean energy technologies like solar, wind and geothermal are on high these days.

(10) CFL lights consume less electricity as against their counterparts. They live longer, consume less electricity, lower electricity bills and also help you to reduce pollution by consuming less energy.[73]

(11) Request that nations enact and enforce strict regulations requiring the use of air scrubbers on all industrial facilities that release atmospheric pollutants.

(12) Apply the carbon credit system to other known atmospheric pollutants such as sulphur oxide, nitrogen oxide, carbon monoxide, methane, and aerosols and annually reduce the total amount of pollutants permitted.

(13) Encourage government-funded research projects to develop clean electric transportation methods to help reduce dependence on fossil fuels.[74]

Water Pollution Control

Within India, Maharashtra state was the front runner to enact Water Pollution and Control Act in 1962. This was followed by passing of Comprehensive Environmental Protection Bill for prevention of air pollution in 1983. Maharashtra, Gujarat, Madhya Pradesh were the first states in Indian union to have pollution control board with attached analytical laboratories. This was followed by the setting of series of laboratories in all remaining states of the nation.[75]

In 1995, the Central Pollution Control Board identified severely polluted stretches on 18 major rivers in India. Not surprisingly, a majority of these stretches were found in and around large urban areas. The level of water pollution in the country can be gauged by the status of water quality around India. The water quality monitoring results carried out by CPCB particularly with respect to the indicator of oxygen consuming substances (biochemical oxygen demand, BOD) and the indicator of pathogenic bacteria. The water quality monitoring results obtained by CPCB during 1995 to 2009 indicate that organic and bacterial contamination was critical in the water bodies.[76]

Water pollution can be controlled in the multiple ways. It is best controlled by the dilution of water. The pollutants must be treated chemically and must be converted into the non-toxic substances. The low level of radioactive wastes in the water is removed by the oxidation of ponds. There are certain chemicals which act on the organic insecticide and are used in the pesticide.[78]

Table 1: Ill Effects of Water Pollutants[77]

Sl. No.	*Pollutant*	*Effects*
1.	Zinc (Zn)	Zinc is essential element for humans, animal and plants. It is also an important cell component in several metalloen zymes. Infants need 3–5 mg/day, adult males 15 mg/day, pregnant and lactating females 20–25 mg Zn/day. However, heavy doses of Zn salts (165 mg) for 26 days causes vomiting, renal damage, cramps, etc.
2.	Copper (Cu)	Excess of Cu in human body (more than 470 mg) is toxic, may cause hypertension, sporadic fever, uremia, coma. Copper also produces pathological changes in brain tissue. However, Cu is an important cell component in several metalloenzymes. Lack of Cu causes anaemia, growth inhibition and blood circulation problem.
3.	Barium (Ba)	Excess of Ba (more than 100 mg) in human body may cause excessive salivation, colic, vomiting, diarrhoea, tremors, paralysis of muscles or nervous system, damage to heart and blood vessels.
4.	Iron (Fe)	It is one of the essential mineral for humans and animals. Degree of absorption depends upon solubility and stability of compound. It is a component of blood cells and liveral metalloenzymes. However, more than 10 mg per kg of body weight causes rapid respiration and pulse rates, congestion of blood vessels, hypertension and drowsiness. It increases hazard of pathogenic organisms, as many of them require Fe for their growth.
5.	Cadmium (Cd)	Cd is very toxic, 50 mg may cause vomiting, diarrhoea, abdominal pains, loss of consciousness. It takes 5–10 years for chronic Cd intoxication. During first phase, discolour ation of teeth, loss of sense of smell, mouth dryness occurs. Afterwards it may cause decrease of red blood cells, impa-irment of bone marrow, lumber pains, disturbance in calcium metabolism, softening of bones, fractures, skeletal deformations, damage of kidney, hypertension, tumor formation, heart disease, impaired reproductive function, genetic mutation, etc.
6.	Mercury (Hg)	Mercury is very toxic. Excess mercury in human body (more than 100 mg) may cause headache, abdominal pain, diarrhoea, destruction of haemoglobin, tremors*, very bad effects on cerebral functions and central nervous system, paralysis, inactivates functional proteins, damage of renal tissues, hyper coagulability of blood, mimamata disease, and even death. It may cause impairment of vision and muscles and even coma. It disturbs reproductive and

(Contd...)

		endocrine system. Also causes insomnia, memory loss, gum inflammation, loosening of teeth, loss of appetite, etc.
7.	Lead (Pb)	More than 400 mg of lead in human body can cause brain damage, vomiting, loss of appetite, convulsions, uncoordinated body movements helplessly amazed state, coma. It is retained in liver, kidney, brain, muscle, soft tissues, bones. Leads to high rate of miscarriages, affects skin, and respiratory system, damages kidney, liver and brain cells. Disturbs endocrine system, causes anaemia,` and long term exposure may cause even death.
8.	Arsenic (As)	Poisonous to fishes, animals and humans. Greater than 25 mg of arsenic causes vomiting, diarrhoea, nausea, irritation of nose and throat, abdominal pain, skin eruptions inflammations and even death. It binds globulin of blood haemoglobin in erythrocytes. May cause cancer of skin, lungs and liver, chromosomal aberration and damage, gangrene, loss of hearing, injury to nerve tissue, liver and kidney damage. Minor symptoms of As poisoning, weight loss, hair loss, nausea, depression, fatigue, white lines across toe nails and finger nails.
9.	Vanadium (V)	It is very toxic, may cause paralysis.
10.	Silver (Ag)	Causes pathological change in kidney, liver and may even damage kidney. May cause Argyria (discolouration of skin). Effects mucous membranes and eyes In high doses, it may be fatal to humans.
11.	Radioactive materials/ metals/ substances	These generally cause 'Gene' mutation, ionisation of body fluids, chromosomnal mutations and cancers. Destroy body cell tissue, adversely effects reproductive system. When mother is exposed to radiation during pregnancy, it causes severe mental retardation and leukaemia in infants. Radioactive metals like heavy metals are nephrotoxic and damage kidneys.
12.	Fluoride	Excess fluoride intake in body results in progressive crippling scourge (sponging)/fluorosis of bones, teeth. May cause metabolic alternations in soft tissues and their functional mechanism.
13.	Selenium (Se)	Signs of Se poisoning (more than 4 mg) are fever, nervousness, vomiting, falling of blood pressure, causes damage to liver, kidney and spleen, loss of nails and hair, causes blindness to animals. Cats are most susceptible. It affects enzyme systems and interfere with sulphur metabolism. It can cause growth inhibition, skin discolouration, bad teeth, psychological problem, gastro intestinal problems, but trace amount of Se is protective against poisoning by Hg, Cd, Ag.

(Contd...)

14.	Chromium (Cr)	Any chromium compound is toxic but haxavalent Cr greater than 70 mg is very toxic. It causes cancer, anuria, nephritis, gastrointestinal ulceration, perforation in partition of nose. It penetrates cell membrane and badly affects central nervous system. Causes respiratory trouble, lung tumors when inhaled. May cause complications during pregnancy. It has adverse effects on aquatic life. Trace amount of CrIII is essential for normal glucose, protein and fat metabolism and hence it is a essential trace element in diet.
15.	Manganese (Mn)	Mn is essential for mammals but in concentration greater than 100 ppm, is toxic, and causes growth retardation, fever, sexual impotence, muscles fatigue, eye blindness.
16.	Cobalt (Co)	High dose (27 mg or above) can cause paralysis, diarrhoea, low blood pressure, lung irritation, bone defects.
17.	Nickel (Ni)	More than 30 mg may cause changes in muscle, brain, lungs, liver, kidney and can also cause cancer, tremor*, paralysis and even death.
18.	Boron (B)	Essential for plant growth in traces. Harmful to crops and affects metabolic activities of plants in higher concentra - tion. Affects central nervous system.
19.	Alkalinity and Acidity	Permissible range of pH value if violated may cause health problems to human and animals and loss of productivity in agriculture.
20.	Phosphate and nitrates	Soil nutrient and not toxic in low concentration. Deplete oxygen by excess Algae production-giving bad odour and taste of water and detrimental to aquatic life. They are toxic for human and animal life if concentration is beyond permissible limits. Nitrates also cause cynosis or blue body disease.
21.	Chlorine (Cl)	Destroys plant and aquatic life and is a biocide.
22.	Sulphide	Gives bad odour, toxic to many aquatic organisms and animals.
23.	Salinity	Very bad for soils which retain salinity. Destroys agricultural land.
24.	Oil/Grease/ Oil Sludge	Petroleum product in general is very harmful for soils, aquatic life, animal, human and plant life. They are very toxic. Agricultural land may suffer accumulation of oily waste affecting aeration and fertility. Many constituents of oily sludge are even carcinogenic and potent immunotoxicants.
25.	Pesticides/ Insecticides	Highly poisonous for humans and animals. Also they lower seed germination, plays a role in development of Parkinson's disease, destruction of nerve cells in certain regions of brain resulting in loss of dopamine which is used by nerve cells to communicate with brain. Some of

(Contd...)

		these are physical poisons, some are protoplasmic poisons causing liver damage, some are respiratory poisons and some are nerve poisons.
26.	Phenols	Toxic and impart objectionable odour Also subdue plant growth generally. Some phenols (nitrophenyl etc) are carcinogens.

Source: http://www.newagepublishers.com/samplechapter/001754.pdf

Several chemical methods have been devised for the treatment of industrial effluents before discharging them in water bodies. Iron exchange is a reversible reaction where in an iron from solution is exchanged for a similar charged ion attached to an immobile solid particle which is either naturally occurring inorganic zeolite or synthetically produced organic resins. Precipitation process transform dissolved contaminants into an insoluble solid, facilitating the contaminant's subsequent removal from the liquid phase by sedimentation or filtration. Chemical coagulation enhances the removal of colloidal particles by destabilising and chemically precipitating them and accumulating the precipitated material into larger floe particles which can either removed by gravity setting or filtration.[79]

The Water (Prevention and Control of Pollution) Act was enacted in 1974 to provide for the prevention and control of water pollution, and for the maintaining or restoring of wholesomeness of water in the country. The Act was amended in 1988. The Water (Prevention and Control of Pollution) Cess Act was enacted in 1977, to provide for the levy and collection of a cess on water consumed by persons operating and carrying or certain types of industrial activities. This cess is collected with a view to augment the resources of the Central Board and the State Boards for the prevention and control of water pollution constituted under the Water (Prevention and Control of Pollution) Act, 1974. The Act was last amended in 2003.[80]

Parliament adopted the Water (Prevention and Control of Pollution) Cess Act, 1977 to provide funds for the Central and State Pollution Control Boards. The Act empowers the Central Government to impose a Cess on water consumed by industries listed in Schedule-I of the Act. The industries as specified Schedule-I in and local authorities are required to pay the water Cess as per the quarterly of water Schedule-I.

1. Industrial cooling, spraying in mine pits, or boiler feed;
2. Domestic purposes;
3. Processing which results in water pollution by biodegradable water pollutants; or
4. Processing which results in water pollution by water pollutants which are not easily biodegradable or are toxic. Schedule-II used for various purposes as specified in Schedule-II.

Under Section 3: The Cess shall be calculated at such rate as may be specified by the Government. The rate notified/specified by the Government indicates two rates for Cess calculation - lower one for industries complying with Section 25 of Water Act, 1974 and standards of effluent as prescribed under EPA, 1986 and higher one for those failing to comply with the above mentioned conditions.

Under Section 4: For the purpose of measuring and recording the quantity of water consumed, every person carrying on any specified industry and every local authority shall affix meters of such standards and at such places as may be prescribed.

Under Section 7: Where any person or local authority, liable to pay the Cess under this act, installs any plant for the treatment of sewage or trade effluents, such person or local authority shall be entitled to a rebate of 25 per cent of the Cess payable by such person or local authority, provided that the person/local authority is not contravening section prescribed 25 of the Water Act 1974 and effluent standards prescribed under EPA, 1986 and is not consuming water in excess of the maximum quantity as may be prescribed by the government for any specified industry or local authority.

Under Section 9: Any officer or authority of the State govt. specially empowered in this behalf can enter any premises at any reasonable time for the purpose of carrying out his duties under this Act.

Under Section 10: If any person carrying on any specified industry or local authority fails to pay any amount of Cess payable under Section 3 within the date specified in the order of assessment made such person or local authority is liable to pay interest on the amount to be paid as laid down.

Under Section 13: Any person or local authority aggrieved by an order of assessment made under Section 6 or by an order imposing any penalty made under Section 11 may within such time as may be prescribed, appear to such authority in such form and in such manner as may be prescribed.[81]

Green infrastructure and low impact development approaches and techniques help manage water and water pollutants at the source, preventing or reducing the impact of development on water and water quality. States, territories, and tribes must protect water bodies and to address water bodies that do not meet water quality standards (i.e., impaired waters). EPA's National Pollutant Discharge Elimination System (NPDES) permit programme plays an important role in minimising the wastes and pollution load released into receiving bodies. Find basic information on the major features and elements of the NPDES permit programme.[82] The various methods for the control of water pollution are discussed below:

1. The sewage pollutants are subject to chemical treatment to change them into non-toxic substances or make them less toxic.
2. Water pollution due to organic insecticides can be reduced by the use of very specific and less stable chemicals in the manufacture of insecticides.

3. Oxidation ponds can be useful in removing low level of radioactive wastes.
4. Suitable strict legislation should be enacted to make it obligatory for the industries to treat the waste water before being discharged into rivers or seas.
5. Polluted water can be reclaimed by proper sewage treatment plants and the same water can be reused in factories and even irrigation.[83]

Soil Pollution Control

Soil pollution is defined as, "contamination of soil by human and natural activities which may cause harmful effect on living organisms". It can be positive or negative. In the negative soil pollution there occur an overuse of soil and erosion. The erosion occurs by water and air. The water erosion occurs by the high speed rivers which remove the top layer of soil. In the positive soil pollution there occur an overuse of chemical fertilizers, air pollutants and pesticides along with herbicides and fumigants. The air pollutants have the ability to move down with the rain. The pesticides and weedicides are defined as the chemicals which have the ability to kill the insects, fungi, rodents, algae, weeds so that the agriculture output is increased.

Modern agricultural practices pollute the soil to a large extent. With the advancing agro-technology, huge quantities of fertilizers, pesticides, herbicides and weedicides are added to increase the crop yield. Radioactive substances resulting from explosions of nuclear testing laboratories and industries giving rise to nuclear dust radioactive wastes penetrate the soil and accumulate giving rise to land/soil pollution.

Soil erosion can be controlled by a variety of forestry and farm practices. Reducing deforestation and substituting chemical manures by animal wastes also helps arrest soil erosion in the long term. The biological control method must be known and implemented. The grazing must be controlled and forest management should be done properly. The afforestation and reforestation must be done. In areas of wind erosion wind breaks and shields must be used.

Applying bio-fertilizers and manures can reduce chemical fertilizer and pesticide use. Biological methods of pest control can also reduce the use of pesticides and thereby minimise soil pollution. Materials such as glass containers, plastic bags, paper, cloth etc. can be reused at domestic levels rather than being disposed, reducing solid waste pollution. Proper methods should be adopted for management of solid waste disposal. Crop rotation or mixed cropping can improve the fertility of the land.

Pollution Control Strategies

Control strategy is a set of discrete and specific measures identified and implemented to achieve reductions in air pollution. These measures may vary by source type, such as stationary or mobile, as well as by the pollutant that is being targeted. The purpose of these measures is to achieve the air quality standard or goal. Costs and benefits are assessed in the development of the control strategy.[84] Pollution controls divert economic resources from other economic activities, thereby reducing the potential size of measured national output. As long as the increase in the value of the environment is at least one dollar for each additional dollar spent on controls, the total value of goods, services, and environmental amenities is not reduced.[85]

The Basic Law for Environmental Pollution Control defines environmental pollution as any activity, by corporations or individuals, which compromises the health and/or environment of other persons in a localised area, where the causal link is clearly established. Pollution prevention reduces the amount of pollution generated by a process, whether it is consumer consumption, driving, or industrial production. With increasing human population, pollution has become a great concern. Pollution from human activities is a problem that does not have to be inevitable. With a comprehensive pollution prevention programme, most pollution can be reduced, reused, or prevented.

Pollution control equipment can reduce emissions by cleaning exhaust and dirty air before it leaves the business. There are other ways to reduce emissions besides using pollution control equipment—prevent emissions to begin with. Air quality permits help minimise, reduce or prevent emissions as much as possible by placing requirements on how things are done. Engineers can also set combustion specifications to minimise emissions.[86]

Methods of air pollution control can be divided into two categories: the control of particulate emissions and the control of gaseous emissions. Methods for particulate control tend to operate on a common principle. The solid particles are separated from the gases in which they are contained by physical procedures such as passage through a settling chamber. Many different methods are available for removing unwanted gases, most of which are acidic. Scrubbers are smokestack devices that contain a moist chemical such as lime, magnesium oxide, or sodium hydroxide. Another method for controlling gaseous emissions is by adsorption.

Methods of controlling water pollution fall into three general categories: physical, chemical, and biological. These materials can be removed from water by simply allowing the water to sit quietly for a period of time, thereby allowing the pollutants to settle out, or by passing the water through a filter. Chemical reactions can be used to remove pollutants from water. Biological agents can also be used to remove pollutants from water.[87] Green infrastructure and low impact development approaches and techniques help manage water and water pollutants at the source, preventing or reducing the impact of development on water and water quality. States, territories, and tribes must protect water bodies and to address water bodies that do not meet water quality standards (i.e., impaired waters).[88]

Cost-Benefit Analysis

Cost–benefit analysis (CBA) is a systematic approach to estimating the strengths and weaknesses of alternatives that satisfy transactions, activities or functional requirements for a business. It is a technique that is used to determine options that provide the best approach for the adoption and practice in terms of benefits in labour, time and cost savings etc. It is often used by governments and other organisations, such as private sector businesses, to appraise the desirability of a given policy. It usually tries to put all relevant costs and benefits on a common temporal footing using time value of money calculations.

A formal CBA tallies all of the planned project costs, quantifies each of the tangible benefits and calculates key financial performance metrics such as return on investment (ROI), net present value (NPV), internal rate of return (IRR) and payback period. A CBA is considered to be a subjective (as opposed to objective) assessment tool because cost and benefit calculations can be influenced by the choice of supporting data and estimation methodologies.[89] A cost benefit analysis is done to determine how well, or how poorly, a planned action will turn out. Although a cost benefit analysis can be used for almost anything, it is most commonly done on financial questions. Since the cost benefit analysis relies on the addition of positive factors and the subtraction of negative ones to determine a net result, it is also known as running the numbers.[90]

The real key to doing a successful cost-benefit analysis is making sure to include all the costs and all the benefits and properly quantify them. Capital budgeting is essentially a cost-benefit analysis that extends the evaluation of costs and benefits into a longer timeframe and greater emphasis is placed on considerations of the time value of money. A formal cost-benefit analysis is a multi-step process which includes a preliminary survey, a feasibility study, and a final report. Cost-benefit analysis is a decision support method used to help answer questions that often start with "what if" or "should we." [91]

Cost–benefit analysis adds up the total costs of a programme or activity and compares it against its total benefits. The technique assumes that a monetary value can be placed on all the costs and benefits of a programme, including tangible and intangible returns to other people and organisations in addition to those immediately impacted. Costs and benefits that occur in the future have less weight attached to them in a cost-benefit analysis.[92]

References

1. Brainy Quote, Available at http://www.brainyquote.com/quotes/keywords/environment.html
2. Introduction to Environmental Pollution, Chapter 1, Retrieved from http://www.newagepublishers.com/samplechapter/000261.pdf

3. Environmental Pollution Control Measures, chapter 6 (http://jica-ri.jica.go.jp/IFIC_and_JBICI-Studies/english/publications/reports/study/topical/health/pdf/health_08.pdf)
4. The Environmental Problems Cause by the Air Pollution (2012) (http://www.directessays.com/viewpaper/15390.html)
5. Water Pollution and its Control (http://www.open.edu/openlearnworks/mod/oucontent/view.php?id=204&printable=1)
6. Effects of Thermal Pollution (http://www.tutorvista.com/biology/effects-of-thermal-pollution)
7. Monty C. Dozier (2012), What Is Water Pollution? What Is Water Pollution? (http://waterandme.tamu.edu/WaterPollution/waterpollution.pdf)
8. What is air pollution? (http://www.conserve-energy-future.com/causes-effects-solutions-of-air-pollution.php)
9. Air Pollution Control, The Environment of Tokyo 2011, Retrieved from http://www.kankyo.metro.tokyo.jp/en/attachement/airpollution.pdf
10. Health & Environmental Effects of Air Pollution (2014) (http://www.mass.gov/eea/docs/dep/air/aq/health-and-env-effects-air-pollutions.pdf)
11. Air Pollution-Effects on the health and the environment (http://www.infoplease.com/encyclopedia/science/air-pollution-effects-health-environment.html)
12. What is light pollution? (http://www.globeatnight.org/light-pollution.php)
13. Light Pollution Harms the Environment (http://physics.fau.edu/observatory/lightpol-environ.html)
14. Verlyn Klinkenborg (2008), Our Vanishing Night: Most city skies have become virtually empty of stars (http://ngm.nationalgeographic.com/2008/11/light-pollution/klinkenborg-text)
15. Sophia Lahey (2012), Light Pollution: Causes, Effects and Solutions (http://www.sustainablefairfax.org/content/view/321/27/)
16. Ron Chepesiuk (2013), missing the Dark: Health Effects of Light Pollution (http://www.ncbi.nlm.nih.gov/pmc/articles/PMC2627884/)
17. Antoine Giraud (2013), The negative effects of light pollution (http://www.alive.com/health/the-negative-effects-of-light-pollution/)
18. Mukesh Kumar Mishra (2014), Basic facts on water pollution in India (http://www.crin.org/docs/KNUC%20WATER%20FILE.pdf)
19. Environmental Pollution and Its Effects (2014) (http://www.uccee.org/Environmental_Pollution.html)
20. F. W. Owa (2014), Water pollution: sources, effects, control and management, International Letters of Natural Sciences Vol. 8 (2014) pp. 1-6.
21. Performance Audit of Water Pollution in India, Ministry of Environment and Forests (2012) (http://saiindia.gov.in/english/home/our_products/noddy/union/report_21_12.pdf)
22. Health impacts of water pollution, Retrieved from http://edugreen.teri.res.in/explore/water/health.htm

23. Understanding noise pollution (2015) (http://www.conserve-energy-future.com/causes-and-effects-of-noise-pollution.php)
24. What is noise pollution? (http://www.thebigger.com/biology/pollution/what-is-noise-pollution/)
25. Lisa Goines (2007), Noise Pollution: A Modern Plague (http://www.medscape.com/viewarticle/554566_3)
26. Noise pollution (2015) (http://www.eoearth.org/view/article/154869/)
27. Daniel G. Nunez (1998), Cause and Effects of Noise Pollution, (http://darwin.bio.uci.edu/sustain/global/sensem/S98/Nunez/Noise.html)
28. Soil pollution (http://www.environmentalpollutioncenters.org/soil/)
29. Soil pollution (http://www.pollutionissues.com/Re-Sy/Soil-Pollution.html)
30. What is soil pollution? (http://www.conserve-energy-future.com/causes-and-effects-of-soil-pollution.php)
31. Rahul Kakkar (2014). What are the Causes and Effects of Land Pollution? (http://www.importantindia.com/11719/what-are-the-causes-and-effects-of-land-pollution/)
32. Status of Soil Contamination in India (http://www.waterandmegacities.org/status-of-soil-contamination-in-india/)
33. Effects of Soil Pollution (http://biology.tutorvista.com/environmental-pollution/effects-of-soil-pollution.html)
34. Long term effects of soil pollution (2014) (http://garden.lovetoknow.com/wiki/Long_Term_Effects_of_Soil_Pollution)
35. Puja Monda (2014), Soil Pollution: Causes, Effects and Control Measures of Soil Pollution | Speech (http://www.yourarticlelibrary.com/speech/soil-pollution-causes-effects-and-control-measures-of-soil-pollution-speech/28290/)
36. A.L. Kennedy (2014), The Effects of Soil Pollution on Humans (http://www.livestrong.com/article/176005-the-effects-of-soil-pollution-on-humans/)
37. What are the different types of pollution? (http://readanddigest.com/what-are-different-types-of-pollution/)
38. Thermal pollution (http://www.pollutionissues.com/Te-Un/Thermal-Pollution.html)
39. Thermal pollution (http://www.eoearth.org/view/article/156599/)
40. Puja Mondal, Thermal Pollution: Effects, Causes and Control of Thermal Pollution | Speech (http://www.yourarticlelibrary.com/speech/thermal-pollution-effects-causes-and-control-of-thermal-pollution-speech/28289/)
41. Thermal pollution - causes, effects and control measures of thermal pollution (http://mjcetenvsci.blogspot.in/2013/11/thermal-pollution-causes-effects-and.html)
42. Environment &Pollution: Thermal Pollution (http://agritech.tnau.ac.in/environment/envi_pollution_intro%20-%20thermal.html)
43. Thermal pollution from coal plants (http://www.sourcewatch.org/index.php/Thermal_pollution_from_coal_plants)
44. Thermal pollution (http://www.ukm.my/ahmadukm/images/stories/data/kuliah/manusia/artikel/thermal.htm)

45. Ill-Effects of Plastic in the Environment (http://www.prokerala.com/going-green/ill-effects-of-plastic.php)
46. Plastic Pollution: Causes and Effects (http://www.buzzle.com/articles/effects-of-plastic-pollution.html)
47. Plastic pollution (http://www.britannica.com/science/plastic-pollution)
48. Solutions to Plastic Pollution in our Oceans (http://www.nrdc.org/oceans/plastic-ocean/)
49. Air pollution in India (https://en.wikipedia.org/wiki/Air_pollution_in_India)
50. Hindustan Times (June 05, 2015), 13 out of world's top 20 polluted cities in India, only three in China, Retrieved from http://www.hindustantimes.com/india-news/india-s-cities-more-polluted-than-china-but-there-is-still-hope/article1-1355013.aspx
51. The Times of India (June 27, 2015), Delhi air has high doses of most toxic pollutant (http://timesofindia.indiatimes.com/home/environment/pollution/Delhi-air-has-high-doses-of-most-toxic-pollutant/articleshow/47836984.cms)
52. The Indian Express (June 9, 2014), Air quality in Mumbai, Navi Mumbai is 'poor to severe', says TERI report (http://indianexpress.com/article/cities/mumbai/air-quality-in-mumbai-navi-mumbai-is-poor-to-severe-says-teri-report/#sthash.lXOEgQN1.dpuf)
53. DNA Report (31Oct, 2014), Kolkata most polluted metro in India, has highest pollution level among eight countries: Study (http://www.dnaindia.com/india/report-kolkata-most-polluted-metro-in-india-has-highest-pollution-level-among-eight-countries-study-2030909)
54. Rashme Sehgal (May 2004), Kolkata has the highest number of lung cancer cases worldwide (http://infochangeindia.org/urban-india/features/kolkata-has-the-highest-number-of-lung-cancer-cases-worldwide.html)
55. Pollution survey: Kanpur is the most polluted city, Chennai the least (http://infochangeindia.org/environment/news/pollution-survey-kanpur-is-the-most-polluted-city-chennai-the-least.html)
56. Mukesh Kumar Mishra (2014), Basic facts on water pollution in India (http://www.crin.org/docs/KNUC%20WATER%20FILE.pdf)
57. What is soil pollution? (http://www.preservearticles.com/2012040429879/what-is-soil-pollution.html)
58. Smriti Chand (2014). Sources of Land Pollution in India: Chemical Fertilizers and Municipal Solid Waste (http://www.yourarticlelibrary.com/land-pollution/sources-of-land-pollution-in-india-chemical-fertilizers-and-municipal-solid-waste/19787/)
59. Michael Greenstone & Rema Hanna (2012), Environmental Regulations, Air and Water Pollution, and Infant Mortality in India, Discussion Paper 12-40, pp. 1-7.
60. Central Pollution Control Board (https://en.wikipedia.org/wiki/Central_Pollution_Control_Board)
61. Official website of Central Pollution Control Board (http://cpcb.nic.in/Introduction.php)

62. NDTV (August 4, 2015), Environment Ministry Proposes Scheme for Developing City Forests (http://www.ndtv.com/india-news/environment-ministry-proposes-scheme-for-developing-city-forests-1203871)

63. P.K. Wattal, Indian programme on radioactive waste management, Sadhana, Vol. 38, Part 5, October 2013, pp. 849–857.

64. Harish C. Sharma, Pollution control acts and regulations in India (http://www.petroleumbazaar.com/admin/actsandcontrols/pollution_control_act.pdf)

65. See https://en.wikipedia.org/wiki/Environment_Protection_Act,_1986

66. C. Srivenkatesh Prabhu, Public Liability Insurance Act 1991 (http://lawyerslaw.org/the-public-liability-insurance-act-1991/)

67. The Hindu (July 16, 2015), Reality check on air quality, Retrieved from http://www.thehindu.com/opinion/editorial/indias-air-quality-index-reality-check-on-air-quality/article7426092.ece

68. Air quality data, Embassy of United States of America in India Website [http://newdelhi.usembassy.gov/airqualitydata.html]

69. Business Standard (May 28, 2015),what's behind Delhi's air pollution? (http://www.business-standard.com/article/economy-policy/what-s-behind-delhi-s-air-pollution-115052801685_1.html)

70. Air Pollution (2015) (http://www.123helpme.com/assets/13173.html)

71. See http://hspcb.gov.in/Air_Act.html

72. Ameer Kumar and Dhruv Katoria, Air Pollution and its Control Measures, International Journal of Environmental Engineering and Management, Volume 4, Number 5 (2013), pp. 445-450.

73. What is Air Pollution? (http://www.conserve-energy-future.com/causes-effects-solutions-of-air-pollution.php)

74. Air pollution solution (2014) (http://web.mit.edu/12.000/www/m2015/2015/airpollutionsolutions.html)

75. Introduction to Environmental Pollution, Chapter 1, Retrieved from http://www.newagepublishers.com/samplechapter/000261.pdf

76. M.N. Murty and Surender Kumar, Water Pollution in India: An Economic Appraisal, chapter 19, Retrieved from http://www.idfc.com/pdf/report/2011/Chp-19-Water-Pollution-in-India-An-Economic-Appraisal.pdf

77. Effects and sources of water pollution (http://www.newagepublishers.com/samplechapter/001754.pdf)

78. How to control water pollution? (http://www.thebigger.com/biology/pollution/how-to-control-water-pollution/)

79. Puja Mondal (2014), Short Notes on 5 Methods to Control Water Pollution (http://www.yourarticlelibrary.com/water-pollution/short-notes-on-5-methods-to-control-water-pollution/12366/)

80. See http://envfor.nic.in/division/water-pollution

81. The Water (Prevention and Control of Pollution) Cess Act, 1977 (http://dpcc.delhigovt.nic.in/actcess.htm)

82. Pollution Control (2014) (http://water.epa.gov/polwaste/)

83. Puja Monda, Essay on Water Pollution: Sources, Effects and Control of Water Pollution (http://www.yourarticlelibrary.com/essay/essay-on-water-pollution-sources-effects-and-control-of-water-pollution/23267/)
84. Control strategy (http://www.epa.gov/airquality/aqmportal/management/control_strategies.htm)
85. See http://www.econlib.org/library/Enc/PollutionControls.html
86. How air pollution is controlled (http://www.iowadnr.gov/Environment/AirQuality/HowAirPollutionIsControlled.aspx)
87. Pollution control (http://www.scienceclarified.com/Ph-Py/Pollution-Control.html)
88. Pollution Control (http://water.epa.gov/polwaste/)
89. Cost-benefit analysis (CBA) (http://whatis.techtarget.com/definition/cost-benefit-analysis-CBA)
90. Cost-benefit analysis (http://management.about.com/cs/money/a/CostBenefit.htm)
91. Cost-benefit analysis (http://www.inc.com/encyclopedia/cost-benefit-analysis.html)
92. Cost-benefit analysis (http://betterevaluation.org/evaluation-options/CostBenefitAnalysis)

Chapter - 7

Environmental Laws

"Why should we think upon things that are lovely? Because thinking determines life. It is a common habit to blame life upon the environment. Environment modifies life but does not govern life. The soul is stronger than its surroundings."

—***William James***[1]

Natural environment is an environment that encompasses the interaction of all living species. The atmosphere of the Earth serves as a key factor in sustaining the planetary ecosystem. The thin layer of gases that envelops the Earth is held in place by the planet's gravity. Dry air consists of 78 per cent nitrogen, 21 per cent oxygen, one per cent argon and other inert gases, such as carbon dioxide. The ozone layer of the Earth's atmosphere plays an important role in depleting the amount of ultraviolet (UV) radiation that reaches the surface. As DNA is readily damaged by UV light, this serves to protect life at the surface. The atmosphere also retains heat during the night, thereby reducing the daily temperature extremes.[2]

Environment is the surrounding things. It includes living things and natural forces. The environment of living things provides conditions for development and growth, also causes danger and damage. Living things do not simply exist in their environment. They constantly interact with it. Environment is the events and culture that a person lived in. A person's beliefs and actions are dependent on his environment. The word environment is used to talk about many things.[3]

Environmental Laws

It is a collective term describing the network of treaties, statutes, regulations, and common and customary laws addressing the effects of human activity on the natural environment. The broad category of "environmental law" may be broken down into a number of more specific regulatory subjects.

While there is no single agreed-upon taxonomy, the core environmental law regimes address environmental pollution. Environmental law has developed in response to emerging awareness of and concern over issues impacting the entire world. While laws have developed piecemeal and for a variety of reasons, some effort has gone into identifying key concepts and guiding principles common to environmental law as a whole.[4] There are three key policies relating to environmental protection in India. They are:

- The National Forest Policy, 1988
- Policy Statement for Abatement of Pollution, 1992
- National Conservation Strategy and Policy Statement on Environment and Development, 1992

The different statutes/legislations enacted in India exclusively for environment protection are:

- The Water (Prevention and Control of Pollution) Act, 1974
- The Water (Prevention and Control of Pollution) Rules, 1975
- The Water (Prevention and Control of Pollution) Cess Act, 1977
- The Water (Prevention and Control of Pollution) Cess Rules, 1978
- The Air (Prevention and Control of Pollution) Act, 1981
- The Air (Prevention and Control of Pollution) Rules, 1982
- The Environment (Protection) Act, 1986
- The Environment (Protection) Rules, 1986
- Hazardous Wastes (Management and Handling) Rules, 1989
- Manufacture, Storage and Import of Hazardous Chemical Rules,1989
- The Forest (Conservation) Act, 1980
- The Forest (Conservation) Rules, 1981
- The Wildlife Protection Act, 1972
- The Wildlife (Transactions and Taxidermy) Rules, 1973
- The Wildlife (Stock Declaration) Central Rules, 1973
- The Wildlife (Protection) Licensing (Additional Matters for Consideration) Rules, 1983
- The Wildlife (Protection) Rules, 1995
- The Wildlife (Specified Plants - Conditions for Possession by Licensee) Rules, 1995
- The Public Liability Insurance Act, 1991
- The Public Liability Insurance Rules, 1991
- The National Environment Tribunal Act, 1995
- The National Environment Appellate Authority Act, 1997[5]

The Indian Penal Code has a chapter on offences affecting Public Health, Safety, Convenience (Chapter XIV). Sec. 268 provides that "a person is guilty of a public nuisance who does any act or is guilty of an illegal omission which causes any common injury, danger or annoyance to the public or to the people in general who dwell or occupy property in the vicinity, or which must necessarily cause injury, obstruction, danger, or annoyance to persons who may have occasion to use any public right."[6]

(1) National Forest Policy, 1988

India is one of the very few countries of the world where forest policy is in operation since 1894. In 1952 and 1988, revisions were made in the forest policy of 1894. The National Forest Policy of 1952 recommended that the country should aim at coverage of one-third of the total land area under forest (60 per cent in hilly and mountainous areas, and 25 per cent in the plains)[7]. The National Forest Policy (NFP) of 1988 marked a watershed in the way forests were perceived by the State Forest Departments. Recognising the serious limitations of the exclusivist approach towards forest conservation that had been followed since independence, the NFP paved the way for bringing in more participatory means of conserving forests and biodiversity in which involvement of local people was a key ingredient.[8]

In Resolution No.13/52/F, dated the 12th May, 1952, the Government of India in the erstwhile Ministry of Food and Agriculture enunciated a Forest Policy to be followed in the management of State Forests in the country. The principal aim of Forest Policy must be to ensure environmental stability and maintenance of ecological balance including atmospheric equilibrium which is vital for sustenance of all life forms, human, animal and plant. The derivation of direct economic benefit must be subordinated to this principal aim.The basic objectives that should govern the National Forest Policy - are the following:

1. Maintenance of environmental stability through preservation and, where necessary, restoration of the ecological balance that has been adversely disturbed by serious depletion of the forests of the country.
2. Conserving the natural heritage of the country by preserving the remaining natural forests with the vast variety of flora and fauna, which represent the remarkable biological diversity and genetic resources of the country.
3. Checking soil erosion and denudation in the catchment areas of rivers, lakes, reservoirs in the interest of soil and water conservation, for mitigating floods and droughts and for the retardation of siltation of reservoirs.
4. Checking the extension of sand-dunes in the desert areas of Rajasthan and along the coastal tracts.
5. Increasing substantially the forest/tree cover in the country through massive afforestation and social forestry programmes, especially on all denuded, degraded and unproductive lands.

6. Meeting the requirements of fuel-wood, fodder, minor forest produce and small timber of the rural and tribal populations.
7. Increasing the productivity of forests to meet essential national needs.
8. Encouraging efficient utilisation of forest produce and maximising substitution of wood.
9. Creating a massive people's movement with the involvement of women, for achieving these objectives and to minimise pressure on existing forests.[9]

(2) Policy Statement for Abatement of Pollution, 1992

The policy statement for abatement of pollution, adopted in 1992 lays emphasis on pollution prevention in place of the conventional end-of-the pipe treatment identified the adoption of best available and practicable technologies as the key element for pollution prevention. The focus of the various programmes and schemes of the Ministry and its associated organisations related to pollution prevention and control is on such issues such as promotion of clear and low waste technologies, waste minimisation, reuse or recycling, improvement of water quality, environment audit, natural resource accounting, development of mass based standards, institutional and human resource development.[10]

(3) National Conservation Strategy and Policy Statement on Environment and Development, 1992

It provides the basis for the integration of environmental considerations in the policies of various sectors. The Outlines government's goals and projects are for achieving sustainable lifestyles and the proper management and conservation of resources The National Conservation Strategy and the Policy Statement on Environment and Development are in response to the need for laying down the guidelines that will help to weave environmental considerations into the fabric of our national life and of our development process. It is an expression of India's commitment for reorienting policies and action in unison with the environmental perspective.[11]

The National Conservation Strategy and Policy Statement on Environment and Development, adopted in June, 1992, provide the basis for the integration and internalisation of environmental considerations in the policies and programmes of different sectors. It also emphasises sustainable lifestyles, and the proper management and conservation of resources. The policy statement announced by the Government in 1992 on Abatement of Pollution reiterates the Government's commitment to arrest deterioration of the environment. The statement reflects a shift in focus from problems to implementation of measures incorporating both short-term and long-term considerations.[12]

(4) The Water (Prevention and Control of Pollution) Act, 1974

The act aims to prevent and control water pollution and to maintain/ restore wholesomeness of water by establishing central and state pollution control board to monitor and enforce the regulations. The Central Pollution Control Board, and State Pollution Control Boards composition, terms and conditions of service of members are defined in Sections 3-12 of Water (Prevention and Control of Pollution) Act, 1974. The Board advises the government on any matter concerning the prevention and control of water pollution. It coordinates the activities and provides technical assistance and guidance. This policy sets the standards and penalties for non-compliance for polluting bodies. The government has power to restrict any unit, and to take samples of effluents and get them analysed in Central or State laboratories. Whoever fails to comply with any provision of this Act is punishable with imprisonment, fine or with both.[13]

The Water (Prevention and Control of Pollution) Act was enacted in 1974 to provide for the prevention and control of water pollution, and for the maintaining or restoring of wholesomeness of water in the country. The Act was amended in 1988. The Water (Prevention and Control of Pollution) Cess Act was enacted in 1977, to provide for the levy and collection of a cess on water consumed by persons operating and carrying on certain types of industrial activities. This cess is collected with a view to augment the resources of the Central Board and the State Boards for the prevention and control of water pollution constituted under the Water (Prevention and Control of Pollution) Act, 1974. The Act was last amended in 2003.[14]

(5) Water (Prevention and Control of Pollution) Cess Act, 1977

Parliament adopted the Water (Prevention and Control of Pollution) Cess Act, 1977 to provide funds for the Central and State Pollution Control Boards. The Act empowers the Central Government to impose a Cess on water consumed by industries listed in Schedule-I of the Act. It is an Act to provide for the levy and collection of a cess on water consumed by persons carrying on certain industries and by local authorities, with a view to augment the resources of the Central Board and the State Boards for the prevention and control of water pollution constituted under the Water (Prevention and Control of Pollution) Act, 1974.

For the purpose of measuring and recording the quantity of water consumed, every person carrying on any specified industry and every local authority shall affix meters of such standards and at such places as may be prescribed and it shall be presumed that the quantity indicated by the meter has been consumed by such person or local authority, as the case may be, until the contrary is proved. The officer of authority to whom or which the return has been furnished under Section 5 shall, after making or causing to be made such inquiry as he or it thinks fit and after satisfying himself or itself that the particulars stated in the return are correct, by order, assess the amount of cess payable by the concerned person carrying or any specified industry or local authority, as the case may be.[15]

(6) Air (Prevention and Control of Pollution) Act, 1981

The Act specifically empowers State Government to designate air pollution areas and to prescribe the type of fuel to be used in these designated areas. According to this Act, no person can operate certain types of industries including the asbestos, cement, fertilizer and petroleum industries without consent of the State Board. The government passed this Act in 1981 to clean up our air by controlling pollution. It states that sources of air pollution such as industry, vehicles, power plants, etc., are not permitted to release particulate matter, lead, carbon monoxide, sulphur dioxide, nitrogen oxide, volatile organic compounds or other toxic substances beyond a prescribed level. This Act is created to take appropriate steps for the preservation of the natural resources of the Earth which among other things includes the preservation of high quality air and ensures controlling the level of air pollution.

The main function of the Central Board is to implement legislation created to improve the quality of air and to prevent and control air pollution in the country. The State Boards have the power to advise the State Government on any matter concerning the prevention and control of air pollution. The persons managing industry are to be penalised if they produce emissions of air pollutants in excess of the standards laid down by the State Board. The Board also makes applications to the court for restraining persons causing air pollution.

The persons managing industry are to be penalised if they produce emissions of air pollutants in excess of the standards laid down by the State Board. The Board also makes applications to the court for restraining persons causing air pollution. Whoever contravenes any of the provision of the Act or any order or direction issued is punishable with imprisonment for a term which may extend to three months or with a fine of Rs 10,000 or with both, and in case of continuing offence with an additional fine which may extend to Rs 5,000 for every day during which such contravention continues after conviction for the first contravention.[16]

(7) The Environment (Protection) Act, 1986

Environment Protection Act, 1986 is an Act of the Parliament of India. In the wake of the Bhopal Tragedy, the Government of India enacted the Environment Protection Act of 1986 under Article 253 of the Constitution. Passed in March 1986, it came into force on 19th November 1986. The purpose of the Act is to implement the decisions of the United Nations Conference on the Human Environments they relate to the protection and improvement of the human environment and the prevention of hazards to human beings, other living creatures, plants and property. The Act is an "umbrella" legislation designed to provide a framework for central government coordination of the activities of various central and state authorities established under previous laws, such as the Water Act and the Air Act. The objectives of the act are:

(1) To co-ordinate the activities of the various regulatory agencies already in existence.

(2) Creation of an authority or authorities with adequate powers for environmental protection.

(3) Regulation of discharge of environmental pollutants and handling of hazardous substance.

(4) Speedy response in the event of accidents threatening environment and punishment to those who endanger human environment, safety and health.[17]

(8) Hazardous Wastes (Management and Handling) Rules, 1989.

Hazardous Waste Management Rules are notified to ensure safe handling, generation, processing, treatment, package, storage, transportation, use reprocessing, collection, conversion, and offering for sale, destruction and disposal of Hazardous Waste. These Rules came into effect in the year 1989 and have been amended later in the years 2000, 2003 and with final notification of the Hazardous Waste (Management, Handling and Transboundary Movement) Rules, 2008 in supersession of former notification. The Rules lay down corresponding duties of various authorities such as MoEF, CPCB, State/ UT Govts., SPCBs/PCCs, DGFT, Port Authority and Custom Authority while State Pollution Control Boards/ Pollution Control Committees have been designated with wider responsibilities touching across almost every aspect of Hazardous wastes generation, handling and their disposal.[18]

(9) Manufacture, Storage and Import of Hazardous Chemicals Rules, 1989

The Ministry of Environment and Forests, Govt. of India has notified the rules under title "Manufacture Storage and Import of Hazardous Chemicals Rules, 1989 to deal with the safety and environmental aspects associated with hazardous chemicals. The salient features of the rules are as follows:

(a) This rule applies to an industrial activity in which a hazardous chemical, subject to schedule 1, is or may be involved.

(b) The occupier is required to inform to the authority, in schedule 6, of any major accident caused due to hazardous chemicals occurring on a site or in a pipeline.

(c) The concerned authority shall undertake full analysis of the major accident and send the requisite information to the MoEF.

(d) The criteria of industries coming under preview of isolated storage are given in the schedule 2.

(e) The occupier is required to submit a written report in schedule 7, to the concerned authority.

(f) The occupier is required to submit safety report as specified in schedule 8.

(g) The occupier shall prepare and keep updated on site emergency plan as per schedule 11, detailing how major accident will be dealt in the industry on the site.

(h) An offsite emergency plan shall be prepared by the concerned authority, as in schedule 5, to deal with the emergencies. The importer of hazardous chemicals shall inform to the authority in the prescribed form.

(i) Authority at the state is to advice to the importer and the concerned port authority for regarding safety measures to be observed by them.

(j) The importer shall maintain the records of hazardous chemicals as specified in schedule 10.

(k) The road transportation of hazardous chemicals should be in accordance in the Central Motor Vehicle Rules 1989.[19]

(10) The Forest (Conservation) Act, 1980

The Parliament has enacted the Forest (Conservation) Act, 1980, to check further deforestation and conserve forests and to provide for matters connected therewith or ancillary or incidental thereto. This Act has five Sections which deal with conservation of forests. The Act was enacted with the twin objectives under Section 2 of restricting the use of forest land for non-forest purposes, and preventing the de-reservation of forests that have been reserved under the Indian Forest Act, 1927. However, in 1988 the Act was further amended to include two new provisions under Section 2, where it sought to restrict leasing of forest land to private individuals, authority, corporations not owned by the government, and to prevent clear felling of naturally grown trees.

The Act empowers the Central Government to constitute a committee to advise the government with a grant of approval under Section 2, as also on any other matter connected with the conservation of forest and referred to it by the Central Government. The Act provides for the punishment of imprisonment, extendable to fifteen days for the contravention of the provisions of the Act. The Act provides for punishment of offenders from the Government Departments, including Head of the Departments and authorities.[20]

(11) The Wildlife Protection Act, 1972

The Wildlife Protection Act, 1972 is an Act of the Parliament of India enacted for protection of plants and animal species. Before 1972, India only had five designated national parks. Among other reforms, the Act established schedules of protected plant and animal species; hunting or harvesting these species was largely outlawed. The Act provides for the protection of wild animals, birds and plants; and for matters connected therewith or ancillary or incidental thereto.

It extends to the whole of India, except the State of Jammu and Kashmir which has its own wildlife act. The hunting to the Enforcement authorities have the power to compound offences under this Schedule (i.e. they impose fines on the offenders). Up to April 2010 there have been 16 convictions under this act relating to the death of tigers. Penalties are prescribed in section 51. Enforcement can be performed by agencies such as the Forest Department, the Police, the Wildlife Crime Control Bureau, the Customs and the Central Bureau of Investigation. Charge sheets can be filed directly by the Forest Department. Other enforcement agencies, often due to the lack of technical expertise, hand over cases to the Forest Department.[21]

(12) The National Environment Tribunal Act, 1995

National Environment Tribunal Act, 1995 consists of 31 Sections to fulfill the broad objectives laid under Act. As the Act enacted with a broad objective to provide compensation to person who got injured, the owner has to pay compensation under Section 3, where there been damage caused to the environment and the death or injury has been resulted due to the accident. The person can make application with respect to claim for compensation to the Tribunal under provision as specified under Section 4(1), Tribunal while dealing with the application of compensation as specified in the provisions of Act shall exercise the same jurisdiction and authority as that of matters as specified in Public Liability Insurance Act, 1991. Central Government to exercise the jurisdiction and powers conferred under the provisions of the Act established a Tribunal known as the National Environment Tribunal under Section 8. Tribunal to perform its functions laid in the Act has certain members in its composition, the composition of Tribunal includes the Chairperson, Vice-chairperson, other members and the Benches under the Act has the power to exercise the authority, jurisdiction and powers of Tribunal.

Tribunal after the commencement of the Act has a specific jurisdiction to deal with the matters relating to the application, claim of compensation. Under Section 23, Tribunal has powers as of Civil Court in matters connected under the provisions of Act, and award made by Tribunal executable as like a decree passed in Civil Court. If the order made by the Tribunal not compiled by the owner, Tribunal can recover the order amount from the owner as arrear of land revenue. Tribunal Constituted under Act has the authority to punish the person who contravene the provisions laid under Act and persons who responsible for environmental hazardous. Indian Penal Code has its wide functioning under the Act as all members of Tribunal deemed to come under the purview of Public Servants under Section 21 of Code and all proceeding taken under the provisions of the enacted Act comes under the term of Judicial proceedings as specified in Sections 193, 219, and 228 of Code.[22]

(13) National Environment Appellate Authority Act, 1997

The National Environment Appellate Authority was set up as an independent body to address cases in which environmental clearances granted by the ministry of environment are challenged by civil society. The Authority was established on April 9, 1997, after the enactment of the National Environment Appellate Authority Act. The most important and critical expectation was that the Authority, appointed under Section 3 (3) of the Environment (Protection) Act, 1986, would address grievances regarding the process of environmental clearances and would implement the 'precautionary principle' and the 'polluter pays principle'.

According to the Appellate Act, the Authority is to consist of a chairperson, a vice-chairperson and up to three other members. While the chairperson is to have been a judge in the Supreme Court or the chief justice of a high court, the vice-chairperson must have been a secretary to the Government of India or any other equivalent post and have expertise or experience in administrative, legal, managerial or technical aspects of problems relating to the environment. Members of the Authority require professional knowledge or practical experience in conservation, environmental management, law or planning, and development.[23]

Protection of Environment

Environmental Protection Act (1986) defined "Environment as the sum total of water, air and land, their interrelationship among themselves and with the human beings, other living beings and property." Ecology is that part of environmental studies in which we study about organisms, plants and animals and their relationship or interdependence on other living and non-living environment. Environmental studies are the scientific study of the environmental system and the status of its inherent or induced changes on organisms. It includes not only the study of physical and biological characters of the environment but also the social and cultural factors and the impact of man on environment.[24]

Environment consists of all living and non-living things which surround humans. Environment influence and shaped our life. It is from the environment that we get food to eat, water to drink, air to breathe and all necessities of day-to-day life are available from our environment. It is the life support system. According to ManTech 1970 environmental science attempts to solve the major environmental problems with the help of interdisciplinary and transdisciplinary approaches i.e., the entire knowledge of all the disciplines of science such as Maths, Physics, Chemistry, Biology, Geology, Geography, Computer Science, Medical, Science and Biotechnology, as well as of social sciences such as Economics, Sociology and Psychology.[25]

Environmental protection is a topical and controversial issue of contemporary Third World development. As a result of the growing crisis of environment and development as well as issues of global environmental balance, divergent views and proposals have been put forward by external governments, international agencies, and environmental groups in resolving the environmental degradation problems of the developing world. However, very little appraisal has been made of the efforts by indigenous Third World governments in facing up to their environmental conservation issues.[26]

Environmental policy refers to the commitment of an organisation to the laws, regulations, and other policy mechanisms concerning environmental issues. These issues generally include air and water pollution, solid waste management, biodiversity, ecosystem management, maintenance of biodiversity, the protection of natural resources, wildlife and endangered species. Policies concerning energy or regulation of toxic substances including pesticides and many types of industrial waste are part of the topic of environmental policy.

Environmental policy instruments are tools used by governments to implement their environmental policies. Governments may use a number of different types of instruments. The concept of Environmental Policy Integration refers to the process of integrating environmental objectives into non-environmental policy areas, such as energy, agriculture and transport, rather than leaving them to be pursued solely through purely environmental policy practices. Such instruments is widely recognised as one of the key elements of sustainable development.[27]

Environmental protection is a practice of protecting the natural environment on individual, organisational or governmental levels, for the benefit of both the natural environment and humans. Due to the pressures of population and technology, the biophysical environment is being degraded, sometimes permanently. This has been recognised, and governments have begun placing restraints on activities that cause environmental degradation. Environmental protection has become an important task for the institutions of the European Community after the Maastricht Treaty for the European Union ratification by all the Member States. The union is already very active in the field of environmental policy with important directives like those on environmental impact assessment and on the access to environmental information for citizens in the Member States.[28]

The Ministry of Environment, Forest and Climate Change is the nodal agency in the administrative structure of the Central Government for the planning, promotion, co-ordination and overseeing the implementation of India's environmental and forestry policies and programmes. The primary concerns of the Ministry are implementation of policies and programmes relating to conservation of the country's natural resources including its lakes and rivers, its biodiversity, forests and wildlife, ensuring the welfare of animals, and the prevention and abatement of pollution. While implementing these policies and programmes, the Ministry is guided by the principle of sustainable development and enhancement of human well-being. The Ministry also serves as the nodal agency in the country for the United Nations Environment Programme, South Asia Co-operative Environment Programme, International Centre for Integrated Mountain Development and for the follow-up of the United Nations Conference on Environment and Development.[29]

Due to growing concern over deteriorating environmental conditions, legal systems around the world have increasingly recognised the interests of future generations and the corresponding responsibilities of present generations. The concept of future generations is based on precedent, ancient and modern, international and domestic. Various legal traditions and documents recognise the interests of future generations in a clean and healthy environment, providing precedent for considering them in contemporary decision-making. A multitude of international and domestic sources acknowledge that the actions of present generations can interfere with the needs of future generations. To address this situation, legal documents commonly highlight the interests of future generations and state that they should receive attention alongside those of present generations.[30]

Environment Agency is a public body whose role that can protect the environment. According to the agency chairman, the environment agency is 'is a leading public body for protecting and improving the environment in England and Wales. It is their job to make sure the air, land and water is looked after by everyone in today's society, so that tomorrow's generation inherit is a cleaner and healthier world'. Good building designs are essential to protect any local and global environment. Good-quality design to a high and global standard, using a sustainable construction technique, can play dividends for an environment. There is many ways to save energy in a building including switching off appliances on standby, using grade A appliances, using low energy light bulbs and filling an kettle with an amount of water needed, these are just the tip of the iceberg.

Environmental Protection Policies (EPPs) are statutory policies developed under Part III of the *Environmental Protection Act 1986* (EP Act). They are whole-of-Government policies that are ratified by Parliament and have the force of law from the day they are published in the Western Australian Government Gazette. Such policies are developed, for instance, to establish environmental values and environmental quality objectives for a particular environment or component of the environment.[31]

Afforestation is the establishment of a forest or stand of trees in an area where there was no forest. Reforestation is the reestablishment of forest cover, either naturally (by natural seeding, coppice, or root suckers) or artificially (by direct seeding or planting). While reforestation is increasing the number of trees of an existing forest, afforestation is the creation of a 'new' forest. By planting trees and creating forests, many of the commercial needs of human beings are fulfilled, while not destroying what is left of the planet. Afforestation is, therefore, a practice that has been propagated by government and non-government agencies of many countries as a way to stop over-exploitation of nature.[32]

The afforestation in and around an industrial region serves in aesthetically enhancing the foreground and background landscape features while contributing to the overall improvement of the environment. Forests have many important and varied functions, and to have a broad idea some of them are listed below: (a) Forests are the renewable resources of nature; (b) They are giant sinks of carbon: they absorb and assimilate carbon dioxide, which accounts for the majority of the greenhouse gases that are now accelerating global warming; (c) They are home to living creatures; (d) They contribute in maintaining biodiversity; (e) They regulate the climate; (f) They provide industrial timber and fuel, and (g) They prevent and mitigate sudden freshets that lead to flooding.[33]*Afforestation* refers to the process of converting a non-forest land into a forest. *Afforestation* is highly *important* to maintain the biodiversity. In *afforestation* programme forest trees are planted in suitable areas and also on waste land.

Vienna Convention

The Vienna Convention was the first international conference on ozone layer depletion. It was held in Vienna, Austria in 1985 when a hole in the stratospheric ozone layer was observed in the South Pole marked by increased UV-B infiltration over Antarctica. On the basis of the Vienna Convention, the Montreal Protocol on Substances that Deplete the Ozone Layer was negotiated and signed by 24 countries and by the European Economic Community in September 1987. The Protocol called for the Parties to phase down the use of CFCs, halons and other man-made ODCs. It acts as a framework for the international efforts to protect the ozone layer. However, it does not include legally binding reduction goals for the use of CFCs, the main chemical agents causing ozone depletion.

The Vienna Convention for the Protection of the Ozone Layer:

Article 1: Definitions	For the purposes of this Convention: (1) "The ozone layer" means the layer of atmospheric ozone above the planetary boundary layer. (2) "Adverse effects" means changes in the physical environment or biota, including changes in climate, which have significant deleterious effects on human health or on the

(Contd...)

	composition, resilience and productivity of natural and managed ecosystems, or on materials useful to mankind. (3) "Alternative technologies or equipment" means technologies or equipment the use of which makes it possible to reduce or effectively eliminate emissions of substances which have or are likely to have adverse effects on the ozone layer. (4) "Alternative substances" means substances which reduce, eliminate or avoid adverse effects on the ozone layer. (5) "Parties" means, unless the text otherwise indicates, Parties to this Convention. (6) "Regional economic integration organisation" means an organisation constituted by sovereign States of a given region which has competence in respect of matters governed by this Convention or its protocols and has been duly authorised, in accordance with its internal procedures, to sign, ratify, accept, approve or accede to the instruments concerned. (7) "Protocols" means protocols to this Convention.
Article 2: General obligations	1. The Parties shall take appropriate measures in accordance with the provisions of this Convention and of those protocols in force to which they are party to protect human health and the environment against adverse effects resulting or likely to result from human activities which modify or are likely to modify the ozone layer. 2. To this end the Parties shall, in accordance with the means at their disposal and their capabilities: (a) Co-operate by means of systematic observations, research and information exchange in order to better understand and assess the effects of human activities on the ozone layer and the effects on human health and the environment from modification of the ozone layer; (b) Adopt appropriate legislative or administrative measures and co-operate in harmonising appropriate policies to control, limit, reduce or prevent human activities under their jurisdiction or control should it be found that these activities have or are likely to have adverse effects resulting from modification or likely modification of the ozone layer; (c) Co-operate in the formulation of agreed measures, procedures and standards for the implementation of this Convention, with a view to the adoption of protocols and annexes; (d) Co-operate with competent international bodies to implement effectively this Convention and protocols to which they are party. 3. The provisions of this Convention shall in no way affect the right of Parties to adopt, in accordance with international law, domestic measures additional to those referred to in paragraphs 1 and 2 above, nor shall they affect additional domestic measures already taken by a Party, provided that these measures are not incompatible with their obligations under this Convention. 4. The application of this article shall be based on relevant scientific and technical considerations.

(Contd...)

Article 3: Research and systematic observations	1.The Parties undertake, as appropriate, to initiate and co-operate in, directly or through competent international bodies, the conduct of research and scientific assessments on: (a) The physical and chemical processes that may affect the ozone layer; (b) The human health and other biological effects deriving from any modifications of the ozone layer, particularly those resulting from changes in ultra-violet solar radiation having biological effects; (c) Climatic effects deriving from any modifications of the ozone layer; (d) Effects deriving from any modifications of the ozone layer and any consequent change in UV-B radiation on natural and synthetic materials useful to mankind; (e) Substances, practices, processes and activities that may affect the ozone layer, and their cumulative effects; (f) Alternative substances and technologies; (g) Related socio-economic matters. 2. The Parties undertake to promote or establish, as appropriate, directly or through competent international bodies and taking fully into account national legislation and relevant ongoing activities at both the national and international levels, joint or complementary programmes for systematic observation of the state of the ozone layer and other relevant parameters. 3. The Parties undertake to co-operate, directly or through competent international bodies, in ensuring the collection, validation and transmission of research and observational data through appropriate world data centres in a regular and timely fashion.
Article 4: Co-operation in the legal, scientificand technical fields	1. The Parties shall facilitate and encourage the exchange of scientific, technical, socio-economic, commercial and legal information relevant to this Convention as further elaborated in annex II. Such information shall be supplied to bodies agreed upon by the Parties. Any such body receiving information regarded as confidential by the supplying Party shall ensure that such information is not disclosed and shall aggregate it to protect its confidentiality before it is made available to all Parties. 2. The Parties shall co-operate, consistent with their national laws, regulations and practices and taking into account in particular the needs of the developing countries, in promoting, directly or through competent international bodies, the development and transfer of technology and knowledge. Such co-operation shall be carried out particularly through: (a) Facilitation of the acquisition of alternative technologies by other Parties; (b) Provision of information on alternative technologies and equipment, and supply of special manuals or guides to them; (c) The supply of necessary equipment and facilities for research and systematic observations; (d) Appropriate training of scientific and technical personnel.

(Contd...)

Article 5: Transmission of information	The Parties shall transmit, through the secretariat, to the Conference of the Parties established under article 6 information on the measures adopted by them in implementation of this Convention and of protocols to which they are party in such form and at such intervals as the meetings of the parties to the relevant instruments may determine.
Article 6: Conference of the Parties	1. A Conference of the Parties is hereby established. The first meeting of the Conference of the Parties shall be convened by the secretariat designated on an interim basis under article 7 not later than one year after entry into force of this Convention. Thereafter, ordinary meetings of the Conference of the Parties shall be held at regular intervals to be determined by the Conference at its first meeting. 2. Extraordinary meetings of the Conference of the Parties shall be held at such other times as may be deemed necessary by the Conference, or at the written request of any Party, provided that, within six months of the request being communicated to them by the secretariat, it is supported by at least one third of the Parties. 3. The Conference of the Parties shall by consensus agree upon and adopt rules of procedure and financial rules for itself and for any subsidiary bodies it may establish, as well as financial provisions governing the functioning of the secretariat. 4. The Conference of the Parties shall keep under continuous review the implementation of this Convention, and, in addition, shall: (a) Establish the form and the intervals for transmitting the information to be submitted in accordance with article 5 and consider such information as well as reports submitted by any subsidiary body; (b) Review the scientific information on the ozone layer, on its possible modification and on possible effects of any such modification; (c) Promote, in accordance with article 2, the harmonisation of appropriate policies, strategies and measures for minimising the release of substances causing or likely to cause modification of the ozone layer, and make recommendations on any other measures relating to this Convention; (d) Adopt, in accordance with articles 3 and 4, programmes for research, systematic observations, scientific and technological co-operation, the exchange of information and the transfer of technology and knowledge; (e) Consider and adopt, as required, in accordance with articles 9 and 10, amendments to this Convention and its annexes; (f) Consider amendments to any protocol, as well as to any annexes thereto, and, if so decided, recommend their adoption to the parties to the protocol concerned; (g) Consider and adopt, as required, in accordance with article 10, additional annexes to this Convention; (h) Consider and adopt, as required, protocols in accordance with article 8; (i) Establish such subsidiary bodies as are deemed

(Contd...)

	necessary for the implementation of this Convention; (j) Seek, where appropriate, the services of competent international bodies and scientific committees, in particular the World Meteorological Organisation and the World Health Organisation as well as the Coordinating Committee on the Ozone Layer, in scientific research, systematic observations and other activities pertinent to the objectives of this Convention, and make use as appropriate of information from these bodies and committees; (k) Consider and undertake any additional action that may be required for the achievement of the purposes of this Convention. 5. The United Nations, its specialised agencies and the International Atomic Energy Agency, as well as any State not party to this Convention, may be represented at meetings of the Conference of the Parties by observers. Anybody or agency, whether national or international, governmental or non-governmental, qualified in fields relating to the protection of the ozone layer which has informed the secretariat of its wish to be represented at a meeting of the Conference of the Parties as an observer may be admitted unless at least one-third of the Parties present object. The admission and participation of observers shall be subject to the rules of procedure adopted by the Conference of the Parties.
Article 7: Secretariat	1.The functions of the secretariat shall be: (a) To arrange for and service meetings provided for in articles 6, 8, 9 and 10; (b) To prepare and transmit reports based upon information received in accordance with articles 4 and 5, as well as upon information derived from meetings of subsidiary bodies established under article 6; (c) To perform the functions assigned to it by any protocol; (d) To prepare reports on its activities carried out in implementation of its functions under this Convention and present them to the Conference of the Parties; (e) To ensure the necessary co-ordination with other relevant international bodies, and in particular to enter into such administrative and contractual arrangements as may be required for the effective discharge of its functions; (f) To perform such other functions as may be determined by the Conference of the Parties. 2. The secretariat functions will be carried out on an interim basis by the United Nations Environment Programme until the completion of the first ordinary meeting of the Conference of the Parties held pursuant to article 6. At its first ordinary meeting, the Conference of the Parties shall designate the secretariat from amongst those existing competent international organisations which have signified their willingness to carry out the secretariat functions under this Convention.
Article 8: Adoption of protocols	1. The Conference of the Parties may at a meeting adopt protocols pursuant to Article 2. 2. The text of any proposed protocol shall be communicated to the Parties by the secretariat at least six months before such a meeting.

(Contd...)

Article 9: Amendment of the Convention or protocols	1. Any Party may propose amendments to this Convention or to any protocol. Such amendments shall take due account, inter alia, of relevant scientific and technical considerations. 2. Amendments to this Convention shall be adopted at a meeting of the Conference of the Parties. Amendments to any protocol shall be adopted at a meeting of the Parties to the protocol in question. The text of any proposed amendment to this Convention or to any protocol, except as may otherwise be provided in such protocol, shall be communicated to the Parties by the secretariat at least six months before the meeting at which it is proposed for adoption. The secretariat shall also communicate proposed amendments to the signatories to this Convention for information. 3. The Parties shall make every effort to reach agreement on any proposed amendment to this Convention by consensus. If all efforts at consensus have been exhausted, and no agreement reached, the amendment shall as a last resort be adopted by a three-fourths majority vote of the Parties present and voting at the meeting, and shall be submitted by the Depositary to all Parties for ratification, approval or acceptance. 4. The procedure mentioned in paragraph 3 above shall apply to amendments to any protocol, except that a two-thirds majority of the parties to that protocol present and voting at the meeting shall suffice for their adoption. 5. Ratification, approval or acceptance of amendments shall be notified to the Depositary in writing. Amendments adopted in accordance with paragraphs 3 or 4 above shall enter into force between parties having accepted them on the ninetieth day after the receipt by the Depositary of notification of their ratification, approval or acceptance by at least three-fourths of the Parties to this Convention or by at least two-thirds of the parties to the protocol concerned, except as may otherwise be provided in such protocol. Thereafter the amendments shall enter into force for any other Party on the ninetieth day after that Party deposits its instrument of ratification, approval or acceptance of the amendments. 6. For the purposes of this article, "Parties present and voting" means Parties present and casting an affirmative or negative vote.
Article 10: Adoption and amendment of annexes	1. The annexes to this Convention or to any protocol shall form an integral part of this Convention or of such protocol, as the case may be, and, unless expressly provided otherwise, a reference to this Convention or its protocols constitutes at the same time a reference to any annexes thereto. Such annexes shall be restricted to scientific, technical and administrative matters. 2. Except as may be otherwise provided in any protocol with respect to its annexes, the following procedure shall apply to

(Contd...)

	the proposal, adoption and entry into force of additional annexes to this Convention or of annexes to a protocol: (a) Annexes to this Convention shall be proposed and adopted according to the procedure laid down in article 9, paragraphs 2 and 3, while annexes to any protocol shall be proposed and adopted according to the procedure laid down in article 9, paragraphs 2 and 4; (b) Any party that is unable to approve an additional annex to this Convention or annex to any protocol to which it is party shall so notify the Depositary, in writing, within six months from the date of the communication of the adoption by the Depositary. The Depositary shall without delay notify all Parties of any such notification received. A Party may at any time substitute an acceptance for a previous declaration of objection and the annexes shall thereupon enter into force for that Party; (c) On the expiry of six months from the date of the circulation of the communication by the Depositary, the annex shall become effective for all Parties to this Convention or to any protocol concerned which have not submitted a notification in accordance with the provision of subparagraph (b) above. 3. The proposal, adoption and entry into force of amendments to annexes to this Convention or to any protocol shall be subject to the same procedure as for the proposal, adoption and entry into force of annexes to the Convention or annexes to a protocol. Annexes and amendments thereto shall take due account, inter alia, of relevant scientific and technical considerations. 4. If an additional annex or an amendment to an annex involves an amendment to this Convention or to any protocol, the additional annex or amended annex shall not enter into force until such time as the amendment to this Convention or to the protocol concerned enters into force.
Article 11: Settlement of disputes	1. In the event of a dispute between Parties concerning the interpretation or application of this Convention, the parties concerned shall seek solution by negotiation. 2. If the parties concerned cannot reach agreement by negotiation, they may jointly seek the good offices of, or request mediation by, a third party. 3.When ratifying, accepting, approving or acceding to this Convention, or at any time thereafter, a State or regional economic integration organisation may declare in writing to the Depositary that for a dispute not resolved in accordance with paragraph 1 or paragraph 2 above, it accepts one or both of the following means of dispute settlement as compulsory: (a) Arbitration in accordance with procedures to be adopted by the Conference of the Parties at its first ordinary meeting; (b) Submission of the dispute to the International Court of Justice.

(Contd...)

	4. If the parties have not, in accordance with paragraph 3 above, accepted the same or any procedure, the dispute shall be submitted to conciliation in accordance with paragraph 5 below unless the parties otherwise agree. 5. A conciliation commission shall be created upon the request of one of the parties to the dispute. The commission shall be composed of an equal number of members appointed by each party concerned and a chairman chosen jointly by the members appointed by each party. The commission shall render a final and recommendatory award, which the parties shall consider in good faith. 6. The provisions of this Article shall apply with respect to any protocol except as provided in the protocol concerned.
Article 12: Signature	This Convention shall be open for signature by States and by regional economic integration organisations at the Federal Ministry for Foreign Affairs of the Republic of Austria in Vienna from 22 March 1985 to 21 September 1985, and at United Nations Headquarters in New York from 22 September 1985 to 21 March 1986.
Article 13: Ratification, acceptance or approval	1. This Convention and any protocol shall be subject to ratification, acceptance or approval by States and by regional economic integration organisations. Instruments of ratification, acceptance or approval shall be deposited with the Depositary. 2. Any organisation referred to in paragraph 1 above which becomes a Party to this Convention or any protocol without any of its member States being a Party shall be bound by all the obligations under the Convention or the protocol, as the case may be. In the case of such organisations, one or more of whose member States is a Party to the Convention or relevant protocol, the organisation and its member States shall decide on their respective responsibilities for the performance of their obligation under the Convention or protocol, as the case may be. In such cases, the organisation and the member States shall not be entitled to exercise rights under the Convention or relevant protocol concurrently. 3. In their instruments of ratification, acceptance or approval, the organisations referred to in paragraph 1 above shall declare the extent of their competence with respect to the matters governed by the Convention or the relevant protocol. These organisations shall also inform the Depositary of any substantial modification in the extent of their competence.
Article 14: Accession	1. This Convention and any protocol shall be open for accession by States and by regional economic integration organisations from the date on which the Convention or the protocol concerned is closed for signature. The instruments of accession shall be deposited with the Depositary.

(Contd...)

	2. In their instruments of accession, the organisations referred to in paragraph 1 above shall declare the extent of their competence with respect to the matters governed by the Convention or the relevant protocol. These organisations shall also inform the Depositary of any substantial modification in the extent of their competence. 3. The provisions of article 13, paragraph 2, shall apply to regional economic integration organisations which accede to this Convention or any protocol.
Article 15: Right to vote	1. Each Party to this Convention or to any protocol shall have one vote. 2. Except as provided for in paragraph 1 above, regional economic integration organisations, in matters within their competence, shall exercise their right to vote with a number of votes equal to the number of their member States which are Parties to the Convention or the relevant protocol. Such organisations shall not exercise their right to vote if their member States exercise theirs, and vice versa.
Article 16: Relationship between the Convention and its protocols	1. A State or a regional economic integration organisation may not become a party to a protocol unless it is, or becomes at the same time, a Party to the Convention. 2. Decisions concerning any protocol shall be taken only by the parties to the protocol concerned.
Article 17: Entry into force	1. This Convention shall enter into force on the ninetieth day after the date of deposit of the twentieth instrument of ratification, acceptance, approval or accession. 2. Any protocol, except as otherwise provided in such protocol, shall enter into force on the ninetieth day after the date of deposit of the eleventh instrument of ratification, acceptance or approval of such protocol or accession thereto. 3. For each Party which ratifies, accepts or approves this Convention or accedes thereto after the deposit of the twentieth instrument of ratification, acceptance, approval or accession, it shall enter into force on the ninetieth day after the date of deposit by such Party of its instrument of ratification, acceptance, approval or accession. 4. Any protocol, except as otherwise provided in such protocol, shall enter into force for a party that ratifies, accepts or approves that protocol or accedes thereto after its entry into force pursuant to paragraph 2 above, on the ninetieth day after the date on which that party deposits its instrument of ratification, acceptance, approval or accession, or on the date which the Convention enters into force for that Party, whichever shall be the later. 5. For the purposes of paragraphs 1 and 2 above, any instrument deposited by a regional economic integration organisation shall

(Contd...)

	not be counted as additional to those deposited by member States of such organisation.
Article 18: Reservations	No reservations may be made to this Convention.
Article 19: Withdrawal	1. At any time after four years from the date on which this Convention has entered into force for a Party that Party may withdraw from the Convention by giving written notification to the Depositary. 2. Except as may be provided in any protocol, at any time after four years from the date on which such protocol has entered into force for a party that party may withdraw from the protocol by giving written notification to the Depositary. 3. Any such withdrawal shall take effect upon expiry of one year after the date of its receipt by the Depositary, or on such later date as may be specified in the notification of the withdrawal. 4. Any Party which withdraws from this Convention shall be considered as also having withdrawn from any protocol to which it is party.
Article 20: Depositary	1. The Secretary-General of the United Nations shall assume the functions of depositary of this Convention and any protocols. 2.The Depositary shall inform the Parties, in particular, of: (a) The signature of this Convention and of any protocol, and the deposit of instruments of ratification, acceptance, approval or accession in accordance with articles 13 and 14; (b) The date on which the Convention and any protocol will come into force in accordance with article 17; (c) Notifications of withdrawal made in accordance with article19; (d) Amendments adopted with respect to the Convention and any protocol, their acceptance by the parties and their date of entry into force in accordance with article 9; (e) All communications relating to the adoption and approval of annexes and to the amendment of annexes in accordance with article 10; (f) Notifications by regional economic integration organisations of the extent of their competence with respect to matters governed by this Convention and any protocols, and of any modifications thereof. (g) Declarations made in accordance with article 11, paragraph 3.
Article 21: Authentic texts	The original of this Convention, of which the Arabic, Chinese, English, French, Russian and Spanish texts are equally authentic, shall be deposited with the Secretary-General of the United Nations.

Montreal Protocol

According to wikipedia, "Montreal Protocol is an international treaty designed to protect the ozone layer by phasing out the production of numerous substances that are responsible for ozone depletion. It was agreed on 16 September 1987, and entered into force on 1 January 1989, followed by a first meeting in Helsinki, May 1989. The stated purpose of the treaty is that the signatory states "Recognising that worldwide emissions of certain substances can significantly deplete and otherwise modify the ozone layer in a manner that is likely to result in adverse effects on human health and the environment. Determined to protect the ozone layer by taking precautionary measures to control equitably total global emissions of substances that deplete it with the ultimate objective of their elimination on the basis of developments in scientific knowledge."

The provisions of the Protocol include the requirement that the Parties to the Protocol base their future decisions on the current scientific, environmental, technical, and economic information that is assessed through panels drawn from the worldwide expert communities. Since the Montreal Protocol came into effect, the atmospheric concentrations of the most important chlorofluorocarbons and related chlorinated hydrocarbons have either leveled off or decreased. It also offers major incentives for non-signatory nations to sign the agreement. The treaty negotiators justified the sanctions because depletion of the ozone layer is an environmental problem most effectively addressed on the global level.

The Montreal Protocol includes a unique adjustment provision that enables the Parties to the Protocol to respond quickly to new scientific information and agree to accelerate the reductions required on chemicals already covered by the Protocol. The Parties to the Montreal Protocol have amended the Protocol to enable, among other things, the control of new chemicals and the creation of a financial mechanism to enable developing countries to comply. It targets 96 chemicals in thousands of applications across more than 240 industrial sectors. The Multilateral Fund has provided more than US $2.5 billion in financial assistance to developing countries to phase out production and consumption of ozone depleting substances since the Protocol's inception in 1987.The Montreal Protocol stipulates that the production and consumption of compounds that deplete ozone in the stratosphere—chlorofluorocarbons (CFCs), halons, carbon tetrachloride, and methyl chloroform—are to be phased out by 2000 (2005 for methyl chloroform)."

The Montreal Protocol on Substances that Deplete the Ozone Layer

Article	Description
Article 1: Definitions	For the purposes of this Protocol: "Convention" means the Vienna Convention for the Protection of the Ozone Layer, adopted on 22 March 1985. "Parties" means, unless the text otherwise indicates, Parties to this Protocol. "Secretariat" means the Secretariat of the Convention. "Controlled substance" means a substance in Annex A, Annex B, Annex C or Annex E to this

(Contd...)

	Protocol, whether existing alone or in a mixture. It includes the isomers of any such substance, except as specified in the relevant Annex, but excludes any controlled substance or mixture which is in a manufactured product other than a container used for the transportation or storage of that substance. "Production" means the amount of controlled substances produced, minus the amount destroyed by technologies to be approved by the Parties and minus the amount entirely used as feedstock in the manufacture of other chemicals. The amount recycled and reused is not to be considered as "production". "Consumption" means production plus imports minus exports of controlled substances. "Calculated levels" of production, imports, exports and consumption means levels determined in accordance with Article 3. "Industrial rationalisation" means the transfer of all or a portion of the calculated level of production of one Party to another, for the purpose of achieving economic efficiencies or responding to anticipated shortfalls in supply as a result of plant closures.
Article 2: Control Measures	1. Incorporated in Article 2A. 2. Replaced by Article 2B. 3. Replaced by Article 2A. 4. Replaced by Article 2A. 5. Any Party may, for one or more control periods, transfer to another Party any portion of its calculated level of production set out in Articles 2A to 2F, and Article 2H, provided that the total combined calculated levels of production of the Parties concerned for any group of controlled substances do not exceed the production limits set out in those Articles for that group. Such transfer of production shall be notified to the Secretariat by each of the Parties concerned, stating the terms of such transfer and the period for which it is to apply. Any Party not operating under paragraph 1 of Article 5 may, for one or more control periods, transfer to another such Party any portion of its calculated level of consumption set out in Article 2F, provided that the calculated level of consumption of controlled substances in Group I of Annex A of the Party transferring the portion of its calculated level of consumption did not exceed 0.25 kilograms per capita in 1989 and that the total combined calculated levels of consumption of the Parties concerned do not exceed the consumption limits set out in Article 2F. Such transfer of consumption shall be notified to the Secretariat by each of the Parties concerned, stating the terms of such transfer and the period for which it is to apply. 6. Any Party not operating under Article 5, that has facilities for the production of Annex A or Annex B controlled substances under construction, or contracted for, prior to 16 September 1987, and provided for in national legislation prior to 1 January

(Contd...)

	1987, may add the production from such facilities to its 1986 production of such substances for the purposes of determining its calculated level of production for 1986, provided that such facilities are completed by 31 December 1990 and that such production does not raise that Party's annual calculated level of consumption of the controlled substances above 0.5 kilograms per capita. 7. Any transfer of production pursuant to paragraph 5 or any addition of production pursuant to paragraph 6 shall be notified to the Secretariat, no later than the time of the transfer or addition. 8. (a) Any Parties which are Member States of a regional economic integration organisation as defined in Article 1 (6) of the Convention may agree that they shall jointly fulfill their obligations respecting consumption under this Article and Articles 2A to 2I provided that their total combined calculated level of consumption does not exceed the levels required by this Article and Articles 2A to 2I; (b) The Parties to any such agreement shall inform the Secretariat of the terms of the agreement before the date of the reduction in consumption with which the agreement is concerned; (c) Such agreement will become operative only if all Member States of the regional economic integration organisation and the organisation concerned are Parties to the Protocol and have notified the Secretariat of their manner of implementation. 9. (a) Based on the assessments made pursuant to Article 6, the Parties may decide whether: (i) Adjustments to the ozone depleting potentials specified in Annex A, Annex B, Annex C and/or Annex E should be made and, if so, what the adjustments should be; and (ii) Further adjustments and reductions of production or consumption of the controlled substances should be undertaken and, if so, what the scope, amount and timing of any such adjustments and reductions should be; (b) Proposals for such adjustments shall be communicated to the Parties by the Secretariat at least six months before the meeting of the Parties at which they are proposed for adoption; (c) In taking such decisions, the Parties shall make every effort to reach agreement by consensus. If all efforts at consensus have been exhausted, and no agreement reached, such decisions shall, as a last resort, be adopted by a two-thirds majority vote of the Parties present and voting representing a majority of the Parties operating under Paragraph 1 of Article 5 present and voting and a majority of the Parties not so operating present and voting; (d) The decisions, which shall be binding on all Parties, shall forthwith be communicated to the Parties by the Depositary. Unless otherwise provided in the decisions, they shall enter into force on the expiry of six months from the date of the circulation of the communication by the Depositary.

(Contd...)

	10. Based on the assessments made pursuant to Article 6 of this Protocol and in accordance with the procedure set out in Article 9 of the Convention, the Parties may decide: (a) whether any substances, and if so which, should be added to or removed from any annex to this Protocol, and (b) the mechanism, scope and timing of the control measures that should apply to those substances; 11. Notwithstanding the provisions contained in this Article and Articles 2A to 2I Parties may take more stringent measures than those required by this Article and Articles 2A to 2I.
Article 2A: CFCs	1. Each Party shall ensure that for the twelve-month period commencing on the first day of the seventh month following the date of entry into force of this Protocol, and in each twelve-month period thereafter, its calculated level of consumption of the controlled substances in Group I of Annex A does not exceed its calculated level of consumption in 1986. By the end of the same period, each Party producing one or more of these substances shall ensure that its calculated level of production of the substances does not exceed its calculated level of production in 1986, except that such level may have increased by no more than ten per cent based on the 1986 level. Such increase shall be permitted only so as to satisfy the basic domestic needs of the Parties operating under Article 5 and for the purposes of industrial rationalisation between Parties. 2. Each Party shall ensure that for the period from 1 July 1991 to 31 December 1992 its calculated levels of consumption and production of the controlled substances in Group I of Annex A do not exceed 150 per cent of its calculated levels of production and consumption of those substances in 1986; with effect from 1 January 1993, the twelve-month control period for these controlled substances shall run from 1 January to 31 December each year. 3. Each Party shall ensure that for the twelve-month period commencing on 1 January 1994, and in each twelve-month period thereafter, its calculated level of consumption of the controlled substances in Group I of Annex A does not exceed, annually, twenty-five per cent of its calculated level of consumption in 1986. Each Party producing one or more of these substances shall, for the same periods, ensure that its calculated level of production of the substances does not exceed, annually, twenty-five per cent of its calculated level of production in 1986. However, in order to satisfy the basic domestic needs of the Parties operating under paragraph 1 of Article 5, its calculated level of production may exceed that limit by up to ten per cent of its calculated level of production in 1986.

(Contd...)

	4. Each Party shall ensure that for the twelve-month period commencing on 1 January 1996, and in each twelve-month period thereafter, its calculated level of consumption of the controlled substances in Group I of Annex A does not exceed zero. Each Party producing one or more of these substances shall, for the same periods, ensure that its calculated level of production of the substances does not exceed zero. However, in order to satisfy the basic domestic needs of the Parties operating under paragraph 1 of Article 5, its calculated level of production may exceed that limit by a quantity equal to the annual average of its production of the controlled substances in Group I of Annex A for basic domestic needs for the period 1995 to 1997 inclusive. This paragraph will apply save to the extent that the Parties decide to permit the level of production or consumption that is necessary to satisfy uses agreed by them to be essential. 5. Each Party shall ensure that for the twelve-month period commencing on 1 January 2003 and in each twelve-month period thereafter, its calculated level of production of the controlled substances in Group I of Annex A for the basic domestic needs of the Parties operating under paragraph 1 of Article 5 does not exceed eighty per cent of the annual average of its production of those substances for basic domestic needs for the period 1995 to 1997 inclusive. 6. Each Party shall ensure that for the twelve-month period commencing on 1 January 2005 and in each twelve-month period thereafter, its calculated level of production of the controlled substances in Group I of Annex A for the basic domestic needs of the Parties operating under paragraph 1 of Article 5 does not exceed fifty per cent of the annual average of its production of those substances for basic domestic needs for the period 1995 to 1997 inclusive. 7. Each Party shall ensure that for the twelve-month period commencing on 1 January 2007 and in each twelve-month period thereafter, its calculated level of production of the controlled substances in Group I of Annex A for the basic domestic needs of the Parties operating under paragraph 1 of Article 5 does not exceed fifteen per cent of the annual average of its production of those substances for basic domestic needs for the period 1995 to 1997 inclusive. 8. Each Party shall ensure that for the twelve-month period commencing on 1 January 2010 and in each twelve-month period thereafter, its calculated level of production of the controlled substances in Group I of Annex A for the basic domestic needs of the Parties operating under paragraph 1 of Article 5 does not exceed zero. For the purposes of calculating basic domestic needs under paragraphs 4 to 8 of this Article, the calculation of the

(Contd...)

	annual average of production by a Party includes any production entitlements that it has transferred in accordance with paragraph 5 of Article 2, and excludes any production entitlements that it has acquired in accordance with paragraph 5 of Article 2.
Article 2B: Halons	1. Each Party shall ensure that for the twelve-month period commencing on 1 January 1992, and in each twelve-month period thereafter, its calculated level of consumption of the controlled substances in Group II of Annex A does not exceed, annually, its calculated level of consumption in 1986. Each Party producing one or more of these substances shall, for the same periods, ensure that its calculated level of production of the substances does not exceed, annually, its calculated level of production in 1986. However, in order to satisfy the basic domestic needs of the Parties operating under paragraph 1 of Article 5, its calculated level of production may exceed that limit by up to ten per cent of its calculated level of production in 1986. 2. Each Party shall ensure that for the twelve-month period commencing on 1 January 1994, and in each twelve-month period thereafter, its calculated level of consumption of the controlled substances in Group II of Annex A does not exceed zero. Each Party producing one or more of these substances shall, for the same periods, ensure that its calculated level of production of the substances does not exceed zero. However, in order to satisfy the basic domestic needs of the Parties operating under paragraph 1 of Article 5, its calculated level of production may, until 1 January 2002 exceed that limit by up to fifteen per cent of its calculated level of production in 1986; thereafter, it may exceed that limit by a quantity equal to the annual average of its production of the controlled substances in Group II of Annex A for basic domestic needs for the period 1995 to 1997 inclusive. This paragraph will apply save to the extent that the Parties decide to permit the level of production or consumption that is necessary to satisfy uses agreed by them to be essential.3. Each Party shall ensure that for the twelve-month period commencing on 1 January 2005 and in each twelve-month period thereafter, its calculated level of production of the controlled substances in Group II of Annex A for the basic domestic needs of the Parties operating under paragraph 1 of Article 5 does not exceed fifty per cent of the annual average of its production of those substances for basic domestic needs for the period 1995 to 1997 inclusive. 4. Each Party shall ensure that for the twelve-month period commencing on 1 January 2010 and in each twelve-month period thereafter, its calculated level of production of the controlled substances in Group II of Annex A for the basic domestic needs of the Parties operating under paragraph 1 of Article 5 does not exceed zero.

(Contd...)

Article 2C: Other fully halogenated CFCs	1. Each Party shall ensure that for the twelve-month period commencing on 1 January 1993, its calculated level of consumption of the controlled substances in Group I of Annex B does not exceed, annually, eighty per cent of its calculated level of consumption in 1989. Each Party producing one or more of these substances shall, for the same period, ensure that its calculated level of production of the substances does not exceed, annually, eighty per cent of its calculated level of production in 1989. However, in order to satisfy the basic domestic needs of the Parties operating under paragraph 1 of Article 5, its calculated level of production may exceed that limit by up to ten per cent of its calculated level of production in 1989. 2. Each Party shall ensure that for the twelve-month period commencing on 1 January 1994, and in each twelve-month period thereafter, its calculated level of consumption of the controlled substances in Group I of Annex B does not exceed, annually, twenty-five per cent of its calculated level of consumption in 1989. Each Party producing one or more of these substances shall, for the same periods, ensure that its calculated level of production of the substances does not exceed, annually, twenty-five per cent of its calculated level of production in 1989. However, in order to satisfy the basic domestic needs of the Parties operating under paragraph 1 of Article 5, its calculated level of production may exceed that limit by up to ten per cent of its calculated level of production in 1989. 3. Each Party shall ensure that for the twelve-month period commencing on 1 January 1996, and in each twelve-month period thereafter, its calculated level of consumption of the controlled substances in Group I of Annex B does not exceed zero. Each Party producing one or more of these substances shall, for the same periods, ensure that its calculated level of production of the substances does not exceed zero. However, in order to satisfy the basic domestic needs of the Parties operating under paragraph 1 of Article 5, its calculated level of production may, until 1 January 2003 exceed that limit by up to fifteen per cent of its calculated level of production in 1989; thereafter, it may exceed that limit by a quantity equal to eighty per cent of the annual average of its production of the controlled substances in Group I of Annex B for basic domestic needs for the period 1998 to 2000 inclusive. This paragraph will apply save to the extent that the Parties decide to permit the level of production or consumption that is necessary to satisfy uses agreed by them to be essential. 4. Each Party shall ensure that for the twelve-month period commencing on 1 January 2007 and in each twelve-month period thereafter, its calculated level of production of the controlled

(Contd...)

	substances in Group I of Annex B for the basic domestic needs of the Parties operating under paragraph 1 of Article 5 does not exceed fifteen per cent of the annual average of its production of those substances for basic domestic needs for the period 1998 to 2000 inclusive. 5. Each Party shall ensure that for the twelve-month period commencing on 1 January 2010 and in each twelve-month period thereafter, its calculated level of production of the controlled substances in Group I of Annex B for the basic domestic needs of the Parties operating under paragraph 1 of Article 5 does not exceed zero.
Article 2D: Carbon tetrachloride	1. Each Party shall ensure that for the twelve-month period commencing on 1 January 1995, its calculated level of consumption of the controlled substance in Group II of Annex B does not exceed, annually, fifteen per cent of its calculated level of consumption in 1989. Each Party producing the substance shall, for the same period, ensure that its calculated level of production of the substance does not exceed, annually, fifteen per cent of its calculated level of production in 1989. However, in order to satisfy the basic domestic needs of the Parties operating under paragraph 1 of Article 5, its calculated level of production may exceed that limit by up to ten per cent of its calculated level of production in 1989. 2. Each Party shall ensure that for the twelve-month period commencing on 1 January 1996, and in each twelve-month period thereafter, its calculated level of consumption of the controlled substance in Group II of Annex B does not exceed zero. Each Party producing the substance shall, for the same periods, ensure that its calculated level of production of the substance does not exceed zero. However, in order to satisfy the basic domestic needs of the Parties operating under paragraph 1 of Article 5, its calculated level of production may exceed that limit by up to fifteen per cent of its calculated level of production in 1989. This paragraph will apply save to the extent that the Parties decide to permit the level of production or consumption that is necessary to satisfy uses agreed by them to be essential.
Article 2E: 1,1,1-Trichloroethane (Methyl chloroform)	1. Each Party shall ensure that for the twelve-month period commencing on 1 January 1993, its calculated level of consumption of the controlled substance in Group III of Annex B does not exceed, annually, its calculated level of consumption in 1989. Each Party producing the substance shall, for the same period, ensure that its calculated level of production of the substance does not exceed, annually, its calculated level of production in 1989. However, in order to satisfy the basic domestic needs of the Parties operating under paragraph 1 of Article 5, its calculated level of production may exceed that limit by up to ten per cent of its calculated level of production in 1989.

(Contd...)

	2. Each Party shall ensure that for the twelve-month period commencing on 1 January 1994, and in each twelve-month period thereafter, its calculated level of consumption of the controlled substance in Group III of Annex B does not exceed, annually, fifty per cent of its calculated level of consumption in 1989. Each Party producing the substance shall, for the same periods, ensure that its calculated level of production of the substance does not exceed, annually, fifty per cent of its calculated level of production in 1989. However, in order to satisfy the basic domestic needs of the Parties operating under paragraph 1 of Article 5, its calculated level of production may exceed that limit by up to ten per cent of its calculated level of production in 1989. 3. Each Party shall ensure that for the twelve-month period commencing on 1 January 1996, and in each twelve-month period thereafter, its calculated level of consumption of the controlled substance in Group III of Annex B does not exceed zero. Each Party producing the substance shall, for the same periods, ensure that its calculated level of production of the substance does not exceed zero. However, in order to satisfy the basic domestic needs of the Parties operating under paragraph 1 of Article 5, its calculated level of production may exceed that limit by up to fifteen per cent of its calculated level of production for 1989. This paragraph will apply save to the extent that the Parties decide to permit the level of production or consumption that is necessary to satisfy uses agreed by them to be essential.
Article 2F: Hydro chloro-fluorocarbons	1. Each Party shall ensure that for the twelve-month period commencing on 1 January 1996, and in each twelve-month period thereafter, its calculated level of consumption of the controlled substances in Group I of Annex C does not exceed, annually, the sum of: (a) Two point eight per cent of its calculated level of consumption in 1989 of the controlled substances in Group I of Annex A; and (b) Its calculated level of consumption in 1989 of the controlled substances in Group I of Annex C. 2. Each Party shall ensure that for the twelve-month period commencing on 1 January 2004, and in each twelve-month period thereafter, its calculated level of consumption of the controlled substances in Group I of Annex C does not exceed, annually, sixty-five per cent of the sum referred to in paragraph 1 of this Article. 3. Each Party shall ensure that for the twelve-month period commencing on 1 January 2010, and in each twelve-month period thereafter, its calculated level of consumption of the controlled substances in Group I of Annex C does not exceed, annually, thirty-five per cent of the sum referred to in paragraph 1 of this Article.

(Contd...)

	4. Each Party shall ensure that for the twelve-month period commencing on 1 January 2015, and in each twelve-month period thereafter, its calculated level of consumption of the controlled substances in Group I of Annex C does not exceed, annually, ten per cent of the sum referred to in paragraph 1 of this Article. 5. Each Party shall ensure that for the twelve-month period commencing on 1 January 2020, and in each twelve-month period thereafter, its calculated level of consumption of the controlled substances in Group I of Annex C does not exceed, annually, zero point five per cent of the sum referred to in paragraph 1 of this Article. Such consumption shall, however, be restricted to the servicing of refrigeration and air conditioning equipment existing at that date. 6. Each Party shall ensure that for the twelve-month period commencing on 1 January 2030, and in each twelve-month period thereafter, its calculated level of consumption of the controlled substances in Group I of Annex C does not exceed zero. 7. As of 1 January 1996, each Party shall endeavour to ensure that: (a) The use of controlled substances in Group I of Annex C is limited to those applications where other more environmentally suitable alternative substances or technologies are not available; (b) The use of controlled substances in Group I of Annex C is not outside the areas of application currently met by controlled substances in Annexes A, B and C, except in rare cases for the protection of human life or human health; and (c) Controlled substances in Group I of Annex C are selected for use in a manner that minimises ozone depletion, in addition to meeting other environmental, safety and economic considerations. 8. Each Party producing one or more of these substances shall ensure that for the twelve-month period commencing on 1 January 2004, and in each twelve-month period thereafter, its calculated level of production of the controlled substances in Group I of Annex C does not exceed, annually, the average of: (a) The sum of its calculated level of consumption in 1989 of the controlled substances in Group I of Annex C and two point eight per cent of its calculated level of consumption in 1989 of the controlled substances in Group I of Annex A; and (b) The sum of its calculated level of production in 1989 of the controlled substances in Group I of Annex C and two point eight per cent of its calculated level of production in 1989 of the controlled substances in Group I of Annex A. However, in order to satisfy the basic domestic needs of the Parties operating under paragraph 1 of Article 5, its calculated level of production may exceed that limit by up to fifteen per cent of its calculated level of production of the controlled substances in Group I of Annex C as defined above.

(Contd...)

Article 2G: Hydrobromo-fluorocarbons	Each Party shall ensure that for the twelve-month period commencing on 1 January 1996, and in each twelve-month period thereafter, its calculated level of consumption of the controlled substances in Group II of Annex C does not exceed zero. Each Party producing the substances shall, for the same periods, ensure that its calculated level of production of the substances does not exceed zero. This paragraph will apply save to the extent that the Parties decide to permit the level of production or consumption that is necessary to satisfy uses agreed by them to be essential.
Article 2H: Methyl bromide	1. Each Party shall ensure that for the twelve-month period commencing on 1 January 1995, and in each twelve-month period thereafter, its calculated level of consumption of the controlled substance in Annex E does not exceed, annually, its calculated level of consumption in 1991. Each Party producing the substance shall, for the same period, ensure that its calculated level of production of the substance does not exceed, annually, its calculated level of production in 1991. However, in order to satisfy the basic domestic needs of the Parties operating under paragraph 1 of Article 5, its calculated level of production may exceed that limit by up to ten per cent of its calculated level of production in 1991. 2. Each Party shall ensure that for the twelve-month period commencing on 1 January 1999, and in the twelve-month period thereafter, its calculated level of consumption of the controlled substance in Annex E does not exceed, annually, seventy-five per cent of its calculated level of consumption in 1991. Each Party producing the substance shall, for the same periods, ensure that its calculated level of production of the substance does not exceed, annually, seventy-five per cent of its calculated level of production in 1991. However, in order to satisfy the basic domestic needs of the Parties operating under paragraph 1 of Article 5, its calculated level of production may exceed that limit by up to ten per cent of its calculated level of production in 1991. 3. Each Party shall ensure that for the twelve-month period commencing on 1 January 2001, and in the twelve-month period thereafter, its calculated level of consumption of the controlled substance in Annex E does not exceed, annually, fifty per cent of its calculated level of consumption in 1991. Each Party producing the substance shall, for the same periods, ensure that its calculated level of production of the substance does not exceed, annually, fifty per cent of its calculated level of production in 1991. However, in order to satisfy the basic domestic needs of the Parties operating under paragraph 1 of Article 5, its calculated level of production may exceed that limit by up to ten per cent of its calculated level of production in 1991.

(Contd...)

	4. Each Party shall ensure that for the twelve-month period commencing on 1 January 2003, and in the twelve-month period thereafter, its calculated level of consumption of the controlled substance in Annex E does not exceed, annually, thirty per cent of its calculated level of consumption in 1991. Each Party producing the substance shall, for the same periods, ensure that its calculated level of production of the substance does not exceed, annually, thirty per cent of its calculated level of production in 1991. However, in order to satisfy the basic domestic needs of the Parties operating under paragraph 1 of Article 5, its calculated level of production may exceed that limit by up to ten per cent of its calculated level of production in 1991.
	5. Each Party shall ensure that for the twelve-month period commencing on 1 January 2005, and in each twelve-month period thereafter, its calculated level of consumption of the controlled substance in Annex E does not exceed zero. Each Party producing the substance shall, for the same periods, ensure that its calculated level of production of the substance does not exceed zero. However, in order to satisfy the basic domestic needs of the Parties operating under paragraph 1 of Article 5, its calculated level of production may, until 1 January 2002 exceed that limit by up to fifteen per cent of its calculated level of production in 1991; thereafter, it may exceed that limit by a quantity equal to the annual average of its production of the controlled substance in Annex E for basic domestic needs for the period 1995 to 1998 inclusive. This paragraph will apply save to the extent that the Parties decide to permit the level of production or consumption that is necessary to satisfy uses agreed by them to be critical uses. Each Party shall ensure that for the twelve-month period commencing on 1 January 2005 and in each twelve-month period thereafter, its calculated level of production of the controlled substance in Annex E for the basic domestic needs of the Parties operating under paragraph 1 of Article 5 does not exceed eighty per cent of the annual average of its production of the substance for basic domestic needs for the period 1995 to 1998 inclusive. Each Party shall ensure that for the twelve-month period commencing on 1 January 2015 and in each twelve-month period thereafter, its calculated level of production of the controlled substance in Annex E for the basic domestic needs of the Parties operating under paragraph 1 of Article 5 does not exceed zero.
	6. The calculated levels of consumption and production under this Article shall not include the amounts used by the Party for quarantine and pre-shipment applications.

(Contd...)

Article 2I: Bromochloro-methane	Each Party shall ensure that for the twelve-month period commencing on 1 January 2002, and in each twelve-month period thereafter, its calculated level of consumption and production of the controlled substance in Group III of Annex C does not exceed zero. This paragraph will apply save to the extent that the Parties decide to permit the level of production or consumption that is necessary to satisfy uses agreed by them to be essential.
Article 3: Calculation of control levels	For the purposes of Articles 2, 2A to 2I and 5, each Party shall, for each group of substances in Annex A, Annex B, Annex C or Annex E determine its calculated levels of: (a) Production by: (i) multiplying its annual production of each controlled substance by the ozone depleting potential specified in respect of it in Annex A, Annex B, Annex C or Annex E; and (ii) adding together, for each such Group, the resulting figures; (b) Imports and exports, respectively, by following, mutatis mutandis, the procedure set out in subparagraph (a); and Consumption by adding together its calculated levels of production and imports and subtracting its calculated level of exports as determined in accordance with subparagraphs (a) and (b). However, beginning on 1 January 1993, any export of controlled substances to non-Parties shall not be subtracted in calculating the consumption level of the exporting Party.
Article 4: Control of trade with non-Parties	1. As of 1 January 1990, each party shall ban the import of the controlled substances in Annex A from any State not party to this Protocol.Within one year of the date of the entry into force of this paragraph, each Party shall ban the import of the controlled substances in Annex B from any State not party to this Protocol.Within one year of the date of entry into force of this paragraph, each Party shall ban the import of any controlled substances in Group II of Annex C from any State not party to this Protocol.Within one year of the date of entry into force of this paragraph, each Party shall ban the import of the controlled substance in Annex E from any State not party to this Protocol. As of 1 January 2004, each Party shall ban the import of the controlled substances in Group I of Annex C from any State not party to this Protocol.Within one year of the date of entry into force of this paragraph, each Party shall ban the import of the controlled substance in Group III of Annex C from any State not party to this Protocol. 2. As of 1 January 1993, each Party shall ban the export of any controlled substances in Annex A to any State not party to this Protocol. Commencing one year after the date of entry into force of this paragraph, each Party shall ban the export of any controlled substances in Annex B to any State not party to this Protocol. Commencing one year after the date of entry into force of this paragraph, each Party shall ban the export of any

(Contd...)

	controlled substances in Group II of Annex C to any State not party to this Protocol. Commencing one year of the date of entry into force of this paragraph, each Party shall ban the export of the controlled substance in Annex E to any State not party to this Protocol. As of 1 January 2004, each Party shall ban the export of the controlled substances in Group I of Annex C to any State not party to this Protocol.Within one year of the date of entry into force of this paragraph, each Party shall ban the export of the controlled substance in Group III of Annex C to any State not party to this Protocol. 3. By 1 January 1992, the Parties shall, following the procedures in Article 10 of the Convention, elaborate in an annex a list of products containing controlled substances in Annex A. Parties that have not objected to the annex in accordance with those procedures shall ban, within one year of the annex having become effective, the import of those products from any State not party to this Protocol.Within three years of the date of the entry into force of this paragraph, the Parties shall, following the procedures in Article 10 of the Convention, elaborate in an annex a list of products containing controlled substances in Annex B. Parties that have not objected to the annex in accordance with those procedures shall ban, within one year of the annex having become effective, the import of those products from any State not party to this Protocol.Within three years of the date of entry into force of this paragraph, the Parties shall, following the procedures in Article 10 of the Convention, elaborate in an annex a list of products containing controlled substances in Group II of Annex C. Parties that have not objected to the annex in accordance with those procedures shall ban, within one year of the annex having become effective, the import of those products from any State not party to this Protocol. 4. By 1 January 1994, the Parties shall determine the feasibility of banning or restricting, from States not party to this Protocol, the import of products produced with, but not containing, controlled substances in Annex A. If determined feasible, the Parties shall, following the procedures in Article 10 of the Convention, elaborate in an annex a list of such products. Parties that have not objected to the annex in accordance with those procedures shall ban, within one year of the annex having become effective, the import of those products from any State not party to this Protocol.Within five years of the date of the entry into force of this paragraph, the Parties shall determine the feasibility of banning or restricting, from States not party to this Protocol, the import of products produced with, but not containing, controlled substances in Annex B. If determined feasible, the Parties shall, following the procedures in Article 10 of the

(Contd...)

	Convention, elaborate in an annex a list of such products. Parties that have not objected to the annex in accordance with those procedures shall ban or restrict, within one year of the annex having become effective, the import of those products from any State not party to this Protocol.Within five years of the date of entry into force of this paragraph, the Parties shall determine the feasibility of banning or restricting, from States not party to this Protocol, the import of products produced with, but not containing, controlled substances in Group II of Annex C. If determined feasible, the Parties shall, following the procedures in Article 10 of the Convention, elaborate in an annex a list of such products. Parties that have not objected to the annex in accordance with those procedures shall ban or restrict, within one year of the annex having become effective, the import of those products from any State not party to this Protocol. Each Party undertakes to the fullest practicable extent to discourage the export to any State not party to this Protocol of technology for producing and for utilizing controlled substances in Annexes A, B, C and E. 6. Each Party shall refrain from providing new subsidies, aid, credits, guarantees or insurance programmes for the export to States not party to this Protocol of products, equipment, plants or technology that would facilitate the production of controlled substances in Annexes A, B, C and E. 7. Paragraphs 5 and 6 shall not apply to products, equipment, plants or technology that improve the containment, recovery, recycling or destruction of controlled substances, promote the development of alternative substances, or otherwise contribute to the reduction of emissions of controlled substances in Annexes A, B, C and E. 8. Notwithstanding the provisions of this Article, imports and exports referred to in paragraphs 1 to 4 ter of this Article may be permitted from, or to, any State not party to this Protocol, if that State is determined, by a meeting of the Parties, to be in full compliance with Article 2, Articles 2A to 2I and this Article, and have submitted data to that effect as specified in Article 7. 9. For the purposes of this Article, the term 'State not party to this Protocol" shall include, with respect to a particular controlled substance, a State or regional economic integration organisation that has not agreed to be bound by the control measures in effect for that substance.10. By 1 January 1996, the Parties shall consider whether to amend this Protocol in order to extend the measures in this Article to trade in controlled substances in Group I of Annex C and in Annex E with States not party to the Protocol.

(Contd...)

Article 4A: Control of trade with Parties	1. Where, after the phase-out date applicable to it for a controlled substance, a Party is unable, despite having taken all practicable steps to comply with its obligation under the Protocol, to cease production of that substance for domestic consumption, other than for uses agreed by the Parties to be essential, it shall ban the export of used, recycled and reclaimed quantities of that substance, other than for the purpose of destruction. 2. Paragraph 1 of this Article shall apply without prejudice to the operation of Article 11 of the Convention and the non-compliance procedure developed under Article 8 of the Protocol.
Article 4B: Licensing	1. Each Party shall, by 1 January 2000 or within three months of the date of entry into force of this Article for it, whichever is the later, establish and implement a system for licensing the import and export of new, used, recycled and reclaimed controlled substances in Annexes A, B, C and E. 2. Notwithstanding paragraph 1 of this Article, any Party operating under paragraph 1 of Article 5 which decides it is not in a position to establish and implement a system for licensing the import and export of controlled substances in Annexes C and E, may delay taking those actions until 1 January 2005 and 1 January 2002, respectively. 3. Each Party shall, within three months of the date of introducing its licensing system, report to the Secretariat on the establishment and operation of that system. 4. The Secretariat shall periodically prepare and circulate to all Parties a list of the Parties that have reported to it on their licensing systems and shall forward this information to the Implementation Committee for consideration and appropriate recommendations to the Parties.
Article 5: Special situation of developing countries	1. Any Party that is a developing country and whose annual calculated level of consumption of the controlled substances in Annex A is less than 0.3 kilograms per capita on the date of the entry into force of the Protocol for it, or any time thereafter until 1 January 1999, shall, in order to meet its basic domestic needs, be entitled to delay for ten years its compliance with the control measures set out in Articles 2A to 2E, provided that any further amendments to the adjustments or Amendment adopted at the Second Meeting of the Parties in London, 29 June 1990, shall apply to the Parties operating under this paragraph after the review provided for in paragraph 8 of this Article has taken place and shall be based on the conclusions of that review. 2. However, any Party operating under paragraph 1 of this Article shall exceed neither an annual calculated level of consumption of the controlled substances in Annex A of 0.3 kilograms per capita nor an annual calculated level of consumption of controlled substances of Annex B of 0.2 kilograms per capita.

(Contd...)

	3. When implementing the control measures set out in Articles 2A to 2E, any Party operating under paragraph 1 of this Article shall be entitled to use: (a) For controlled substances under Annex A, either the average of its annual calculated level of consumption for the period 1995 to 1997 inclusive or a calculated level of consumption of 0.3 kilograms per capita, whichever is the lower, as the basis for determining its compliance with the control measures relating to consumption. (b) For controlled substances under Annex B, the average of its annual calculated level of consumption for the period 1998 to 2000 inclusive or a calculated level of consumption of 0.2 kilograms per capita, whichever is the lower, as the basis for determining its compliance with the control measures relating to consumption. (c) For controlled substances under Annex A, either the average of its annual calculated level of production for the period 1995 to 1997 inclusive or a calculated level of production of 0.3 kilograms per capita, whichever is the lower, as the basis for determining its compliance with the control measures relating to production. (d) For controlled substances under Annex B, either the average of its annual calculated level of production for the period 1998 to 2000 inclusive or a calculated level of production of 0.2 kilograms per capita, whichever is the lower, as the basis for determining its compliance with the control measures relating to production. 4. If a Party operating under paragraph 1 of this Article, at any time before the control measures obligations in Articles 2A to 2I become applicable to it, finds itself unable to obtain an adequate supply of controlled substances, it may notify this to the Secretariat. The Secretariat shall forthwith transmit a copy of such notification to the Parties, which shall consider the matter at their next Meeting, and decide upon appropriate action to be taken.
Article 6: Assessment and review of control measures	Beginning in 1990, and at least every four years thereafter, the Parties shall assess the control measures provided for in Article 2 and Articles 2A to 2I on the basis of available scientific, environmental, technical and economic information. At least one year before each assessment, the Parties shall convene appropriate panels of experts qualified in the fields mentioned and determine the composition and terms of reference of any such panels. Within one year of being convened, the panels will report their conclusions, through the Secretariat, to the Parties.
Article 7: Reporting of data	Each Party shall provide to the Secretariat, within three months of becoming a Party, statistical data on its production, imports and exports of each of the controlled substances in Annex A for the year 1986, or the best possible estimates of such data where actual data are not available.

(Contd...)

Article 8: Non-compliance	The Parties, at their first meeting, shall consider and approve procedures and institutional mechanisms for determining noncompliance with the provisions of this Protocol and for treatment of Parties found to be in non-compliance.
Article 9: Research, development, public awareness and exchange of information	1. The Parties shall co-operate, consistent with their national laws, regulations and practices and taking into account in particular the needs of developing countries, in promoting, directly or through competent international bodies, research, development and exchange of information on: (a) best technologies for improving the containment, recovery, recycling, or destruction of controlled substances or otherwise reducing their emissions; (b) possible alternatives to controlled substances, to products containing such substances, and to products manufactured with them; and (c) costs and benefits of relevant control strategies. 2. The Parties, individually, jointly or through competent international bodies, shall co-operate in promoting public awareness of the environmental effects of the emissions of controlled substances and other substances that deplete the ozone layer. 3. Within two years of the entry into force of this Protocol and every two years thereafter, each Party shall submit to the Secretariat a summary of the activities it has conducted pursuant to this Article.
Article 10: Financial mechanism	1. The Parties shall establish a mechanism for the purposes of providing financial and technical co-operation, including the transfer of technologies, to Parties operating under paragraph 1 of Article 5 of this Protocol to enable their compliance with the control measures set out in Articles 2A to 2E and Article 2I, and any control measures in Articles 2F to 2H that are decided pursuant to paragraph 1 bis of Article 5 of the Protocol. The mechanism, contributions to which shall be additional to other financial transfers to Parties operating under that paragraph, shall meet all agreed incremental costs of such Parties in order to enable their compliance with the control measures of the Protocol. An indicative list of the categories of incremental costs shall be decided by the meeting of the Parties. 2. The mechanism established under paragraph 1 shall include a Multilateral Fund. It may also include other means of multilateral, regional and bilateral co-operation. 3. The Multilateral Fund shall: (a) Meet, on a grant or concessional basis as appropriate, and according to criteria to be decided upon by the Parties, the agreed incremental costs; (b) Finance clearing-house functions to: (i) Assist Parties operating under paragraph 1 of Article 5, through country specific studies and

(Contd...)

	other technical co-operation, to identify their needs for co-operation; (ii) Facilitate technical co-operation to meet these identified needs; (iii) Distribute, as provided for in Article 9, information and relevant materials, and hold workshops, training sessions, and other related activities, for the benefit of Parties that are developing countries; and (iv) Facilitate and monitor other multilateral, regional and bilateral co-operation available to Parties that are developing countries; (c) Finance the secretarial services of the Multilateral Fund and related support costs. 4. The Multilateral Fund shall operate under the authority of the Parties who shall decide on its overall policies. 5. The Parties shall establish an Executive Committee to develop and monitor the implementation of specific operational policies, guidelines and administrative arrangements, including the disbursement of resources, for the purpose of achieving the objectives of the Multilateral Fund. The Executive Committee shall discharge its tasks and responsibilities, specified in its terms of reference as agreed by the Parties, with the co-operation and assistance of the International Bank for Reconstruction and Development (World Bank), the United Nations Environment Programme, the United Nations Development Programme or other appropriate agencies depending on their respective areas of expertise. The members of the Executive Committee, which shall be selected on the basis of a balanced representation of the Parties operating under paragraph 1 of Article 5 and of the Parties not so operating, shall be endorsed by the Parties. 6. The Multilateral Fund shall be financed by contributions from Parties not operating under paragraph 1 of Article 5 in convertible currency or, in certain circumstances, in kind and/or in national currency, on the basis of the United Nations scale of assessments. Contributions by other Parties shall be encouraged. Bilateral and, in particular cases agreed by a decision of the Parties, regional co-operation may, up to a percentage and consistent with any criteria to be specified by decision of the Parties, be considered as a contribution to the Multilateral Fund, provided that such co-operation, as a minimum: (a) Strictly relates to compliance with the provisions of this Protocol; (b) Provides additional resources; and (c) Meets agreed incremental costs. 7. The Parties shall decide upon the programme budget of the Multilateral Fund for each fiscal period and upon the percentage of contributions of the individual Parties thereto. 8. Resources under the Multilateral Fund shall be disbursed with the concurrence of the beneficiary Party 9. Decisions by the Parties under this Article shall be taken by consensus whenever possible. If all efforts at consensus have

(Contd...)

	been exhausted and no agreement reached, decisions shall be adopted by a two-thirds majority vote of the Parties present and voting, representing a majority of the Parties operating under paragraph 1 of Article 5 present and voting and a majority of the Parties not so operating present and voting.10. The financial mechanism set out in this Article is without prejudice to any future arrangements that may be developed with respect to other environmental issues.
Article 10A: Transfer of technology	Each Party shall take every practicable step, consistent with the programmes supported by the financial mechanism, to ensure: (a) that the best available, environmentally safe substitutes and related technologies are expeditiously transferred to Parties operating under paragraph 1 of Article 5; and (b) that the transfers referred to in subparagraph (a) occur under fair and most favourable conditions.
Article 11: Meetings of the parties	1. The Parties shall hold meetings at regular intervals. The Secretariat shall convene the first meeting of the Parties not later than one year after the date of the entry into force of this Protocol and in conjunction with a meeting of the Conference of the Parties to the Convention, if a meeting of the latter is scheduled within that period. 2. Subsequent ordinary meetings of the parties shall be held, unless the Parties otherwise decide, in conjunction with meetings of the Conference of the Parties to the Convention. Extraordinary meetings of the Parties shall be held at such other times as may be deemed necessary by a meeting of the Parties, or at the written request of any Party, provided that within six months of such a request being communicated to them by the Secretariat, it is supported by at least one third of the Parties.
Article 13: Financial provisions	The funds required for the operation of this Protocol, including those for the functioning of the Secretariat related to this Protocol, shall be charged exclusively against contributions from the Parties. The Parties, at their first meeting, shall adopt by consensus financial rules for the operation of this Protocol.
Article 14: Relationship of this Protocol to the Convention	Except as otherwise provided in this Protocol, the provisions of the Convention relating to its protocols shall apply to this Protocol.
Article 15: Signature	This Protocol shall be open for signature by States and by regional economic integration organisations in Montreal on 16 September 1987, in Ottawa from 17 September 1987 to 16 January 1988, and at United Nations Headquarters in New York from 17 January 1988 to 15 September 1988.

(Contd...)

Article 16: Entry into force	This Protocol shall enter into force on 1 January 1989, provided that at least eleven instruments of ratification, acceptance, approval of the Protocol or accession thereto have been deposited by States or regional economic integration organisations representing at least two-thirds of 1986 estimated global consumption of the controlled substances, and the provisions of paragraph 1 of Article 17 of the Convention have been fulfilled. In the event that these conditions have not been fulfilled by that date, the Protocol shall enter into force on the ninetieth day following the date on which the conditions have been fulfilled. 2. For the purposes of paragraph 1, any such instrument deposited by a regional economic integration organisation shall not be counted as additional to those deposited by member States of such organisation. 3. After the entry into force of this Protocol, any State or regional economic integration organisation shall become a Party to it on the ninetieth day following the date of deposit of its instrument of ratification, acceptance, approval or accession.
Article 17: Parties joining after entry into force	Subject to Article 5, any State or regional economic integration organisation which becomes a Party to this Protocol after the date of its entry into force, shall fulfil forthwith the sum of the obligations under Article 2, as well as under Articles 2A to 2I and Article 4, that apply at that date to the States and regional economic integration organisations that became Parties on the date the Protocol entered into force.
Article 18: Reservations	No reservations may be made to this Protocol.
Article 19: Withdrawal	Any Party may withdraw from this Protocol by giving written notification to the Depositary at any time after four years of assuming the obligations specified in paragraph 1 of Article 2A. Any such withdrawal shall take effect upon expiry of one year after the date of its receipt by the Depositary, or on such later date as may be specified in the notification of the withdrawal.
Article 20: Authentic texts	The original of this Protocol, of which the Arabic, Chinese, English, French, Russian and Spanish texts are equally authentic, shall be deposited with the Secretary-General of the United Nations.

Kyoto Protocol

According to wikipedia, "Kyoto Protocol is an international treaty, which extends the 1992 United Nations Framework Convention on Climate Change that commits State Parties to reduce greenhouse gases emissions, based on the premise that (a) global warming exists and (b) man-made CO_2 emissions have caused it. The Kyoto Protocol was adopted in Kyoto, Japan, on 11 December 1997 and entered into force on 16 February 2005. There are currently 192 Parties (Canada withdrew effective December 2012) to the Protocol.

The main goal of the Kyoto Protocol is to control emissions of the main anthropogenic (i.e., human-emitted) greenhouse gases (GHGs) in ways that reflect underlying national differences in GHG emissions, wealth, and capacity to make the reductions.

The Kyoto Protocol is an international agreement linked to the United Nations Framework Convention on Climate Change, which commits its Parties by setting internationally binding emission reduction targets. Recognising that developed countries are principally responsible for the current high levels of GHG emissions in the atmosphere as a result of more than 150 years of industrial activity, the Protocol places a heavier burden on developed nations under the principle of "common but differentiated responsibilities."

The Kyoto Protocol's first round commitments are the first detailed step taken within the UN Framework Convention on Climate Change. The ultimate objective of the UNFCCC is the "stabilisation of greenhouse gas concentrations in the atmosphere at a level that would stop dangerous anthropogenic interference with the climate system." Under the Kyoto Protocol, 37 industrialised countries and the European Community commit themselves to binding targets for GHG emissions. The Protocol also reaffirms the principle that developed countries have to pay billions of dollars, and supply technology to other countries for climate-related studies and projects.

Kyoto Protocol was structured on the principles of the Convention. It only binds developed countries because it recognises that they are largely responsible for the current high levels of GHG emissions in the atmosphere, which are the result of more than 150 years of industrial activity. It places a heavier burden on developed nations under its central principle: that of "common but differentiated responsibility". In Doha, Qatar, on 8 December 2012, the Doha Amendment to the Kyoto Protocol was adopted. This launched a second commitment period, starting on 1 January 2013 until 2020.

Kyoto Protocol to the United Nations Framework Convention on Climate Change:

Article	Description
Article 1	For the purposes of this Protocol, the definitions contained in Article 1 of the Convention shall apply. In addition: "Conference of the Parties" means the Conference of the Parties to the Convention. "Convention" means the United Nations Framework Convention on Climate Change, adopted in New York on 9 May 1992. "Intergovernmental Panel on Climate Change" means the Intergovernmental Panel on Climate Change established in 1988 jointly by the World Meteorological Organisation and the United Nations Environment Programme. "Montreal Protocol" means the Montreal Protocol on Substances that Deplete the Ozone Layer, adopted in Montreal on 16 September 1987 and as subsequently adjusted and amended. "Parties present and voting" means Parties present and casting an affirmative

(Contd...)

	or negative vote. "Party" means, unless the context otherwise indicates, a Party to this Protocol. "Party included in Annex I" means a Party included in Annex I to the Convention, as may be amended, or a Party which has made a notification under Article 4, paragraph 2 (g), of the Convention.
Article 2	1. Each Party included in Annex I, in achieving its quantified emission limitation and reduction commitments under Article 3, in order to promote sustainable development, shall: (a) Implement and/or further elaborate policies and measures in accordance with its national circumstances, such as: (i) Enhancement of energy efficiency in relevant sectors of the national economy; (ii) Protection and enhancement of sinks and reservoirs of greenhouse gases not controlled by the Montreal Protocol, taking into account its commitments under relevant international environmental agreements; promotion of sustainable forest management practices, afforestation and reforestation; (iii) Promotion of sustainable forms of agriculture in light of climate change considerations; (iv) Research on, and promotion, development and increased use of, new and renewable forms of energy, of carbon dioxide sequestration technologies and of advanced and innovative environmentally sound technologies; (v) Progressive reduction or phasing out of market imperfections, fiscal incentives, tax and duty exemptions and subsidies in all greenhouse gas emitting sectors that run counter to the objective of the Convention and application of market instruments; (vi) Encouragement of appropriate reforms in relevant sectors aimed at promoting policies and measures which limit or reduce emissions of greenhouse gases not controlled by the Montreal Protocol; (vii) Measures to limit and/or reduce emissions of greenhouse gases not controlled by the Montreal Protocol in the transport sector; (viii) Limitation and/or reduction of methane emissions through recovery and use in waste management, as well as in the production, transport and distribution of energy.(b) Cooperate with other such Parties to enhance the individual and combined effectiveness of their policies and measures adopted under this Article, pursuant to Article 4, paragraph 2 (e) (i), of the Convention. To this end, these Parties shall take steps to share their experience and exchange information on such policies and measures, including developing ways of improving their comparability, transparency and effectiveness. The Conference of the Parties serving as the meeting of the Parties to this Protocol shall, at its first session or as soon as practicable thereafter, consider ways to facilitate such cooperation, taking into account all relevant information. 2. The Parties included in Annex I shall pursue limitation or reduction of emissions of greenhouse gases not controlled by the Montreal Protocol from aviation and marine bunker fuels, working through the International Civil Aviation Organisation and the International Maritime Organisation, respectively.

(Contd...)

	3.The Parties included in Annex I shall strive to implement policies and measures under this Article in such a way as to minimise adverse effects, including the adverse effects of climate change, effects on international trade, and social, environmental and economic impacts on other Parties, especially developing country Parties and in particular those identified in Article 4, paragraphs 8 and 9, of the Convention, taking into account Article 3 of the Convention. The Conference of the Parties serving as the meeting of the Parties to this Protocol may take further action, as appropriate, to promote the implementation of the provisions of this paragraph. 4.The Conference of the Parties serving as the meeting of the Parties to this Protocol, if it decides that it would be beneficial to coordinate any of the policies and measures in paragraph 1 (a) above, taking into account different national circumstances and potential effects, shall consider ways and means to elaborate the coordination of such policies and measures.
Article 3	1. The Parties included in Annex I shall, individually or jointly, ensure that their aggregate anthropogenic carbon dioxide equivalent emissions of the greenhouse gases listed in Annex A do not exceed their assigned amounts, calculated pursuant to their quantified emission limitation and reduction commitments inscribed in Annex B and in accordance with the provisions of this Article, with a view to reducing their overall emissions of such gases by at least 5 per cent below 1990 levels in the commitment period 2008 to 2012. 2. Each Party included in Annex I shall, by 2005, have made demonstrable progress in achieving its commitments under this Protocol. 3. The net changes in greenhouse gas emissions by sources and removals by sinks resulting from direct human-induced land-use change and forestry activities, limited to afforestation, reforestation and deforestation since 1990, measured as verifiable changes in carbon stocks in each commitment period, shall be used to meet the commitments under this Article of each Party included in Annex I. The greenhouse gas emissions by sources and removals by sinks associated with those activities shall be reported in a transparent and verifiable manner and reviewed in accordance with Articles 7 and 8. 4. Prior to the first session of the Conference of the Parties serving as the meeting of the Parties to this Protocol, each Party included in Annex I shall provide, for consideration by the Subsidiary Body for Scientific and Technological Advice, data to establish its level of carbon stocks in 1990 and to enable an estimate to be made of its changes in carbon stocks in subsequent years. The Conference of the Parties serving as the meeting of the Parties to this Protocol shall, at its first session or as soon as practicable thereafter, decide upon modalities, rules and guidelines as to how, and which, additional human-induced activities related to changes in greenhouse gas emissions by sources

(Contd...)

and removals by sinks in the agricultural soils and the land-use change and forestry categories shall be added to, or subtracted from, the assigned amounts for Parties included in Annex I, taking into account uncertainties, transparency in reporting, verifiability, the methodological work of the Intergovernmental Panel on Climate Change, the advice provided by the Subsidiary Body for Scientific and Technological Advice in accordance with Article 5 and the decisions of the Conference of the Parties. Such a decision shall apply in the second and subsequent commitment periods. A Party may choose to apply such a decision on these additional human-induced activities for its first commitment period, provided that these activities have taken place since 1990.

5. The Parties included in Annex I undergoing the process of transition to a market economy whose base year or period was established pursuant to decision 9/CP.2 of the Conference of the Parties at its second session shall use that base year or period for the implementation of their commitments under this Article. Any other Party included in Annex I undergoing the process of transition to a market economy which has not yet submitted its first national communication under Article 12 of the Convention may also notify the Conference of the Parties serving as the meeting of the Parties to this Protocol that it intends to use an historical base year or period other than 1990 for the implementation of its commitments under this Article. The Conference of the Parties serving as the meeting of the Parties to this Protocol shall decide on the acceptance of such notification.

6. Taking into account Article 4, paragraph 6, of the Convention, in the implementation of their commitments under this Protocol other than those under this Article, a certain degree of flexibility shall be allowed by the Conference of the Parties serving as the meeting of the Parties to this Protocol to the Parties included in Annex I undergoing the process of transition to a market economy.

7. In the first quantified emission limitation and reduction commitment period, from 2008 to 2012, the assigned amount for each Party included in Annex I shall be equal to the percentage inscribed for it in Annex B of its aggregate anthropogenic carbon dioxide equivalent emissions of the greenhouse gases listed in Annex A in 1990, or the base year or period determined in accordance with paragraph 5 above, multiplied by five. Those Parties included in Annex I for whom land-use change and forestry constituted a net source of greenhouse gas emissions in 1990 shall include in their 1990 emissions base year or period the aggregate anthropogenic carbon dioxide equivalent emissions by sources minus removals by sinks in 1990 from land-use change for the purposes of calculating their assigned amount

8. Any Party included in Annex I may use 1995 as its base year for hydrofluorocarbons, perfluorocarbons and sulphur hexafluoride, for the purposes of the calculation referred to in paragraph 7 above.

(Contd...)

	9. Commitments for subsequent periods for Parties included in Annex I shall be established in amendments to Annex B to this Protocol, which shall be adopted in accordance with the provisions of Article 21, paragraph 7. The Conference of the Parties serving as the meeting of the Parties to this Protocol shall initiate the consideration of such commitments at least seven years before the end of the first commitment period referred to in paragraph 1 above. 10. Any emission reduction units, or any part of an assigned amount, which a Party acquires from another Party in accordance with the provisions of Article 6 or of Article 17 shall be added to the assigned amount for the acquiring Party. 11. Any emission reduction units, or any part of an assigned amount, which a Party transfers to another Party in accordance with the provisions of Article 6 or of Article 17 shall be subtracted from the assigned amount for the transferring Party. 12. Any certified emission reductions which a Party acquires from another Party in accordance with the provisions of Article 12 shall be added to the assigned amount for the acquiring Party. 13. If the emissions of a Party included in Annex I in a commitment period are less than its assigned amount under this Article, this difference shall, on request of that Party, be added to the assigned amount for that Party for subsequent commitment periods. 14. Each Party included in Annex I shall strive to implement the commitments mentioned in paragraph 1 above in such a way as to minimise adverse social, environmental and economic impacts on developing country Parties, particularly those identified in Article 4, paragraphs 8 and 9, of the Convention. In line with relevant decisions of the Conference of the Parties on the implementation of those paragraphs, the Conference of the Parties serving as the meeting of the Parties to this Protocol shall, at its first session, consider what actions are necessary to minimise the adverse effects of climate change and/or the impacts of response measures on Parties referred to in those paragraphs. Among the issues to be considered shall be the establishment of funding, insurance and transfer of technology.
Article 4	1. Any Parties included in Annex I that have reached an agreement to fulfil their commitments under Article 3 jointly, shall be deemed to have met those commitments provided that their total combined aggregate anthropogenic carbon dioxide equivalent emissions of the greenhouse gases listed in Annex A do not exceed their assigned amounts calculated pursuant to their quantified emission limitation and reduction commitments inscribed in Annex B and in accordance with the provisions of Article 3. The respective emission level allocated to each of the Parties to the agreement shall be set out in that agreement. 2. The Parties to any such agreement shall notify the secretariat of the terms of the agreement on the date of deposit of their instruments of

(Contd...)

	ratification, acceptance or approval of this Protocol, or accession thereto. The secretariat shall in turn inform the Parties and signatories to the Convention of the terms of the agreement. 3. Any such agreement shall remain in operation for the duration of the commitment period specified in Article 3, paragraph 7. 4. If Parties acting jointly do so in the framework of, and together with, a regional economic integration organisation, any alteration in the composition of the organisation after adoption of this Protocol shall not affect existing commitments under this Protocol. Any alteration in the composition of the organisation shall only apply for the purposes of those commitments under Article 3 that are adopted subsequent to that alteration. 5. In the event of failure by the Parties to such an agreement to achieve their total combined level of emission reductions, each Party to that agreement shall be responsible for its own level of emissions set out in the agreement. 6. If Parties acting jointly do so in the framework of, and together with, a regional economic integration organisation which is itself a Party to this Protocol, each member State of that regional economic integration organisation individually, and together with the regional economic integration organisation acting in accordance with Article 24, shall, in the event of failure to achieve the total combined level of emission reductions, be responsible for its level of emissions as notified in accordance with this Article.
Article 5	1. Each Party included in Annex I shall have in place, no later than one year prior to the start of the first commitment period, a national system for the estimation of anthropogenic emissions by sources and removals by sinks of all greenhouse gases not controlled by the Montreal Protocol. Guidelines for such national systems, which shall incorporate the methodologies specified in paragraph 2 below, shall be decided upon by the Conference of the Parties serving as the meeting of the Parties to this Protocol at its first session. 2. Methodologies for estimating anthropogenic emissions by sources and removals by sinks of all greenhouse gases not controlled by the Montreal Protocol shall be those accepted by the Intergovernmental Panel on Climate Change and agreed upon by the Conference of the Parties at its third session. Where such methodologies are not used, appropriate adjustments shall be applied according to methodologies agreed upon by the Conference of the Parties serving as the meeting of the Parties to this Protocol at its first session. Based on the work of, inter alia, the Intergovernmental Panel on Climate Change and advice provided by the Subsidiary Body for Scientific and Technological Advice, the Conference of the Parties serving as the meeting of the Parties to this Protocol shall regularly review and, as appropriate, revise such methodologies and adjustments, taking fully into account any relevant decisions by the Conference of the Parties. Any revision

(Contd...)

	to methodologies or adjustments shall be used only for the purposes of ascertaining compliance with commitments under Article 3 in respect of any commitment period adopted subsequent to that revision.3. The global warming potentials used to calculate the carbon dioxide equivalence of Anthropogenic emissions by sources and removals by sinks of greenhouse gases listed in Annex A shall be those accepted by the Intergovernmental Panel on Climate Change and agreed upon by the Conference of the Parties at its third session. Based on the work of, inter alia, the Intergovernmental Panel on Climate Change and advice provided by the Subsidiary Body for Scientific and Technological Advice, the Conference of the Parties serving as the meeting of the Parties to this Protocol shall regularly review and, as appropriate, revise the global warming potential of each such greenhouse gas, taking fully into account any relevant decisions by the Conference of the Parties. Any revision to a global warming potential shall apply only to commitments under Article 3 in respect of any commitment period adopted subsequent to that revision. 1. For the purpose of meeting its commitments under Article 3, any Party included in Annex I may transfer to, or acquire from, any other such Party emission reduction units resulting from projects aimed at reducing anthropogenic emissions by sources or enhancing anthropogenic removals by sinks of greenhouse gases in any sector of the economy, provided that: (a) Any such project has the approval of the Parties involved; (b) Any such project provides a reduction in emissions by sources, or an enhancement of removals by sinks, that is additional to any that would otherwise occur; (c) It does not acquire any emission reduction units if it is not in compliance with its obligations under Articles 5 and 7; and (d) The acquisition of emission reduction units shall be supplemental to domestic actions for the purposes of meeting commitments under Article 3.2. The Conference of the Parties serving as the meeting of the Parties to this Protocol may, at its first session or as soon as practicable thereafter, further elaborate guidelines for the implementation of this Article, including for verification and reporting. 3. A Party included in Annex I may authorize legal entities to participate, under its responsibility, in actions leading to the generation, transfer or acquisition under this Article of emission reduction units. 4. If a question of implementation by a Party included in Annex I of the requirements referred to in this Article is identified in accordance with the relevant provisions of Article 8, transfers and acquisitions of emission reduction units may continue to be made after the question has been identified, provided that any such units may not be used by a Party to meet its commitments under Article 3 until any issue of compliance is resolved.
Article 7	1. Each Party included in Annex I shall incorporate in its annual inventory of anthropogenic emissions by sources and removals by sinks of greenhouse gases not controlled by the Montreal Protocol,

(Contd...)

	submitted in accordance with the relevant decisions of the Conference of the Parties, the necessary supplementary information for the purposes of ensuring compliance with Article 3, to be determined in accordance with paragraph 4 below. 2. Each Party included in Annex I shall incorporate in its national communication, submitted under Article 12 of the Convention, the supplementary information necessary to demonstrate compliance with its commitments under this Protocol, to be determined in accordance with paragraph 4 below. 3. Each Party included in Annex I shall submit the information required under paragraph 1 above annually, beginning with the first inventory due under the Convention for the first year of the commitment period after this Protocol has entered into force for that Party. Each such Party shall submit the information required under paragraph 2 above as part of the first national communication due under the Convention after this Protocol has entered into force for it and after the adoption of guidelines as provided for in paragraph 4 below. The frequency of subsequent submission of information required under this Article shall be determined by the Conference of the Parties serving as the meeting of the Parties to this Protocol, taking into account any timetable for the submission of national communications decided upon by the Conference of the Parties. 4.The Conference of the Parties serving as the meeting of the Parties to this Protocol shall adopt at its first session, and review periodically thereafter, guidelines for the preparation of the information required under this Article, taking into account guidelines for the preparation of national communications by Parties included in Annex I adopted by the Conference of the Parties. The Conference of the Parties serving as the meeting of the Parties to this Protocol shall also, prior to the first commitment period, decide upon modalities for the accounting of assigned amounts.
Article 8	1. The information submitted under Article 7 by each Party included in Annex I shall be reviewed by expert review teams pursuant to the relevant decisions of the Conference of the Parties and in accordance with guidelines adopted for this purpose by the Conference of the Parties serving as the meeting of the Parties to this Protocol under paragraph 4 below. The information submitted under Article 7, paragraph 1, by each Party included in Annex I shall be reviewed as part of the annual compilation and accounting of emissions inventories and assigned amounts. Additionally, the information submitted under Article 7, paragraph 2, by each Party included in Annex I shall be reviewed as part of the review of communications. 2. Expert review teams shall be coordinated by the secretariat and shall be composed of experts selected from those nominated by Parties to the Convention and, as appropriate, by intergovernmental

(Contd...)

	organisations, in accordance with guidance provided for this purpose by the Conference of the Parties. 3. The review process shall provide a thorough and comprehensive technical assessment of all aspects of the implementation by a Party of this Protocol. The expert review teams shall prepare a report to the Conference of the Parties serving as the meeting of the Parties to this Protocol, assessing the implementation of the commitments of the Party and identifying any potential problems in, and factors influencing, the fulfilment of commitments. Such reports shall be circulated by the secretariat to all Parties to the Convention. The secretariat shall list those questions of implementation indicated in such reports for further consideration by the Conference of the Parties serving as the meeting of the Parties to this Protocol. 4. The Conference of the Parties serving as the meeting of the Parties to this Protocol shall adopt at its first session, and review periodically thereafter, guidelines for the review of implementation of this Protocol by expert review teams taking into account the relevant decisions of the Conference of the Parties. 5. The Conference of the Parties serving as the meeting of the Parties to this Protocol shall, with the assistance of the Subsidiary Body for Implementation and, as appropriate, the Subsidiary Body for Scientific and Technological Advice, consider: (a) The information submitted by Parties under Article 7 and the reports of the expert reviews thereon conducted under this Article; and (b) Those questions of implementation listed by the secretariat under paragraph 3 above, as well as any questions raised by Parties. 6. Pursuant to its consideration of the information referred to in paragraph 5 above, the Conference of the Parties serving as the meeting of the Parties to this Protocol shall take decisions on any matter required for the implementation of this Protocol.
Article 9	1. The Conference of the Parties serving as the meeting of the Parties to this Protocol shall periodically review this Protocol in the light of the best available scientific information and assessments on climate change and its impacts, as well as relevant technical, social and economic information. Such reviews shall be coordinated with pertinent reviews under the Convention, in particular those required by Article 4, paragraph 2 (d), and Article 7, paragraph 2 (a), of the Convention. Based on these reviews, the Conference of the Parties serving as the meeting of the Parties to this Protocol shall take appropriate action. 2. The first review shall take place at the second session of the Conference of the Parties serving as the meeting of the Parties to this Protocol. Further reviews shall take place at regular intervals and in a timely manner.
Article 10	All Parties, taking into account their common but differentiated responsibilities and their specific national and regional development priorities, objectives and circumstances, without introducing any new

(Contd...)

	commitments for Parties not included in Annex I, but reaffirming existing commitments under Article 4, paragraph 1, of the Convention, and continuing to advance the implementation of these commitments in order to achieve sustainable development, taking into account Article 4, paragraphs 3, 5 and 7, of the Convention, shall: (a) Formulate, where relevant and to the extent possible, cost-effective national and, where appropriate, regional programmes to improve the quality of local emission factors, activity data and/or models which reflect the socio-economic conditions of each Party for the preparation and periodic updating of national inventories of anthropogenic emissions by sources and removals by sinks of all greenhouse gases not controlled by the Montreal Protocol, using comparable methodologies to be agreed upon by the Conference of the Parties, and consistent with the guidelines for the preparation of national communications adopted by the Conference of the Parties; (b) Formulate, implement, publish and regularly update national and, where appropriate, regional programmes containing measures to mitigate climate change and measures to facilitate adequate adaptation to climate change: (i) Such programmes would, inter alia, concern the energy, transport and industry sectors as well as agriculture, forestry and waste management. Furthermore, adaptation technologies and methods for improving spatial planning would improve adaptation to climate change; and (ii) Parties included in Annex I shall submit information on action under this Protocol, including national programmes, in accordance with Article 7; and other Parties shall seek to include in their national communications, as appropriate, information on programmes which contain measures that the Party believes contribute to addressing climate change and its adverse impacts, including the abatement of increases in greenhouse gas emissions, and enhancement of and removals by sinks, capacity building and adaptation measures; (c) Cooperate in the promotion of effective modalities for the development, application and diffusion of, and take all practicable steps to promote, facilitate and finance, as appropriate, the transfer of, or access to, environmentally sound technologies, know-how, practices and processes pertinent to climate change, in particular to developing countries, including the formulation of policies and programmes for the effective transfer of environmentally sound technologies that are publicly owned or in the public domain and the creation of an enabling environment for the private sector, to promote and enhance the transfer of, and access to, environmentally sound technologies; (d) Cooperate in scientific and technical research and promote the maintenance and the development of systematic observation systems and development of data archives to reduce uncertainties related to the climate system, the adverse impacts of climate change and the economic and social consequences of various response strategies, and promote the development and strengthening of endogenous capacities and capabilities to participate in international

(Contd...)

	and intergovernmental efforts, programmes and networks on research and systematic observation, taking into account Article 5 of the Convention; (e) Cooperate in and promote at the international level, and, where appropriate, using existing bodies, the development and implementation of education and training programmes, including the strengthening of national capacity building, in particular human and institutional capacities and the exchange or secondment of personnel to train experts in this field, in particular for developing countries, and facilitate at the national level public awareness of, and public access to information on, climate change. Suitable modalities should be developed to implement these activities through the relevant bodies of the Convention, taking into account Article 6 of the Convention; (f) Include in their national communications information on programmes and activities undertaken pursuant to this Article in accordance with relevant decisions of the Conference of the Parties; and (g) Give full consideration, in implementing the commitments under this Article, to Article 4, paragraph 8, of the Convention.
Article 11	1.In the implementation of Article 10, Parties shall take into account the provisions ofArticle 4, paragraphs 4, 5, 7, 8 and 9, of the Convention. 2. In the context of the implementation of Article 4, paragraph 1, of the Convention, inaccordance with the provisions of Article 4, paragraph 3, and Article 11 of the Convention, and through the entity or entities entrusted with the operation of the financial mechanism of the Convention, the developed country Parties and other developed Parties included in Annex II to the Convention shall:Provide new and additional financial resources to meet the agreed full costs incurred by developing country Parties in advancing the implementation of existing commitments under Article 4, paragraph 1 (a), of the Convention that are covered in Article 10, subparagraph (a); and Also provide such financial resources, including for the transfer of technology, needed by the developing country Parties to meet the agreed full incremental costs of advancing the implementation of existing commitments under Article 4, paragraph 1, of the Convention that are covered by Article 10 and that are agreed between a developing country Party and the international entity or entities referred to in Article 11 of the Convention, in accordance with that Article.The implementation of these existing commitments shall take into account the need for adequacy and predictability in the flow of funds and the importance of appropriate burden sharing among developed country Parties. The guidance to the entity or entities entrusted with the operation of the financial mechanism of the Convention in relevant decisions of the Conference of the Parties, including those agreed before the adoption of this Protocol, shall apply mutatis mutandis to the provisions of this paragraph. 3. The developed country Parties and other developed Parties in Annex II to the Convention may also provide, and developing country Parties

(Contd...)

	avail themselves of, financial resources for the implementation of Article 10, through bilateral, regional and other multilateral channels.
Article 12	1. A clean development mechanism is hereby defined. 2. The purpose of the clean development mechanism shall be to assist Parties not included in Annex I in achieving sustainable development and in contributing to the ultimate objective of the Convention, and to assist Parties included in Annex I in achieving compliance with their quantified emission limitation and reduction commitments under Article 3. 3. Under the clean development mechanism: (a) Parties not included in Annex I will benefit from project activities resulting in certified emission reductions; and (b) Parties included in Annex I may use the certified emission reductions accruing from such project activities to contribute to compliance with part of their quantified emission limitation and reduction commitments under Article 3, as determined by the Conference of the Parties serving as the meeting of the Parties to this Protocol. 4. The clean development mechanism shall be subject to the authority and guidance of the Conference of the Parties serving as the meeting of the Parties to this Protocol and be supervised by an executive board of the clean development mechanism. 5. Emission reductions resulting from each project activity shall be certified by operational entities to be designated by the Conference of the Parties serving as the meeting of the Parties to this Protocol, on the basis of: (a) Voluntary participation approved by each Party involved; (b) Real, measurable, and long-term benefits related to the mitigation of climate change; and (c) Reductions in emissions that are additional to any that would occur in the absence of the certified project activity. 6. The clean development mechanism shall assist in arranging funding of certified project activities as necessary. 7. The Conference of the Parties serving as the meeting of the Parties to this Protocol shall, at its first session, elaborate modalities and procedures with the objective of ensuring transparency, efficiency and accountability through independent auditing and verification of project activities. 8. The Conference of the Parties serving as the meeting of the Parties to this Protocol shall ensure that a share of the proceeds from certified project activities is used to cover administrative expenses as well as to assist developing country Parties that are particularly vulnerable to the adverse effects of climate change to meet the costs of adaptation. 9. Participation under the clean development mechanism, including in activities mentioned in paragraph 3 (a) above and in the acquisition of certified emission reductions, may involve private and/or public entities, and is to be subject to whatever guidance may be provided by the executive board of the clean development mechanism.10. Certified

(Contd...)

	emission reductions obtained during the period from the year 2000 up to the beginning of the first commitment period can be used to assist in achieving compliance in the first commitment period.
Article 13	1. The Conference of the Parties, the supreme body of the Convention, shall serve as the meeting of the Parties to this Protocol. 2. Parties to the Convention that are not Parties to this Protocol may participate as observers in the proceedings of any session of the Conference of the Parties serving as the meeting of the Parties to this Protocol. When the Conference of the Parties serves as the meeting of the Parties to this Protocol, decisions under this Protocol shall be taken only by those that are Parties to this Protocol. 3. When the Conference of the Parties serves as the meeting of the Parties to this Protocol, any member of the Bureau of the Conference of the Parties representing a Party to the Convention but, at that time, not a Party to this Protocol, shall be replaced by an additional member to be elected by and from amongst the Parties to this Protocol. 4. The Conference of the Parties serving as the meeting of the Parties to this Protocol shall keep under regular review the implementation of this Protocol and shall make, within its mandate, the decisions necessary to promote its effective implementation. It shall perform the functions assigned to it by this Protocol and shall: (a) Assess, on the basis of all information made available to it in accordance with the provisions of this Protocol, the implementation of this Protocol by the Parties, the overall effects of the measures taken pursuant to this Protocol, in particular environmental, economic and social effects as well as their cumulative impacts and the extent to which progress towards the objective of the Convention is being achieved; (b) Periodically examine the obligations of the Parties under this Protocol, giving due consideration to any reviews required by Article 4, paragraph 2 (d), and Article 7, paragraph 2, of the Convention, in the light of the objective of the Convention, the experience gained in its implementation and the evolution of scientific and technological knowledge, and in this respect consider and adopt regular reports on the implementation of this Protocol; (c) Promote and facilitate the exchange of information on measures adopted by the Parties to address climate change and its effects, taking into account the differing circumstances, responsibilities and capabilities of the Parties and their respective commitments under this Protocol; (d) Facilitate, at the request of two or more Parties, the coordination of measures adopted by them to address climate change and its effects, taking into account the differing circumstances, responsibilities and capabilities of the Parties and their respective commitments under this Protocol; (e) Promote and guide, in accordance with the objective of the Convention and the provisions of this Protocol, and taking fully into account the relevant decisions by the Conference of the Parties, the development and periodic refinement of comparable methodologies for the effective implementation of this

(Contd...)

	Protocol, to be agreed on by the Conference of the Parties serving as the meeting of the Parties to this Protocol; (f) Make recommendations on any matters necessary for the implementation of this Protocol; (g) Seek to mobilise additional financial resources in accordance with Article 11,paragraph 2; (h) Establish such subsidiary bodies as are deemed necessary for the implementation of this Protocol; (i) Seek and utilise, where appropriate, the services and cooperation of, and information provided by, competent international organisations and intergovernmental and non-governmental bodies; and (j) Exercise such other functions as may be required for the implementation of this Protocol, and consider any assignment resulting from a decision by the Conference of the Parties. 5.The rules of procedure of the Conference of the Parties and financial procedures applied under the Convention shall be applied mutatis mutandis under this Protocol, except as may be otherwise decided by consensus by the Conference of the Parties serving as the meeting of the Parties to this Protocol. 6. The first session of the Conference of the Parties serving as the meeting of the Parties to this Protocol shall be convened by the secretariat in conjunction with the first session of the Conference of the Parties that is scheduled after the date of the entry into force of this Protocol. Subsequent ordinary sessions of the Conference of the Parties serving as the meeting of the Parties to this Protocol shall be held every year and in conjunction with ordinary sessions of the Conference of the Parties, unless otherwise decided by the Conference of the Parties serving as the meeting of the Parties to this Protocol. 7. Extraordinary sessions of the Conference of the Parties serving as the meeting of the Parties to this Protocol shall be held at such other times as may be deemed necessary by the Conference of the Parties serving as the meeting of the Parties to this Protocol, or at the written request of any Party, provided that, within six months of the request being communicated to the Parties by the secretariat, it is supported by at least one third of the Parties. 8.The United Nations, its specialised agencies and the International Atomic Energy Agency, as well as any State member thereof or observers thereto not party to the Convention, may be represented at sessions of the Conference of the Parties serving as the meeting of the Parties to this Protocol as observers. Any body or agency, whether national or international, governmental or non-governmental, which is qualified in matters covered by this Protocol and which has informed the secretariat of its wish to be represented at a session of the Conference of the Parties serving as the meeting of the Parties to this Protocol as an observer, may be so admitted unless at least one-third of the Parties present object. The admission and participation of observers shall be subject to the rules of procedure, as referred to in paragraph 5 above.

(Contd...)

Article 14	1. The secretariat established by Article 8 of the Convention shall serve as the secretariat of this Protocol. 2. Article 8, paragraph 2, of the Convention on the functions of the secretariat, and Article 8, paragraph 3, of the Convention on arrangements made for the functioning of the secretariat, shall apply mutatis mutandis to this Protocol. The secretariat shall, in addition, exercise the functions assigned to it under this Protocol.
Article 15	1. The Subsidiary Body for Scientific and Technological Advice and the Subsidiary Body for Implementation established by Articles 9 and 10 of the Convention shall serve as, respectively, the Subsidiary Body for Scientific and Technological Advice and the Subsidiary Body for Implementation of this Protocol. The provisions relating to the functioning of these two bodies under the Convention shall apply mutatis mutandis to this Protocol. Sessions of the meetings of the Subsidiary Body for Scientific and Technological Advice and the Subsidiary Body for Implementation of this Protocol shall be held in conjunction with the meetings of, respectively, the Subsidiary Body for Scientific and Technological Advice and the Subsidiary Body for Implementation of the Convention. 2. Parties to the Convention that are not Parties to this Protocol may participate as observers in the proceedings of any session of the subsidiary bodies. When the subsidiary bodies serve as the subsidiary bodies of this Protocol, decisions under this Protocol shall be taken only by those that are Parties to this Protocol. 3. When the subsidiary bodies established by Articles 9 and 10 of the Convention exercise their functions with regard to matters concerning this Protocol, any member of the Bureaux of those subsidiary bodies representing a Party to the Convention but, at that time, not a party to this Protocol, shall be replaced by an additional member to be elected by and from amongst the Parties to this Protocol.
Article 16	The Conference of the Parties serving as the meeting of the Parties to this Protocol shall, as soon as practicable, consider the application to this Protocol of, and modify as appropriate, the multilateral consultative process referred to in Article 13 of the Convention, in the light of any relevant decisions that may be taken by the Conference of the Parties. Any multilateral consultative process that may be applied to this Protocol shall operate without prejudice to the procedures and mechanisms established in accordance with Article 18.
Article 17	The Conference of the Parties shall define the relevant principles, modalities, rules and guidelines, in particular for verification, reporting and accountability for emissions trading. The Parties included in Annex B may participate in emissions trading for the purposes of fulfilling their commitments under Article 3. Any such trading shall be supplemental to domestic actions for the purpose of meeting quantified emission limitation and reduction commitments under that article.

(Contd...)

Article 18	The Conference of the Parties serving as the meeting of the Parties to this Protocol shall, at its first session, approve appropriate and effective procedures and mechanisms to determine and to address cases of non-compliance with the provisions of this Protocol, including through the development of an indicative list of consequences, taking into account the cause, type, degree and frequency of non-compliance. Any procedures and mechanisms under this Article entailing binding consequences shall be adopted by means of an amendment to this Protocol.
Article 19	The provisions of Article 14 of the Convention on settlement of disputes shall apply mutatis mutandis to this Protocol.
Article 20	1. Any Party may propose amendments to this Protocol. 2. Amendments to this Protocol shall be adopted at an ordinary session of the Conference of the Parties serving as the meeting of the Parties to this Protocol. The text of any proposed amendment to this Protocol shall be communicated to the Parties by the secretariat at least six months before the meeting at which it is proposed for adoption. The secretariat shall also communicate the text of any proposed amendments to the Parties and signatories to the Convention and, for information, to the Depositary. 3. The Parties shall make every effort to reach agreement on any proposed amendment to this Protocol by consensus. If all efforts at consensus have been exhausted, and no agreement reached, the amendment shall as a last resort be adopted by a three-fourths majority vote of the Parties present and voting at the meeting. The adopted amendment shall be communicated by the secretariat to the Depositary, who shall circulate it to all Parties for their acceptance. 4. Instruments of acceptance in respect of an amendment shall be deposited with the Depositary. An amendment adopted in accordance with paragraph 3 above shall enter into force for those Parties having accepted it on the ninetieth day after the date of receipt by the Depositary of an instrument of acceptance by at least three fourths of the Parties to this Protocol. 5. The amendment shall enter into force for any other Party on the ninetieth day after the date on which that Party deposits with the Depositary its instrument of acceptance of the said amendment.
Article 21	1. Annexes to this Protocol shall form an integral part thereof and, unless otherwise expressly provided, a reference to this Protocol constitutes at the same time a reference to any annexes thereto. Any annexes adopted after the entry into force of this Protocol shall be restricted to lists, forms and any other material of a descriptive nature that is of a scientific, technical, procedural or administrative character. 2. Any Party may make proposals for an annex to this Protocol and may propose amendments to annexes to this Protocol. 3. Annexes to this Protocol and amendments to annexes to this Protocol shall be adopted at an ordinary session of the Conference of the

(Contd...)

	Parties serving as the meeting of the Parties to this Protocol. The text of any proposed annex or amendment to an annex shall be communicated to the Parties by the secretariat at least six months before the meeting at which it is proposed for adoption. The secretariat shall also communicate the text of any proposed annex or amendment to an annex to the Parties and signatories to the Convention and, for information, to the Depositary. 4. The Parties shall make every effort to reach agreement on any proposed annex or amendment to an annex by consensus. If all efforts at consensus have been exhausted, and no agreement reached, the annex or amendment to an annex shall as a last resort be adopted by a three-fourths majority vote of the Parties present and voting at the meeting. The adopted annex or amendment to an annex shall be communicated by the secretariat to the Depositary, who shall circulate it to all Parties for their acceptance. 5. An annex, or amendment to an annex other than Annex A or B, that has been adopted in accordance with paragraphs 3 and 4 above shall enter into force for all Parties to this Protocol six month after the date of the communication by the Depositary to such Parties of the adoption of the annex or adoption of the amendment to the annex, except for those Parties that have notified the Depositary, in writing, within that period of their non-acceptance of the annex or amendment to the annex. The annex or amendment to an annex shall enter into force for Parties which withdraw their notification of non-acceptance on the ninetieth day after the date on which withdrawal of such notification has been received by the Depositary. 6. If the adoption of an annex or an amendment to an annex involves an amendment to this Protocol, that annex or amendment to an annex shall not enter into force until such time as the amendment to this Protocol enters into force.7.Amendments to Annexes A and B to this Protocol shall be adopted and enter into force in accordance with the procedure set out in Article 20, provided that any amendment to Annex B shall be adopted only with the written consent of the Party concerned.
Article 22	1. Each Party shall have one vote, except as provided for in paragraph 2 below. 2. Regional economic integration organisations, in matters within their competence, shall exercise their right to vote with a number of votes equal to the number of their member States that are Parties to this Protocol. Such an organisation shall not exercise its right to vote if any of its member States exercises its right, and vice versa.
Article 23	The Secretary-General of the United Nations shall be the Depositary of this Protocol.
Article 24	1. This Protocol shall be open for signature and subject to ratification, acceptance or approval by States and regional economic integration

(Contd...)

	organisations which are Parties to the Convention. It shall be open for signature at United Nations Headquarters in New York from 16 March 1998 to 15 March 1999. This Protocol shall be open for accession from the day after the date on which it is closed for signature. Instruments of ratification, acceptance, approval or accession shall be deposited with the Depositary. 2. Any regional economic integration organisation which becomes a Party to this Protocol without any of its member States being a Party shall be bound by all the obligations under this Protocol. In the case of such organisations, one or more of whose member States is a Party to this Protocol, the organisation and its member States shall decide on their respective responsibilities for the performance of their obligations under this Protocol. In such cases, the organisation and the member States shall not be entitled to exercise rights under this Protocol concurrently. 3. In their instruments of ratification, acceptance, approval or accession, regional economic integration organisations shall declare the extent of their competence with respect to the matters governed by this Protocol. These organisations shall also inform the Depositary, who shall in turn inform the Parties, of any substantial modification in the extent of their competence.
Article 25	1. This Protocol shall enter into force on the ninetieth day after the date on which not less than 55 Parties to the Convention, incorporating Parties included in Annex I which accounted in total for at least 55 per cent of the total carbon dioxide emissions for 1990 of the Parties included in Annex I, have deposited their instruments of ratification, acceptance, approval or accession. 2. For the purposes of this Article, "the total carbon dioxide emissions for 1990 of the Parties included in Annex I" means the amount communicated on or before the date of adoption of this Protocol by the Parties included in Annex I in their first national communications submitted in accordance with Article 12 of the Convention. 3. For each State or regional economic integration organisation that ratifies, accepts or approves this Protocol or accedes thereto after the conditions set out in paragraph 1 above for entry into force have been fulfilled, this Protocol shall enter into force on the ninetieth day following the date of deposit of its instrument of ratification, acceptance, approval or accession. 4. For the purposes of this Article, any instrument deposited by a regional economic integration organisation shall not be counted as additional to those deposited by States members of the organisation.
Article 26	No reservations may be made to this Protocol.
Article 27	1. At any time after three years from the date on which this Protocol has entered into force for a Party that Party may withdraw from this Protocol by giving written notification to the Depositary.

(Contd...)

	2. Any such withdrawal shall take effect upon expiry of one year from the date of receipt by the Depositary of the notification of withdrawal, or on such later date as may be specified in the notification of withdrawal. 3. Any Party that withdraws from the Convention shall be considered as also having withdrawn from this Protocol.
Article 28	The original of this Protocol, of which the Arabic, Chinese, English, French, Russian and Spanish texts are equally authentic, shall be deposited with the Secretary-General of the United Nations.

Environment and Development

Economics is positioned at the intersection of environmental, resource and development economics. The fourth GEO assesses the current state of the world's atmosphere, land, water and biodiversity, providing a description of the state of environment, and demonstrating that the environment is essential for improving and sustaining human well-being. It shows that environmental degradation is diminishing the potential for sustainable development. Policies for action are highlighted to facilitate alternative development paths. Two decades ago the Brundtland Commission report – Our Common Future – addressed the links between development and environment, and challenged policy-makers to consider the interrelationships among environment, economic and social issues when it comes to solving global problems.

The Brundtland Commission is widely attributed with popularising sustainable development internationally. It defined sustainable development as "development that meets the needs of the present generation without compromising the ability of future generations to meet their own needs." Key commitments in the Rio Declaration included integration of environment and development in decision-making, provision for polluters to pay for costs of pollution, recognition of common but differentiated responsibilities, and application of the precautionary approach to decision making. Two years after the Millennium Declaration and a decade after the Rio Earth Summit, world leaders reaffirmed sustainable development as a central goal on the international agenda at the 2002 Johannesburg World Summit on Sustainable Development.

The last 20 years has also seen a growth in the number of scientific assessments, such as the Intergovernmental Panel on Climate Change, the Millennium Ecosystem Assessment and the Global Environment Outlook. The Intergovernmental Panel on Climate Change was established in 1988 to assess on an objective, open and transparent basis the scientific, technical and socio-economic information relevant to climate change. Environmental governance has changed since the Brundtland Commission. The number of non-governmental stakeholders involved in environmental governance has grown considerably, with organisations playing key roles from local to global levels. NGOs and advocacy groups devoted to public interest and environmental causes have multiplied exponentially, particularly in countries undertaking democratic transitions.

Before the Brundtland Commission, "development progress" was associated with industrialisation, and measured solely by economic activity and increases in wealth. Environmental protection was perceived by many as an obstacle to development. While a healthy environment can support development, the relationship is not always reciprocal. Many alternative views exist on the benefits and disadvantages of modern development. Environmental degradation due to development raises deep ethical questions that go beyond economic cost-benefit ratios. Despite changes in environmental governance, and greater understanding of the links between environment and development, real progress towards sustainable development has been slow. Many governments continue to create policies concerned with environmental, economic and social matters as single issues.[34]

At the global level, green economy was called on by Rio+20 Summit in 2012. Asia and the Pacific have already pioneered the concept of green growth in 2005. Green growth – as a pre-requisite for building a green economy in the context of sustainable development and poverty reduction – was brought into the context of intergovernmental discussions for the first time at the Fifth Ministerial Conference on Environment and Development in Asia and the Pacific held in 2005 in Seoul, Republic of Korea.[35]

The Millennium Development Goals are the world's time-bound and quantified targets for addressing extreme poverty in its many dimensions-income poverty, hunger, disease, lack of adequate shelter, and exclusion-while promoting gender equality, education, and environmental sustainability.

The importance of environment and its link to development and the quality of human life were first addressed on a global level at the Stockholm Conference on Human Environment in 1972. It was the then Prime Minister, Mrs. Indira Gandhi, who focused attention of the Conference on this link, stating that "environment cannot be improved in conditions of poverty". Following the Stockholm Conference, set up a separate Ministry of Environment and Forests. Recognising the need for specialised institutions in various fields of environment and development, the Ministry created centres of excellence in partnership with NGOs and academic institutions. The Centre for Environment Education, established in 1984, was on of the first such institutions.[36]

Table 1. Links between the Environment and the Millennium Development Goals.

Millennium Development Goal	Selected Environmental Link
1. Eradicate extreme poverty and hunger	Livelihood strategies and food security of the poor often depend directly on healthy ecosystems and the diversity of goods and ecological services they provide. Natural capital a

(Contd...)

	counts for 26 per cent of the wealth of low-income countries. Climate change affects agricultural productivity. Ground-level ozone damages crops.
2. Achieve universal primary education	Cleaner air will decrease the illnesses of children due to exposure to harmful air pollutants. As a result, they will miss fewer days of school. Water-related diseases such as diarrhoeal infections cost about 443 million school days each year, and diminish learning potential.
3. Promote gender equality, and empower women	Indoor and outdoor air pollution is responsible for more than 2 million premature deaths annually. Poor women are particularly vulnerable to respiratory infections, as they have high levels of exposure to indoor air pollution. Women and girls bear the brunt of collecting water and fuelwood, tasks made harder by environmental degradation, such as water contamination and deforestation.
4. Reduce child mortality	Acute respiratory infections are the leading cause of death in children. Pneumonia kills more children under the age of 5 than any other illness. Environmental factors such as indoor air pollution may increase children's susceptibility to pneumonia. Water-related diseases, such as diarrhoea and cholera, kill an estimated 3 million people/year in developing countries, the majority of whom are children under the age of five. Diarrhoea has become the second biggest killer of children, with 1.8 million children dying every year (almost 5000/day).
5. Improve maternal health	Indoor air pollution and carrying heavy loads of water and fuelwood adversely affect women's health, and can make women less fit for childbirth and at greater risk of complications during pregnancy. Provision of clean water reduces the incidence of diseases that undermine maternal health and contribute to maternal mortality.
6. Combat major diseases	Up to 20 per cent of the total burden of disease in developing countries may be associated with environmental risk factors. Preventative environmental health measures are as important and at times more cost-effective than health treatment. New biodiversity-derived medicines hold promises for fighting major diseases
7. Ensure environmental sustainability	Current trends in environmental degradation must be reversed in order to sustain the health and productivity of the world's ecosystems.
8. Develop a global partnership for development	Poor countries and regions are forced to exploit their natural resources to generate revenue and make huge debt repayments. Unfair globalisation practices export their harmful side-effects to countries that often do not have effective governance regimes.

Source: Adapted from DFID and others 2002, UNDP 2006, UNICEF 2006.

Increased extraction of natural resources, accumulation of waste and concentration of pollutants will therefore overwhelm the carrying capacity of the biosphere and result in the degradation of environmental quality and a decline in human welfare, despite rising incomes. Furthermore, it is argued that degradation of the resource base will eventually put economic activity itself at risk.[37] The universal drive for higher incomes in the face of mounting environmental destruction has heightened the expressed tension between fast growth and environmental protection. The economic costs, including the losses caused by air pollution, water contamination and solid wastes as well as deforestation are estimated to amount to some three per cent of GNP in China as well as India, Argentina, Turkey and elsewhere.[38]

The relationship between economic growth and the environment is, and will always remain, controversial. Some see the emergence of new pollution problems, the lack of success in dealing with global warming and the still rising population in the Third World as proof positive that humans are a short-sighted and rapacious species.[39] While economic growth has produced many benefits, it has also resulted in the depletion of natural resources and the degradation of ecosystems. There has been much debate over whether or not it is possible to achieve economic growth without unsustainably degrading the environment, and a growing realisation that economic growth at the current rate of depletion and degradation of environmental assets cannot continue indefinitely.

The natural environment provides the raw materials for economic production of goods and services. Non-renewable resources are those with a finite endowment, which can be depleted over time. Non-renewable resources like fossil fuels, minerals, metals, and basic aggregates are extracted from the natural environment to produce energy, machinery, consumer products, the built environment. Renewable resources are those which are capable of being replenished through natural processes or their own reproduction. The indirect inputs provided by ecosystems facilitate the processes of production and act as a sink for the adverse environmental effects of economic activity.

Ecosystems also have a wide range of impacts on both the quantity and quality of labour. The World Health Organisation estimates that the apportioned burden of disease from water and air pollution accounts for the loss of over 100 million disability-adjusted life years globally each year. The natural environment contributes to human capital in other ways too. The demand for a clean and healthy natural environment provides opportunities for employment and wealth creation; for example, organic agriculture and industries responsible for managing and protecting natural resources.

Sustainable Development

The concept of sustainable development can be interpreted in many different ways, but at its core is an approach to development that looks to balance different, and often competing, needs against an awareness of the environmental, social and economic limitations we face as a society.[40] The Brundtland Commission's defined sustainable development as "ability to make development sustainable to ensure that it is meets the needs of the present without compromising the ability of future generations to meet their own needs". According to the classical definition given by the United Nations World Commission on Environment and Development in 1987, development is sustainable if it "meets the needs of the present without compromising the ability of future generations to meet their own needs."

It is a process for meeting human development goals while maintaining the ability of natural systems to continue to provide the natural resources and ecosystem services upon which the economy and society depend. It is the organising principle for sustaining finite resources necessary to provide for the needs of future generations of life on the planet. It is a process that envisions a desirable future state for human societies in which living conditions and resource-use continue to meet human needs without undermining the "integrity, stability and beauty" of natural biotic systems.

The 2002 World Summit on Sustainable Development marked a further expansion of the standard definition with the widely used three pillars of sustainable development: economic, social, and environmental. The Johannesburg Declaration created "a collective responsibility to advance and strengthen the interdependent and mutually reinforcing pillars of sustainable development—economic development, social development and environmental protection—at local, national, regional and global levels."[41] The ecological sustainability of human settlements is part of the relationship between humans and their natural, social and built environments. It is the scientific analysis and study of interactions among organisms and their environment. It is an interdisciplinary field that includes biology and Earth science. Ecology includes the study of interactions organisms have with each other, other organisms, and with abiotic components of their environment.

The United Nations Conference on Sustainable Development, also known as Rio 2012, Rio+20, or Earth Summit 2012, was the third international conference on sustainable development, which aimed at reconciling the economic and environmental goals of the global community. Few nations met the World Wide Fund for Nature's definition of sustainable development criteria established in 2006.[42] Sustainable Development stands for meeting the needs of present generations without jeopardising the ability of futures generations to meet their own needs – in other words, a better quality of life for everyone, now and for generations to come. It offers a vision of progress that integrates immediate and longer-term objectives, local and global action, and regards social, economic and environmental issues as inseparable and interdependent components of human progress.[43]

To achieve sustainable development, countries need to achieve three goals simultaneously: economic growth, broad-based social inclusion, and environmental sustainability. While many countries have solved the growth puzzles, few have succeeded in achieving all three aspects of sustainable development. Sustainable development could probably be otherwise called equitable and balanced. The key principle of sustainable development underlying all others is the integration of environmental, social, and economic concerns into all aspects of decision making. All other principles in the SD framework have integrated decision-making at their core.[44]

The essential needs of vast numbers of people in developing countries for food, clothing, shelter, jobs - are not being met, and beyond their basic needs these people have legitimate aspirations for an improved quality of life. A world in which poverty and inequity are endemic will always be prone to ecological and other crises. Sustainable development requires meeting the basic needs of all and extending to all the opportunity to satisfy their aspirations for a better life. Meeting essential needs depends in part on achieving full growth potential, and sustainable development clearly requires economic growth in places where such needs are not being met.[45]

The link between climate change and sustainable development stems from the fact that climate change is a constraint to development, and sustainable development is a key to capacities for mitigation and adaptation. It follows that strategies for dealing with sustainable development and climate change have many common elements so that applying them together creates synergies. It also follows that since dealing with climate change exclusively could be very expensive, it has to be factored into the development agenda.[46]

Population Growth

In biology, population growth is the increase in the number of individuals in a population. The population growth rate is the rate at which the number of individuals in a population increases in a given time period as a fraction of the initial population. It took hundreds of thousands of years for the world population to grow to one billion, and in just another 200 years or so it grew sevenfold. In 2011, the global population reached the seven billion mark, and it is projected to climb to over nine billion by 2050.[47] Demographic transition explains a form of relationship between population and economic development. In the western countries it has been found that they have moved from a condition of high birth and death rates, to a condition of low birth and death rates which led to a slow rate of growth of population. This demographic change is known as 'Demographic Transition'. In other words, demographic transition describes the passage through which countries move from high birth and death rates to low ones.[48]

The population growth rate measures how populations change in size over time. The units of population growth rate are individuals per time. Population size can only be changed by four factors. Births add new individuals to a population whereas deaths remove individuals from a population. Although immigration and emigration can be important factors influencing patterns of population growth in some human populations, for simplicity, most population growth models focus on how population growth rates are affected by birth and death rates.[49]

Population explosion refers to the rapid and dramatic rise in world population that has occurred over the last few hundred years. Most of the growth is currently taking place in the developing world, where rates of natural increase are much higher than in industrialised countries. The combination of a continuing high birth rate and a low death rate is creating a rapid population increase in many countries in Asia, Latin America and Africa and people generally lived longer. Until recently, birth rates and death rates were about the same, keeping the population stable. People had many children, but a large number of them died before age of five.[50]

More than seven billion people currently inhabit the planet, compared to only three billion in 1967. Every year about 135 million people are born and 55 million people die, adding 80 million to our global population. That's about one United States every four years, or one billion more every 12 years. Almost half of the global population is under the age of 25 and their decisions during their reproductive years will determine whether we have six billion or 14 billion people by 2100. As Martin Luther King Jr. said- "Unlike plagues of the dark ages or contemporary diseases we do not understand, the modern plague of overpopulation is soluble by means we have discovered and with resources we possess. What is lacking is not sufficient knowledge of the solution but universal consciousness of the gravity of the problem and education of the billions who are its victim."[51]

In less developed countries, lack of access to birth control, as well as cultural traditions that encourage women to stay home and have babies, lead to rapid population growth. The result is ever increasing numbers of poor people across Africa, the Middle East, Southeast Asia, and elsewhere who suffer from malnourishment, lack of clean water, overcrowding, inadequate shelter, and AIDS and other diseases. And while population numbers in most developed nations are leveling off or diminishing today, high levels of consumption make for a huge drain on resources. Americans, who represent only four per cent of world population, consume 25 per cent of all resources.[52]

At the root of overpopulation is the difference between the overall birth rate and death rate in populations. If the number of children born each year equals the number of adults that die, then the population will stabilise.

Technological advancement was perhaps the biggest reason why the balance has been permanently disturbed. Many people prefer to move to developed countries like US, UK, Canada and Australia where best facilities are available in terms of medical, education, security and employment. The end result is that those people settle over there and those places become overcrowded.

Most developing nations have large number of people who are illiterate, live below the poverty line and have little or no knowledge about family planning. Getting their children married at an early age increase the chances of producing more kids. Families that have been through poverty, natural disasters or are simply in need of more hands to work are a major factor for overpopulation. As compared to earlier times, most of these extra children survive and consume resources that are not sufficient in nature.[53]

Even though legally the marriageable age of a girl is 18 years, the concept of early marriage still prevails and getting married at young age prolongs the child bearing age. In India, marriage is an obligation and a universal practice, where almost every woman is married at a reproductive age. Another factor for the rapid growth of population is poverty. Impoverished families have notion that more the number of members in the family, more will be the numbers to earn income. Sons are the bread earners of the families in India.[54]

The rapid growth of the world's population over the past one hundred years results from a difference between the rate of birth and the rate of death. The growth in human population around the world affects all people through its impact on the economy and environment. The current rate of population growth is now a significant burden to human well-being. Understanding the factors which affect population growth patterns can help us plan for the future. Population growth is usually related to economic development. There occurs a typical fall in death rates and birth rates due to improved living conditions leading to low population growth, a phenomenon called demographic transition. India is the second most populous country of the world with one billion people. If the current growth rates continue, it will have 1.63 billion people by 2050 and will become the most populous country surpassing China[55].

The total population in India was last recorded at 1238.9 million people in 2014 from 359.0 million in 1950, changing 245 per cent during the last 50 years. Population in India averaged 744.18 Million from 1950 until 2014, reaching an all-time high of 1238.89 Million in 2014 and a record low of 359 Million in 1950. Population in India is reported by the Ministry of Statistics and Programme Implementation (MOSPI). The population of India represents 17.99 per cent of the world's total population which arguably means that one person in every six people on the planet is a resident of India.[56]

Table 2: Current Population of India

Rank	*State or Union Territory*	*Population (2011 Census)*	*Density (per km²)*	*Sex ratio*
1.	Uttar Pradesh	199,581,477	828	908
2.	Maharashtra	112,372,972	365	946
3.	Bihar	103,804,637	1102	916
4.	West Bengal	91,347,736	1029	947
5.	Andhra Pradesh	84,665,533	308	992
6.	Madhya Pradesh	72,597,565	236	930
7.	Tamil Nadu	72,138,958	555	995
8.	Rajasthan	68,621,012	201	926
9.	Karnataka	61,130,704	319	968
10.	Gujarat	60,383,628	308	918
11.	Odisha	41,947,358	269	978
12.	Kerala	33,387,677	859	1,084
13.	Jharkhand	32,966,238	414	947
14.	Assam	31,169,272	397	954
15.	Punjab	27,704,236	550	893
16.	Haryana	25,353,081	573	877
17.	Chhattisgarh	25,540,196	189	991
18.	Jammu and Kashmir	12,548,926	56	883
19.	Uttarakhand	10,116,752	189	963
20.	Himachal Pradesh	6,856,509	123	974
21.	Tripura	3,671,032	350	961
22.	Meghalaya	2,964,007	132	986
23.	Manipur	2,721,756	122	987
24.	Nagaland	1,980,602	119	931
25.	Goa	1,457,723	394	968
26.	Arunachal Pradesh	1,382,611	17	920
27.	Mizoram	1,091,014	52	975
28.	Sikkim	607,688	86	889
UT1	Delhi	16,753,235	9,340	866
UT2	Puducherry	1,244,464	2,598	1,038
UT3	Chandigarh	1,054,686	9,252	818
UT4	Andaman and Nicobar Islands	379,944	46	878
UT5	Dadra and Nagar Haveli	342,853	698	775
UT6	Daman and Diu	242,911	2,169	618
UT7	Lakshadweep	64,429	2,013	946
Total	**India**	**1,210,193,422**	**382**	**940**

Source: http://www.indiaonlinepages.com/population/india-current-population.html

Let discuss population in various states of India. Jharkhand has a population of 32.96 million, consisting of 16.93 million males and 16.03 million females. The sex ratio is 947 females to 1000 males. The population consists of 28 per cent tribal peoples, 12 per cent Scheduled Castes and 60 per cent others. Census data since 1881 has shown a gradual decline of tribal population in Jharkhand as against the gradual increase of non-tribal population in the region.

Table 3: Population in Jharkhand

District	*Population*	*Male Population*	*Female Population*	*Growth*	*Sex Ratio*	*Literacy*	*Density*
Bokaro	2061918	1076270	985648	15.99	916	73.48	716
Chatra	1042304	534209	508095	28.98	951	62.14	275
Deoghar	1491879	776741	715138	28.02	921	66.34	602
Dhanbad	2682662	1405847	1276815	11.91	908	75.71	1284
Dumka	1321096	669240	651856	19.39	974	62.54	300
Garhwa	1322387	683984	638403	27.71	933	62.18	327
Giridih	2445203	1258607	1186596	28.33	943	65.12	497
Godda	1311382	678504	632878	25.14	933	57.68	622
Gumla	1025656	514730	510926	23.21	993	66.92	193
Hazaribagh	1734005	891179	842826	25.75	946	70.48	403
Jamtara	790207	403450	386757	21	959	63.73	439
Khunti	530299	265939	264360	21.96	994	64.51	215
Kodarma	717169	367952	349217	32.59	949	68.35	427
Latehar	725673	369534	356139	29.38	964	61.23	200
Lohardaga	461738	232575	229163	26.67	985	68.29	310
Pakur	899200	453101	446099	28.15	985	50.17	498
Palamu	1936319	1003876	932443	25.94	929	65.5	381
Pashchimi Singhbhum	1501619	749314	752305	21.69	1004	59.54	209
Purbi Singhbhum	2291032	1175696	1115336	15.53	949	76.13	648
Ramgarh	949159	494037	455122	13.06	921	73.92	684
Ranchi	2912022	1493376	1418646	23.9	950	77.13	557
Sahibganj	1150038	590390	559648	23.96	948	53.73	719
Saraikela Kharsawan	1063458	543232	520226	25.28	958	68.85	390
Simdega	599813	299905	299908	16.62	1000	67.59	160

Source: http://www.mapsofindia.com/census2011/jharkhand-sex-ratio.html.6

According to the 2011 census of India, the total population of Odisha is 41,947,358, of which 21,201,678 (50.54 per cent) are male and 20,745,680 (49.46 per cent) are female, or 978 females per 1000 males. This represents a

13.97 percent increase over the population in 2001. The population density is 269 per km².

Table 4: Population of Odisha

State/District	*Population in 2011*	*Sex Ratio*	*Literacy Rate*
Odisha	**41,947,358**	**978**	**73.45**
Bargarh	1,478,833	976	75.16
Jharsuguda	579,499	951	78.36
Sambalpur	1,044,410	973	76.91
Debagarh	312,164	976	73.07
Sundargarh	2,080,664	971	74.13
Kendujhar	1,802,777	987	69.00
Mayurbhanj	2,513,895	1005	63.98
Baleshwar	2,317,419	957	80.66
Bhadrak	1,506,522	981	83.25
Kendrapara	1,439,891	1006	85.93
Jagatsinghapur	1,136,604	967	87.13
Cuttack	2,618,708	955	84.20
Jaipur	1,826,275	972	80.44
Dhenkanal	1,192,948	947	79.41
Aungul	1,271,703	942	78.96
Nayagarh	962,215	916	79.17
Khardha	2,246,341	925	87.51
Puri	1,697,983	963	85.37
Ganjam	3,520,151	981	71.88
Gajapati	575,880	1042	54.29
Kandhamal	731,952	1037	65.12
Baudh	439,917	991	72.51
Subarnapur	652,107	959	74.42
Balangir	1,648,574	983	65.50
Nuapada	606,490	1020	58.20
Kalahandi	1,573,054	1003	60.22
Rayagada	961,959	1048	50.88
Nabarangapur	1,218,762	1018	48.20
Koraput	1,376,934	1031	49.87
Malkangiri	612,727	1016	49.49

Source: http://www.indiaonlinepages.com/population/orissa-population.html

Uttar Pradesh is the most populous state in India, with 199,581,477 people on 1 March 2011. The state contributes 16.16 per cent of India's population. The population density is 828 people per square kilometer, making it one of the most densely populated states in the country.

Table 5: Population of Uttar Pradesh

State/ District	*Population in 2011*			*Sex Ratio*	*Population Density per sq. km.*
	Persons	*Males*	*Females*	*2011*	*2011*
Uttar Pradesh	**199,581,477**	**104,596,415**	**94,985,062**	**908**	**828**
Saharanpur	3,464,228	1,835,740	1,628,488	887	939
Muzaffarnagar	4,138,605	2,194,540	1,944,065	886	1033
Bijnor	3,683,896	1,925,787	1,758,109	913	808
Moradabad	4,773,138	2,508,299	2,264,839	903	1284
Rampur	2,335,398	1,226,175	1,109,223	905	987
Jyotiba Phule Nagar	1,838,771	964,319	874,452	907	818
Meerut	3,447,405	1,829,192	1,618,213	885	1347
Baghpat	1,302,156	700,724	601,432	858	986
Ghaziabad	4,661,452	2,481,803	2,179,649	878	3954
Gautam Buddha Nagar	1,674,714	904,505	770,209	852	1306
Bulandshahar	3,498,507	1,848,643	1,649,864	892	775
Aligarh	3,673,849	1,958,536	1,715,313	876	1007
Mahamaya Nagar	1,565,678	837,446	728,232	870	851
Mathura	2,541,894	1,368,445	1,173,449	858	761
Agra	4,380,793	2,356,104	2,024,689	859	1084
Firozabad	2,496,761	1,337,141	1,159,620	867	1037
Mainpuri	1,847,194	984,892	862,302	876	669
Budaun	3,712,738	1,997,242	1,715,496	859	718
Bareilly	4,465,344	2,371,454	2,093,890	883	1084
Pilibhit	2,037,225	1,078,525	958,700	889	553
Shahjahanpur	3,002,376	1,610,182	1,392,194	865	684
Kheri	4,013,634	2,126,782	1,886,852	887	523
Sitapur	4,474,446	2,380,666	2,093,780	879	779
Hardoi	4,091,380	2,204,264	1,887,116	856	683
Unnao	3,110,595	1,636,295	1,474,300	901	682
Lucknow	4,588,455	2,407,897	2,180,558	906	1815
Rae Bareli	3,404,004	1,753,344	1,650,660	941	739
Farrukhabad	1,887,577	1,007,479	880,098	874	865
Kannauj	1,658,005	882,546	775,459	879	792
Etawah	1,579,160	845,893	733,267	867	683
Auraiya	1,372,287	736,144	636,143	864	681
Kanpur Dehat	1,795,092	964,284	830,808	862	594
Kanpur Nagar	4,572,951	2,469,114	2,103,837	852	1449

(Contd...)

Jalaun	1,670,718	895,804	774,914	865	366
Jhansi	2,000,755	1,061,310	939,445	885	398
Lalitpur	1,218,002	639,392	578,610	905	242
Hamirpur	1,104,021	593,576	510,445	860	275
Mahoba	876,055	465,937	410,118	880	279
Banda	1,799,541	966,123	833,418	863	408
Chitrakoot	990,626	527,101	463,525	879	308
Fatehpur	2,632,684	1,385,556	1,247,128	900	634
Pratapgarh	3,173,752	1,591,480	1,582,272	994	854
Kaushambi	1,596,909	838,095	758,814	905	897
Allahabad	5,959,798	3,133,479	2,826,319	902	1087
Barabanki	3,257,983	1,707,951	1,550,032	908	740
Faizabad	2,468,371	1,258,455	1,209,916	961	1054
Ambedkar Nagar	2,398,709	1,214,225	1,184,484	976	1021
Sultanpur	3,790,922	1,916,297	1,874,625	978	855
Bahraich	3,478,257	1,838,988	1,639,269	891	664
Shrawasti	1,114,615	594,318	520,297	875	679
Balarampur	2,149,066	1,117,984	1,031,082	922	642
Gonda	3,431,386	1,785,629	1,645,757	922	857
Siddharthnagar	2,553,526	1,296,046	1,257,480	970	882
Basti	2,461,056	1,256,158	1,204,898	959	916
Sant Kabir Nagar	1,714,300	870,547	843,753	969	1041
Maharajganj	2,665,292	1,375,367	1,289,925	938	903
Gorakhpur	4,436,275	2,281,763	2,154,512	944	1336
Kushinagar	3,560,830	1,821,242	1,739,588	955	1226
Deoria	3,098,637	1,539,608	1,559,029	1,013	1220
Azamgarh	4,616,509	2,289,336	2,327,173	1,017	1139
Mau	2,205,170	1,114,888	1,090,282	978	1287
Ballia	3,223,642	1,667,557	1,556,085	933	1081
Jaunpur	4,476,072	2,217,635	2,258,437	1,018	1108
Ghazipur	3,622,727	1,856,584	1,766,143	951	1073
Chandauli	1,952,713	1,020,789	931,924	913	768
Varanasi	3,682,194	1,928,641	1,753,553	909	2399
Sant Ravidas Nagar (Bhadohi)	1,554,203	797,164	757,039	950	1531
Mirzapur	2,494,533	1,312,822	1,181,711	900	566
Sonbhadra	1,862,612	973,480	889,132	913	270
Etah	1,761,152	945,157	815,995	863	724
Kanshiram Nagar	1,438,156	765,529	672,627	879	736

Source: http://www.indiaonlinepages.com/population/uttar-pradesh-population.html

Rajasthan has mainly Rajasthani population of approximately 68,621,012. Rajasthan's population is made up mainly of Hindus, who account for 88.8 per cent of the population. Muslims make up 8.5 per cent, Sikhs 1.4 per cent and Jains 1.2 per cent of the population.

Table 6: Population of Rajasthan 2011

State/ District	*Population in 2011*	*Gender*		*Percentage Decadal Growth Rate of Population*	*Sex Ratio (No. of Females per 1000 Males)*	*Population density per Sq. Km*
	Person	**Male**	**Female**	**2001-11**	**2011**	**2011**
Rajasthan	**68621012**	**35620086**	**33000926**	**21.44**	**926**	**201**
Ganganagar	1969520	1043730	925790	10.06	887	179
Hanumangarh	1779650	933660	845990	17.24	906	184
Bikaner	2367745	1243916	1123829	24.48	903	78
Churu	2041172	1053375	987797	20.35	938	148
Jhunjhunun	2139658	1097390	1042268	11.81	950	361
Alwar	3671999	1938929	1733070	22.75	894	438
Bharatpur	2549121	1357896	1191225	21.39	877	503
Dhaulpur	1207293	654344	552949	22.78	845	398
Karauli	1458459	784943	673516	20.94	858	264
Sawai Madhopur	1338114	706558	631556	19.79	894	297
Dausa	1637226	859821	777405	23.75	904	476
Jaipur	6663971	3490787	3173184	26.91	909	598
Sikar	2677737	1377120	1300617	17.04	944	346
Nagaur	3309234	1698760	1610474	19.25	948	187
Jodhpur	3685681	1924326	1761355	27.69	915	161
Jaisalmer	672008	363346	308662	32.22	849	17
Barmer	2604453	1370494	1233959	32.55	900	92
Jalor	1830151	937918	892233	26.31	951	172
Sirohi	1037185	535115	502070	21.86	938	202
Pali	2038533	1025895	1012638	11.99	987	165
Ajmer	2584913	1325911	1259002	18.66	950	305
Tonk	1421711	729390	692321	17.33	949	198
Bundi	1113725	579385	534340	15.7	922	193
Bhilwara	2410459	1224483	1185976	19.27	969	230
Rajsamand	1158283	582670	575613	17.89	988	302
Dungarpur	1388906	698069	690837	25.39	990	368
Banswara	1798194	908755	889439	26.58	979	399
Chittaurgarh	1544392	784054	760338	16.09	970	193
Kota	1950491	1023153	927338	24.34	906	374
Baran	1223921	635495	588426	19.82	926	175
Jhalawar	1411327	725667	685660	19.57	945	22
Udaipur	3067549	1566781	1500768	23.63	958	242
Pratapgarh	868231	437950	430281	22.84	982	211

Source: http://www.indiaonlinepages.com/population/rajasthan-population.html

The population of Punjab in 1991 was estimated to be 20.19 million. It reached further 24.3 million by the end of 2001. Around 20 per cent of total Population in Punjab is migratory from other regions in India. According to recent figures, there are only 850 females per 1000 males in Punjab.

Table 7: Current Population of Punjab (2011 census)

State /District	*Total Population*	*Sex Ratio*	*Density*	*Literacy Rate*
Punjab	**3,60,04,423**	**893**	**550**	**76.7**
Gurdaspur	22,99,026	895	649	81.1
Kapurthala	8,17,668	912	501	80.2
Jalandhar	21,81,753	913	831	82.4
Hoshiarpur	15,82,793	962	466	85.4
Shahid Bhagat Singh Nagar	6,14,362	954	479	80.3
Fatehgarh Sahib	5,99,814	871	508	80.3
Ludhiana	34,87,882	869	975	82.5
Moga	9,92,289	893	444	71.6
Firozpur	20,26,831	893	380	69.8
Muktsar	9,02,702	895	348	66.8
Faridkot	6,18,008	889	424	70.6
Bathinda	13,88,859	865	414	69.6
Mansa	7,68,808	880	350	62.8
Patiala	18,92,282	888	596	76.3
Amritsar	24,90,891	884	932	77.2
Tarn-Taran	11,20,070	898	464	69.4
Rupnagar	6,83,349	913	488	83.3
Sahibzada Ajit Singh Nagar	9,86,147	878	830	84.9
Sangrur	16,54,408	883	449	68.9
Barnala	5,96,294	876	419	68.9

Source: http://www.indiaonlinepages.com/population/punjab-population.html

As per the 2011 Census, Haryana has a total population of 25,353,081; previously it was 21,144,564 in the 2001 Census. Out of the total population of Haryana, the population of male are 13,505,130 and female are 11,847,951. The total population growth in the last decade was 19.90 per cent and the population of the state forms 2.09 per cent of the total population in India.

Table 8: Population of Haryana (2011 Census)

District	*Population*	*Male Population*	*Female Population*	*Growth*	*Sex Ratio*	*Liter acy*	*Den sity*
Ambala	1136784	604044	532740	12.06	882	82.9	722
Bhiwani	1629109	864616	764493	14.32	884	76.7	341
Faridabad	1798954	961532	837422	31.75	871	83	2298
Fatehabad	941522	494834	446688	16.79	903	69.1	371
Gurgaon	1514085	817274	696811	73.93	853	84.4	1241
Hisar	1742815	931535	811280	13.38	871	73.2	438
Jhajjar	956907	514303	442604	8.73	861	80.8	522

(Contd...)

Jind	1332042	712254	619788	11.95	870	72.7	493
Kaithal	1072861	570595	502266	13.39	880	70.6	463
Karnal	1506323	798840	707483	18.22	886	76.4	598
Kurukshetra	964231	510370	453861	16.81	889	76.7	630
Mahendra-garh	921680	486553	435127	13.43	894	78.9	485
Mewat	1089406	571480	517926	37.94	906	56.1	729
Palwal	1040493	553704	486789	25.49	879	70.3	761
Panchkula	558890	298919	259971	19.32	870	83.4	622
Panipat	1202811	646324	556487	24.33	861	77.5	949
Rewari	896129	472254	423875	17.09	898	82.2	562
Rohtak	1058683	566708	491975	12.61	868	80.4	607
Sirsa	1295114	683242	611872	15.98	896	70.4	303
Sonipat	1480080	798948	681132	15.71	853	80.8	697
Yamunanagar	1214162	646801	567361	16.56	877	78.9	687

Source: http://www.mapsofindia.com/census2011/haryana-sex-ratio.html

Jammu and Kashmir is a state in northern India. The state has special autonomy under Article 370 of the Constitution of India. Jammu and Kashmir consists of three regions: Jammu, the Kashmir Valley and Ladakh. Jammu and Kashmir is the only Indian state that has its own official flag and constitution, and Indians from other states cannot purchase land or property in the state.

Table 9: Population of Jammu and Kashmir (2011 Census)

District	*Persons (2001 census)*	*Persons (2011 census)*	*Male*	*Female*	*Density*	*Rural*	*Urban*
Srinagar	1202447	1250173	665789	584384	1056	15928	1234245
Ganderbal	NA	297003	158900	138103	284	250203	46800
Budgam	629309	755331	400583	354748	550	666620	88711
Anantnag	1172434	1069749	552203	517546	366	791237	278512
Kulgam	NA	423181	216873	206308	396	343739	79442
Pulwama	652607	570060	297988	272072	525	491370	78690
Shopian	NA	265960	136302	129658	852	251010	14950
Baramulla	1169780	1015503	542171	473332	242	40948	174555
Bandipora	NA	385099	201531	183568	967	320070	65029
Kupwara	650393	875564	475126	400438	368	776322	99242
Leh	117232	147104	92907	54197	3	83901	63203
Kargil	119307	143388	80791	62597	10	130635	12753
Jammu	1588772	1526406	815727	710679	653	768577	757829
Samba	NA	318611	168948	149663	350	264990	53621
Kathua	550084	615711	327953	287758	246	527176	88535

(Contd...)

Poonch	372613	476820	252240	224580	284	438176	38644
Rajouri	483284	619266	332424	286842	235	575332	43934
Udhampur	743509	555357	298094	257263	224	445850	109507
Reasi	NA	314714	166392	148322	185	288010	26704
Doda	691929	409576	213091	196485	137	377003	32573
Kishtwar	NA	231037	120496	110541	29	216196	14841
Ramban	NA	283313	149032	134281	210	271527	11786
Total	**10143700**	**12548926**	**6665561**	**5883365**	**124**	**9134820**	**3414106**

Source: http://www.jkenvis.nic.in/administrative_demography.html

According to recent Census of India 2011, Population of Himachal Pradesh was 6,856,509. These further include 3,473,892 males and 3,382,617 females in the state. Population of Himachal Pradesh is growing at a descent rate as compared to growth in other states of India.

From a small figure of 50,671,017 in 2001, the population of Gujarat has gone to 60,383,628 in 2011. Population growth has witnessed an increase of 19.17 in this decade. Out of this figures, total male population stands at 31,482,282 and female at 28,901,346 in state of Gujarat. According to recently concluded Census of India in 2011, the total number of people living in Gujarat in 2011 was 60,383,628. These include 31,482,282 males and 28,901,346 females.

Table 10: Population of Himachal Pradesh

Name	***Population***			***Growth Rate 2001-2011***	***Density (per Sq. Km)***		***Sex Ratio***	
	Persons	***Males***	***Females***					
Himachal Pradesh	***68,56,509***	***34,73,892***	***33,82,617***	***+12.81***	***109***	***123***	***968***	***974***
Chamba	5,18,844	2,60,848	2,57,996	+12.58	71	80	959	989
Kangra	15,07,223	7,48,559	7,58,664	+12.56	233	263	1025	1013
Lahul & Spiti	31,528	16,455	15,073	-5.10	2	2	802	916
Kullu	4,37,474	2,24,320	2,13,154	+14.65	69	79	927	950
Mandi	9,99,518	4,96,787	5,02,731	+10.89	228	253	1013	1012
Hamirpur	4,54,293	2,16,742	2,37,551	+10.08	369	406	1099	1096
Una	5,21,057	2,63,541	2,57,516	+16.24	291	338	997	977
Bilaspur	3,82,056	1,92,827	1,89,229	+12.08	292	327	990	981
Solan	5,76,670	3,06,162	2,70,508	+15.21	259	298	852	884
Sirmaur	5,30,164	2,76,801	2,53,363	+15.61	162	188	901	915
Shimla	8,13,384	4,24,486	3,88,898	+12.58	141	159	896	916
Kinnaur	84,298	46,364	37,934	+07.61	12	13	857	818

Source:http://www.indiaonlinepages.com/population/himachal-pradesh-population. htm

Table 11: Population of Gujarat

State/District	*Population 2011*			*Sex Ratio*	*Population density per sq. km.*
	Persons	*Males*	*Females*	*2011*	*2011*
Gujarat	**60,383,628**	**31,482,282**	**28,901,346**	**918**	**308**
Kachchh	2,090,313	1,096,343	993,970	907	46
Banaskantha	3,116,045	1,609,148	1,506,897	936	290
Patan	1,342,746	694,062	648,684	935	234
Mahesana	2,027,727	1,053,337	974,390	925	462
Sabarkantha	2,427,346	1,244,491	1,182,855	950	328
Gandhinagar	1,387,478	722,459	665,019	920	660
Ahmedabad	7,208,200	3,787,050	3,421,150	903	890
Surendranagar	1,755,873	910,266	845,607	929	167
Rajkot	3,799,770	1,975,131	1,824,639	924	339
Jamnagar	2,159,130	1,114,360	1,044,770	938	153
Porbandar	586,062	300,967	285,095	947	255
Junagadh	2,742,291	1,404,506	1,337,785	952	310
Amreli	1,513,614	770,651	742,963	964	205
Bhavnagar	2,877,961	1,490,465	1,387,496	931	288
Anand	2,090,276	1,088,253	1,002,023	921	711
Kheda	2,298,934	1,187,098	1,111,836	937	541
Panch Mahals	2,388,267	1,227,805	1,160,462	945	458
Dohad	2,126,558	1,070,843	1,055,715	986	582
Vadodara	4,157,568	2,150,229	2,007,339	934	551
Narmada	590,379	301,270	289,109	960	214
Bharuch	1,550,822	805,945	744,877	924	238
The Dangs	226,769	112,976	113,793	1007	129
Navsari	1,330,711	678,423	652,288	961	602
Valsad	1,703,068	884,064	819,004	926	561
Surat	6,079,231	3,399,742	2,679,489	788	1376
Tapi	806,489	402398	404091	1004	249

Source: http://www.indiaonlinepages.com/population/gujarat-population.html

According to the 2001 census of India, the total population of Karnataka was 52,850,562, of which 26,898,918 (50.9 per cent) were male and 25,951,644 (49.1 per cent) were female, or 1000 males for every 964 females. This represents a 17.3 per cent increase over the population in 1991. The population density was 275.6 per km^2 and 34.0 per cent of the people lived in urban areas.

Table 12: Current Population of Karnataka

Districts	*Population in 2011*			*Growth Rate 2001-2011*	*Density (per Sq. Km)*	*Sex Ratio (females per 1000 males)*
Name	*Persons*	*Males*	*Females*	*2001-2011*	*2011*	*2011*
Karnataka	6,11,30,704	3,10,57,742	3,00,72,962	15.67	319	968
Belgaum	47,78,439	24,27,104	23,51,335	13.38	356	969
Bagalkot	18,90,826	9,52,902	9,37,924	14.46	288	984
Bijapur	21,75,102	11,12,953	1,06,21,49	20.38	207	954
Bidar	17,00,018	8,70,850	8,29,168	13.16	312	952
Raichur	19,24,773	9,66,493	9,58,280	15.27	228	992
Koppal	13,91,292	7,01,479	6,89,813	16.32	250	983
Gadag	10,65,235	5,38,477	5,26,758	9.61	229	978
Dharwad	18,46,993	9,39,127	9,07,866	15.13	434	967
Uttara Kannada	14,36,847	7,27,424	7,09,423	6.15	140	975
Haveri	15,8,506	8,19,295	7,79,211	11.08	331	951
Bellary	25,32,383	12,80,402	12,51,981	24.92	300	978
Chitradurga	16,60,378	8,43,411	8,16,967	9.39	197	969
Davanagere	19,46,905	9,89,602	9,57,303	8.71	329	967
Shimoga	17,55,512	8,79,817	8,75,695	6.88	207	995
Udupi	11,77,908	5,62,896	6,15,012	5.90	304	1,093
Chikmagalur	11,37,753	5,67,483	5,70,270	-0.28	158	1005
Tumkur	26,81,449	13,54,770	13,26,679	3.74	253	979
Bangalore	95,88,910	50,25,498	45,63,412	46.68	4,378	908
Mandya	18,08,680	9,09,441	8,99,239	2.55	365	989
Hassan	17,76,221	8,85,807	8,90,414	3.17	261	1,005
Dakshina Kannada	20,83,625	10,32,577	10,51,048	9.80	457	1,018
Kodagu	5,54,762	2,74,725	2,80,037	1.13	135	1,019
Mysore	29,94,744	15,11,206	14,83,538	13.39	437	982
Chamarajanagar	10,20,962	5,13,359	5,07,603	5.75	200	989
Gulbarga	25,64,892	13,07,061	12,57,831	17.94	233	962
Yadgir	11,72,985	5,91,104	5,81,881	22.67	224	984
Kolar	15,40,231	7,79,401	7,60,830	11.04	384	976
Chikkaballapura	12,54,377	6,37,504	6,16,873	9.17	298	968
Bangalore Rural	9,87,257	5,07,514	4,79,743	16.02	441	945
Ramanagara	10,82,739	5,48,060	5,34,679	5.06	303	976

Source: http://www.indiaonlinepages.com/population/karnataka-population.html

As of 2011 Census of India, the Andhra Pradesh had a population of 49,386,799 with a population density of 308/km^2 (800/sq mi). The total population constitutes 70.4 per cent of rural population with 34,776,389 inhabitants and 29.6 per cent of urban population with 14,610,410 inhabitants.

Table 13: Population in Andhra Pradesh (2011 Census)

District	*Population*	*Growth Rate (per cent)*	*Sex Ratio*	*Literacy (per cent)*	*Density*
Rangareddy	5,296,741	48.16	961	75.87	707
East Godavari	5,154,296	5.16	1006	70.99	477
Guntur	4,887,813	9.47	1003	67.40	429
Krishna	4,517,398	7.87	992	73.74	518
Visakhapatnam	4,290,589	11.96	1006	66.91	384
Chittoor	4,174,064	11.43	997	71.53	275
Anantapur	4,081,148	12.10	977	63.57	213
Kurnool	4,053,463	14.85	988	59.97	230
Mahbubnagar	4,053,028	15.34	977	55.04	220
Hyderabad	3,943,323	2.97	954	83.25	18172
West Godavari	3,936,966	3.51	1004	74.63	509
Karimnagar	3,776,269	8.15	1008	64.15	319
Warangal	3,512,576	8.21	997	65.11	273
Nalgonda	3,488,809	7.41	983	64.20	245
Prakasam	3,397,448	11.05	981	63.08	193
Medak	3,033,288	13.60	992	61.42	313
Sri Potti Sriramulu Nellore	2,963,557	11.05	985	68.90	227
YSR	2,882,469	10.79	985	67.30	188
Khammam	2,797,370	8.47	1011	64.81	175
Adilabad	2,741,239	10.18	1001	61.01	170
Srikakulam	2,703,114	6.52	1015	61.74	463
Nizamabad	2,551,335	8.77	1040	61.25	321
Vizianagaram	2,344,474	4.23	1019	58.89	359

Source: http://www.census2011.co.in/census/state/districtlist/andhra+pradesh.html

Chhattisgarh is primarily a rural state with only 20 per cent of population (around 5.1 million people in 2011) residing in urban areas. According to the report from the government of India, at least 34 per cent are Scheduled Tribes, 12 per cent are Scheduled Castes and over 50 per cent belong to official list of OBC.

Table 14: Population of Chhattisgarh (2011 Census)

District	*Population*	*Male Population*	*Female Population*	*Growth*	*Sex Ratio*	*Literacy*	*Density*
Bastar	1411644	697359	714285	17.83	1024	54.94	140
Bijapur	255180	128761	126419	8.76	982	41.58	39
Bilaspur	2662077	1349928	1312149	33.21	972	71.59	322
Dantewada	532791	263562	269229	11.9	1022	42.67	59
Dhamtari	799199	397250	401949	13.11	1012	78.95	236
Durg	3343079	1681521	1661558	18.95	988	79.69	391
Janjgir Champa	1620632	816057	804575	23.01	986	73.7	421
Jashpur	852043	425085	426958	14.65	1004	68.6	146
Kabirdham	822239	411637	410602	40.66	997	61.95	195
Kanker	748593	372987	375606	15	1007	70.97	115
Korba	1206563	612158	594405	19.25	971	73.22	183
Korea	659039	334336	324703	12.4	971	71.41	100
Mahasamund	1032275	511475	520800	20	1018	71.54	216
Narayanpur	140206	70189	70017	19.49	998	49.59	20
Raigarh	1493627	749439	744188	18.02	993	73.7	211
Raipur	4062160	2048856	2013304	34.65	983	76.43	310
Rajnandgaon	1537520	762170	775350	19.82	1017	76.97	191
Surguja	2361329	1195145	1166184	19.74	976	61.16	150

Source: http://www.mapsofindia.com/census2011/chhattisgarh-sex-ratio.html

Maharashtra occupies the western and central part of the country and has a long coastline stretching nearly 720 kilometres along the Arabian Sea. According to the provisional results of the 2011 national census, Maharashtra is the second most populous state in India with a population of 112,374,333 (9.28 per cent of India's population) of which male and female are 58,243,056 and 54,131,277 respectively.

Table 15: Population in Maharashtra

State/District Name	*Population 2011*			*Percentage Decadal Growth Rate of Population*	*Sex Ratio (Number of Females per 1000 Males)*
	Persons	*Males*	*Females*	*2001-11*	*2011*
Nandurbar	1646177	834866	811311	25.50	972
Dhule	2048781	1055669	993112	19.96	941
Jalgaon	4224442	2197835	2026607	14.71	922
Buldana	2588039	1342152	1245887	15.93	928

(Contd...)

Akola	1818617	936226	882391	11.60	942
Washim	1196714	621228	575486	17.23	926
Amravati	2887826	1482845	1404981	10.77	947
Wardha	1296157	665925	630232	4.80	946
Nagpur	4653171	2388558	2264613	14.39	948
Bhandara	1198810	604371	594439	5.52	984
Gondiya	1322331	662524	659807	10.13	996
Gadchiroli	1071795	542813	528982	10.46	975
Chandrapur	2194262	1120316	1073946	5.95	959
Yavatmal	2775457	1425593	1349864	12.90	947
Nanded	3356566	1732567	1623999	16.70	937
Hingoli	1178973	609386	569587	19.43	935
Parbhani	1835982	946185	889797	20.18	940
Jalna	1958483	1015116	943367	21.84	929
Aurangabad	3695928	1928156	1767772	27.33	917
Nashik	6109052	3164261	2944791	22.33	931
Thane	11054131	5879387	5174744	35.94	880
Mumbai (Suburban)	9332481	5025165	4307316	8.01	857
Mumbai	3145966	1711650	1434316	-5.75	838
Raigarh	2635394	1348089	1287305	19.36	955
Pune	9426959	4936362	4490597	30.34	910
Bid	2585962	1352468	1233494	19.65	912
Latur	2455543	1276262	1179281	18.04	924
Osmanabad	1660311	864674	795637	11.69	920
Solapur	4315527	2233778	2081749	12.10	932
Satara	3003922	1512524	1491398	6.94	986
Ratnagiri	1612672	759703	852969	-4.96	1123
Sindhudurg	848868	416695	432173	-2.30	1037
Kolhapur	3874015	1983274	1890741	9.96	953
Sangli	2820575	1435972	1384603	9.18	964

*Source:*http://www.indiaonlinepages.com/population/population-of-maharashtra.html

From 1951 to 1991, population growth in Kerala was steady, from there on there has been a decrease in the population growth rate. Between 1991 to 2001, there was a growth of 9.4 per cent in population of Kerala; this further was down to 4.9 per cent in last finished Census of 2011.

Table 16: Population in Kerala (2011 Census)

District	*Population*	*Males*	*Females*
Thiruvananthapuram	33,07,284	15,84,200	17,23,084
Kollam	26,29,703	1244815	1384888
Alappuzha	2121943	1010252	1111691
Pathanamthitta	1195537	561620	633917
Kottayam	1979384	970140	1009244
Idukki	1107453	551944	555509
Ernakulam	3279860	1617602	1662258
Thrissur	3110327	1474665	1635662
Palakkad	2810892	1360067	1450825
Kozhikode	3089543	1473028	1616515
Wayanad	816558	401314	415244
Malappuram	4110956	1961014	2124942
Kannur	2525637	1184012	1341625
Kasargod	1302600	626617	675983
Total	**33387677**	**16021290**	**17366387**

Source: http://www.prokerala.com/kerala/population.htm

According to the 2001 census, the total number of workers in Tamil Nadu amounts to 27,878,282 with the Work Participation rate being 44.67 per cent. The total number of non-workers amounts to 34,527,397 or 55.33 per cent of the population.

Table 17: Population in Tamil Nadu

District	*Population (2011)*	*Growth*	*Sex Ratio*	*Literacy*	*Area (km^2)*	*Density (/km^2)*
Ariyalur	754894	8.54	1015	71.34	3208	387
Chennai	4646732	6.98	989	90.18	174	26903
Coimbatore	3458045	18.56	1000	83.98	7469	748
Cuddalore	2605914	14.02	987	78.04	3999	702
Dharmapuri	1506843	16.34	946	68.54	4532	332
Dindigul	2159775	12.31	998	76.26	6058	357
Erode	2251744	11.66	993	72.58	5714	397
Kancheepuram	3998252	38.95	986	84.49	4433	927
Kanniyakumari	1870374	11.60	1019	91.75	1685	1106
Karur	1064493	13.77	1015	75.6	2901	371

(Contd...)

Krishnagiri	1879809	20.41	958	71.46	5086	370
Madurai	3038252	17.84	990	83.45	3676	823
Nagapattinam	1616450	8.57	1025	83.59	2716	668
Namakkal	1726601	15.61	986	74.63	3429	506
Perambalur	565223	14.50	1003	74.32	1752	323
Pudukkottai	1618345	10.8	1015	77.19	4651	348
Ramanathapuram	1353445	13.96	983	80.72	4123	320
Salem	3482056	15.44	954	72.86	5245	663
Sivaganga	1339101	15.90	1003	79.85	4086	324
Thanjavur	2405890	8.56	1035	82.64	3397	691
The Nilgiris	735394	-3.51	1042	85.2	2549	288
Theni	1245899	13.89	991	77.26	3066	433
Thiruvallur	3728104	35.33	987	84.03	3424	1049
Thiruvarur	1264277	8.11	1017	82.86	2377	533
Thoothukkudi	1750176	11.32	1023	86.16	4594	378
Tiruchirappalli	2722290	12.57	1013	83.23	4407	602
Tirunelveli	3077233	12.97	1023	82.5	6703	458
Tiruppur	2479052	29.11	989	78.68	5106	476
Tiruvannamalai	2464875	12.75	994	74.21	6191	399
Vellore	3936331	13.20	1007	79.17	6077	646
Viluppuram	3458873	16.84	987	71.88	7190	462
Virudhunagar	1942288	10.91	1007	80.15	3446	454

Source: http://www.mapsofindia.com/maps/tamilnadu/districts/

A comprehensive Pew Research Centre study shows that by 2050, India will surpass Indonesia to have the largest Muslim population by any country in the world. However, India will continue to have a Hindu majority, the study noted. The Muslim population in India is likely to exceed 18 per cent (310 million) while Hindus will comprise of 77 per cent of the country's population. In 2010, the percentage of Hindus in the country was about 80 per cent, which is likely to come down to 77 per cent. At the same time, over the course of four decades, the Muslim population will increase by four percentage points from 14 per cent to 18 per cent.

As of 2010, Indonesia has the largest Muslim population (209 million) followed by India (176 million) and Pakistan (167 million). The largest share of Hindus as of 2010 is in India, followed by Nepal and Bangladesh. By 2050, India and Nepal will be the only two countries with a majority Hindu population, the same situation as of 2010, the study said. Globally, the most interesting aspect from the study is the fact that by 2050, the number of Muslims will nearly equal the number of Christians in the world.

Over the course of four decades, while Christians will go from 2.17 to 2.92 billion in India, Muslims are seen to have the fastest pace of growth to go from 1.6 billion to 2.76 billion. The study notes that Hindus will go from 1.03 billion to 1.38 billion. The world's total population itself is expected to rise up to 9.3 billion, a rise of 35 per cent. Region-wise, Muslims are likely to be dominant in the Asia-Pacific region but their size itself will reduce from 62 per cent in 2010 to 53 per cent in 2050. They are also projected to surpass Hindus as the largest religious group in the region. Hindus will also be predominantly living in the Asia-Pacific region by 2050.[57]

Rapidly increasing population exacerbates existing problems, such as transnational crime, economic interdependency, climate change, the spread of diseases such as HIV/AIDS and various other pandemics, and such social issues as gender equality, reproductive health, safe motherhood, human rights, emergency situations, and so much more. The UN Population Fund was established in 1973 to assume a leading role within the UN system in promoting population programmes. At the International Conference on Population and Development, its mandate was fleshed out in greater detail, to give more emphasis to the gender and human rights dimensions of population issues, and UNFPA was given the lead role in helping countries carry out the Conference's Programme of Action.[58]

Rapid human population growth has a variety of consequences. Population grows fastest in the world's poorest countries. High fertility rates have historically been strongly correlated with poverty and high childhood mortality rates. Falling fertility rates are generally associated with improved standards of living, increased life expectancy, and lowered infant mortality. Overpopulation and poverty have long been associated with increased death, and disease. People tightly packed into unsanitary housing are inordinately vulnerable to natural disasters and health problems. Poverty is a condition of chronic deprivation and need at the family level. Rich and poor countries alike are affected by population growth, though the population of industrial countries is growing more slowly than those of developing one[59].

Over population leads to number of not only national but also individual's family problems. If in a family there are more persons and the income is less, so naturally it becomes poor. With the addition of every child, the poverty increases. If the population increases and the production of food do not increase, this will lead to a shortage of food supply. More number of people means more jobs and if sufficient number of jobs is not available, it leads to unemployment. More people in a small area generally make the hygienic conditions bad. It becomes difficult for the government to provide education to all.[60]

Global Warming

Global warming and climate change are terms for the observed century-scale rise in the average temperature of the Earth's climate system and its related effects. It is the increase of Earth's average surface temperature due to effect of greenhouse gases, such as carbon dioxide emissions from burning fossil fuels or from deforestation, which trap heat that would otherwise escape from Earth. It is the increase of Earth's average surface temperature due to effect of greenhouse gases, such as carbon dioxide emissions from burning fossil fuels or from deforestation, which trap heat that would otherwise escape from Earth. This is a type of greenhouse effect.[61]

Global warming can be defined as an increase in the earth's atmospheric, oceanic temperatures and an overall change in earth's atmosphere including a rise in sea levels and variability of snow falls. Climate change and associated impacts vary from region to region around the globe. Due to increase in the greenhouse effect resulting especially from pollution and other activities such as, greenhouse gas emissions produced by human activities mainly industrial processes and transportation.[62]

There is great debate among many people, and sometimes in the news, on whether global warming is real. But climate scientists looking at the data and facts agree the planet is warming. While many view the effects of global warming to be more substantial and more rapidly occurring than others do, the scientific consensus on climatic changes related to global warming is that the average temperature of the Earth has risen between 0.4 and 0.8 °C over the past 100 years.[63] Global warming is primarily a problem of too much carbon dioxide in the atmosphere—which acts as a blanket, trapping heat and warming the planet. As we burn fossil fuels like coal, oil and natural gas for energy or cut down and burn forests to create pastures and plantations, carbon accumulates and overloads our atmosphere.[64]

Methane is another extremely potent greenhouse gas, ranking right behind CO_2. When organic matter is broken down by bacteria under oxygen-starved conditions (anaerobic decomposition) as in rice paddies, methane is produced. As methane escapes from the Arctic seabed, the rate of global warming will increase significantly. Forests remove and store carbon dioxide from the atmosphere, and this deforestation releases large amounts of carbon, as well as reducing the amount of carbon capture on the planet. The high rate of application of nitrogen-rich fertilizers has effects on the heat storage of cropland and the run-off of excess fertilizers creates 'dead-zones' in our oceans. According to research published in *Nature,* by 2050, rising temperatures could lead to the extinction of more than a million species. And because we can't exist without a diverse population of species on Earth, this is scary news for humans.[65]

Atmospheric aerosols are able to alter climate in two important ways. First, they scatter and absorb solar and infrared radiation and, second, they may change the microphysical and chemical properties of clouds and possibly their lifetime and extent. The scattering of solar radiation acts to cool the planet, while absorption of solar radiation by aerosols warms the air directly instead of allowing sunlight to be absorbed by the surface of the Earth. The human contribution to the amount of aerosols in the atmosphere takes many forms. Dust is a byproduct of agriculture. Biomass burning produces a combination of organic droplets and soot particles.[66]

Regional effects of global warming vary in nature. Some are the result of a generalised global change, such as rising temperature, resulting in local effects, such as melting ice. In other cases, a change may be related to a change in a particular ocean current or weather system. There are three major ways in which global warming will make changes to regional climate: melting or forming ice, changing the hydrological cycle and changing currents in the oceans and air flows in the atmosphere. The coast can also be considered a region, and will suffer severe impacts from sea level rise. The impacts of climate change can be thought of in terms of sensitivity and vulnerability. Climate change will impact agriculture and food production around the world due to: the effects of elevated CO_2 in the atmosphere, higher temperatures, altered precipitation and transpiration regimes, increased frequency of extreme events, and modified weed, pest, and pathogen pressure. General circulation models project that the future climate change will bring wetter coasts, drier mid-continent areas, and further sea level rise.[67]

Average global sea level has increased eight inches since 1880, but is rising much faster on the U.S. East Coast and Gulf of Mexico. Global warming is now accelerating the rate of sea level rise, increasing flooding risks to low-lying communities and high-risk coastal properties whose development has been encouraged by today's flood insurance system.[68] Though Bangladesh has contributed little to industrial air pollution, other kinds of environmental degradation have left it especially vulnerable. Bangladesh relies almost entirely on groundwater for drinking supplies because the rivers are so polluted. The resultant pumping causes the land to settle. So as sea levels are rising, Bangladesh's cities are sinking, increasing the risks of flooding. Poorly constructed seawalls compound the problem.[69]

Climate change is already responsible for 300,000 deaths a year and is affecting 300 m people, according to the first comprehensive study of the human impact of global warming. It projects that increasingly severe heat waves, floods, storms and forest fires will be responsible for as many as 500,000 deaths a year by 2030, making it the greatest humanitarian challenge the world faces. Nobel peace prize winner Wangari Maathai, said: "Climate change is life or death. It is the new global battlefield. It is being presented as if it is the problem of the developed world. But it's the developed world that has precipitated global warming."

As the concentration of greenhouse gases grows, more heat is trapped in the atmosphere and less escapes back into space. This increase in trapped heat changes the climate and alters weather patterns, which may hasten species extinction, influence the length of seasons, cause coastal flooding, and lead to more frequent and severe storms. The climate is changing, but so are the political and business climates. There's a path forward, and thousands of people like you are helping but not by doing things like recycling and buying local produce.

Deforestation is the cutting down of trees and plants to make way for any development activity. Mother Nature taking out an entire forest is one thing, but man doing it for the use of crop cultivation, fuel, and other consumption, is another. This means that it is very important to protect our trees to stop the greenhouse effect, and also so we can breathe and live. It is blamed for rise in the greenhouse gases present in the atmosphere by cutting or burning them. New development projects, requirement of land for homes and factories, requirement for wood and also soil erosion are the major factors that are causing deforestation, which in turn leading to global warming.[70]

Climate Change

Climate change means that the average weather on Earth is different than it used to be. Consequences of a changed climate can include freak weather, increased flooding, hotter heat waves, stronger hurricanes and more droughts. It is a change in the statistical distribution of weather patterns when that change lasts for an extended period of time (i.e., decades to millions of years). Such change may refer to a change in average weather conditions, or in the time variation of weather around longer-term average conditions. The changes in weather create still more results. For instance, more droughts create the dry conditions that fuel massive wildfires. Meanwhile, climate change affects Earth's biodiversity, and biodiversity is needed for healthy ecosystems.[71]

A wide range of other observations provides a more comprehensive picture of warming throughout the climate system. For example, the lower atmosphere and the upper layers of the ocean have also warmed, snow and ice cover are decreasing in the Northern Hemisphere, the Greenland ice sheet is shrinking, and sea level is rising. These measurements are made with a variety of monitoring systems, which gives added confidence in the reality that Earth's climate is warming.[72]

Climate variability and change affects birdlife and animals in a number of ways; birds lay eggs earlier in the year than usual, plants bloom earlier and mammals are come out of hibernation sooner. Distribution of animals is also affected; with many species moving closer to the poles as a response to the rise in global temperatures. Birds are migrating and arriving at their nesting grounds earlier, and the nesting grounds that they are moving to are not as far away as they used to be and in some countries the birds do not even leave anymore, as the climate is suitable all year round.[73] Scientists generally define the five components of earth's climate system to include atmosphere, hydrosphere, cryosphere, lithosphere, and biosphere.

The atmosphere of Earth is the layer of gases surrounding the planet Earth that is retained by Earth's gravity. The common name air is given to the atmospheric gases used in breathing and photosynthesis. Solar radiation is the energy Earth receives from the Sun. Earth also emits radiation back into space, but at longer wavelengths that we cannot see. Atmospheric circulation is the large-scale movement of air through the troposphere, and the means by which heat is distributed around Earth.

The hydrosphere in physical geography describes the combined mass of water found on, under, and over the surface of a planet. The hydrological cycle transfers water from one state or reservoir to another. Reservoirs include atmospheric moisture (snow, rain and clouds) oceans, rivers, lakes, groundwater, subterranean aquifers, polar icecaps and saturated soil.

The cryosphere is those portions of Earth's surface where water is in solid form, including sea ice, lake ice, river ice, snow cover, glaciers, ice caps, ice sheets, and frozen ground.The lithosphere is the solid outer section of Earth, which includes Earth's crust (the "skin" of rock on the outer layer of planet Earth), as well as the underlying cool, dense, and rigid upper part of the upper mantle. The lithosphere extends from the surface of Earth to a depth of about 44–62 mi (70–100 km).The biosphere is the global sum of all ecosystems. It can also be termed as the zone of life on Earth, a closed system (apart from solar and cosmic radiator and heat from the interior of the Earth), and largely self-regulating (wikipedia).

Most climate scientists agree the main cause of the current global warming trend is human expansion of the "greenhouse effect." Certain gases in the atmosphere block heat from escaping. Long-lived gases that remain semi-permanently in the atmosphere and do not respond physically or chemically to changes in temperature are described as "forcing" climate change. On Earth, human activities are changing the natural greenhouse. Over the last century the burning of fossil fuels like coal and oil has increased the concentration of atmospheric carbon dioxide.[74]

Rising fossil fuel burning and land use changes have emitted, and are continuing to emit, increasing quantities of greenhouse gases into the Earth's atmosphere. These greenhouse gases include carbon dioxide, methane and nitrogen dioxide, and a rise in these gases has caused a rise in the amount of heat from the sun withheld in the Earth's atmosphere, heat that would normally be radiated back into space. At the centre of efforts to address climate change on the international stage is the United Nations Framework Convention on Climate Change. It provides the basis for concerted international action to mitigate climate change and to adapt to its impacts. Its provisions are far-sighted, innovative and firmly embedded in the concept of sustainable development.[75]

The Earth's climate can be affected by natural factors that are external to the climate system, such as changes in volcanic activity, solar output, and the Earth's orbit around the Sun. Of these, the two factors relevant on timescales of contemporary climate change are changes in volcanic activity and changes in solar radiation.[76] Greenland and Antarctic ice sheets are melting. Unless checked, warming from emissions may trigger the irreversible meltdown of the Greenland ice sheet in the coming decades, which would add up to a seven meters rise in sea-level over some centuries. New evidence showing the rate of ice discharge from parts of the Antarctic means that it is also facing a risk of meltdown. The greatest impacts will be on the poorer countries least able to protect themselves from rising sea levels. There will be spread of disease and declines in agricultural production in the developing countries of Africa, Asia and the Pacific.[77]

Among the most serious and potentially catastrophic effects of global warming is sea level rise, caused by a combination of melting glaciers all over the world and the "thermal expansion" of the seas as oceans warm. By the end of the century, if nothing is done to rein in emissions of greenhouse gases, global sea level may be three feet higher than today and rising. Rising sea level will have severe impacts in low-lying coastal communities throughout the world. Scientists predict that climate change will have a significant effect on global weather patterns, causing both more floods and more droughts. Other weather impacts from climate change include a higher incidence of drought and flooding and changes in precipitation patterns. A recent United Nations report blamed climate change, along with worsening air and water quality and poor disposal of solid waste, for an increase in malaria, cholera and lower respiratory tract infections in African societies. Africans also are suffering from the effects of reduced crop yields and decreased availability of water.[78]

The potential future effects of global climate change include more frequent wildfires, longer periods of drought in some regions and an increase in the number, duration and intensity of tropical storms. Global climate change has already had observable effects on the environment. Some of the most dangerous consequences of climate change are[79]:

(a) **Higher Temperature:** High temperatures are to blame for an increase in heat-related deaths and illness, rising seas, increased storm intensity, and many of the other dangerous consequences of climate change. During the twentieth century, the Earth's average temperature rose one degree Fahrenheit to its highest level in the past four centuries – believed to be the fastest rise in a thousand years.[80]

(b) **Changing Landscapes:** Rising temperatures and changing patterns of rain and snow are forcing trees and plants around the world to move toward Polar Regions and up mountain slopes. These vegetation shifts will undermine much of the work the conservation community has accomplished to date, with the potential to permanently change the face of Conservancy preserves, local land trusts, and even our national parks.[81]

(c) **Wildlife at Risk:** Rising temperatures are changing weather and vegetation patterns across the globe, forcing animal species to migrate to new, cooler areas in order to survive. The rapid nature of climate change is likely to exceed the ability of many species to migrate or adjust. Experts predict that one-fourth of Earth's species will be headed for extinction by 2050 if the warming trend continues at its current rate.[82]

(d) Rising Seas: Rising seas has threatened to inundate low-lying areas and islands, threaten dense coastal populations, erode shorelines, damage property and destroy ecosystems such as mangroves and wetlands that protect coasts against storms. Sea levels have risen between four and eight inches in the past 100 years. Current projections suggest that sea levels could continue to rise between 4 inches and 36 inches over the next 100 years. Sea level rise associated with climate change could displace tens of millions of people in low-lying areas – especially in developing countries.[83]

(e) Increased Risk of Drought, Fire, and Floods: Higher temperatures increase the amount of moisture that evaporates from land and water, leading to drought in many areas. As temperatures rise globally, droughts will become more frequent and more severe, with potentially devastating consequences for agriculture, water supply and human health. Hot temperatures and dry conditions also increase the likelihood of forest fires.[84]

(f) Stronger Storms and Hurricanes: Scientists point to higher ocean temperatures as the main culprit, since hurricanes and tropical storms get their energy from warm water. As sea surface temperatures rise, developing storms will contain more energy.[85]

(g) Heat-Related Illness and Disease: As temperatures rise, so do the risks of heat-related illness and even death for the most vulnerable human populations. In addition to heat-related illness, climate change may increase the spread of infectious diseases, mainly because warmer temperatures allow disease-carrying insects, animals and microbes to survive in areas where they were once thwarted by cold weather.[86]

(h) Economic Loss and Damage: Climate change is affecting businesses and economies at home and around the world. Globally, more intense hurricanes and downpours could cause billions of dollars in damage to property and infrastructure. Declining crop yields due to prolonged drought and high temperatures, especially in Africa, could put hundreds of thousands of people at risk for starvation.[87]

Green House Effect

Greenhouse gases are those that absorb and emit infrared radiation in the wavelength range emitted by Earth. In order, the most abundant greenhouse gases in Earth's atmosphere are:

(a) Water vapour (H_2O): It is the gaseous phase of water. It is one state of water within the hydrosphere. Water vapour can be produced from the evaporation or boiling of liquid water or from the sublimation of ice. Unlike other forms of water, water vapour is invisible. Water vapour is a significant component of the Earth's atmosphere and a greenhouse gas. It is also common in the Solar System and by extension, other planetary systems. Its signature has been detected in the atmospheres of the Sun, occurring in sunspots. Measuring the quantity of water vapour in a medium can be done directly or remotely with varying degrees of accuracy. Remote methods such electromagnetic absorption are possible from satellites above planetary atmospheres. Direct methods may use electronic transducers, moistened thermometers or hygroscopic materials measuring changes in physical properties or dimensions.[88]

(b) **Carbon dioxide (CO_2):** It is a colourless, odourless gas vital to life on Earth. It exists in the Earth's atmosphere as a trace gas at a concentration of about 0.04 per cent by volume. Atmospheric carbon dioxide is the primary source of carbon in life on Earth and its concentration in Earth's pre-industrial atmosphere since late in the Precambrian was regulated by photosynthetic organisms. Carbon dioxide is an important greenhouse gas. Burning of carbon-based fuels since the industrial revolution has rapidly increased its concentration in the atmosphere, leading to global warming. It is colourless. Carbon dioxide can be obtained by distillation from air, but the method is inefficient. Liquid carbon dioxide is a good solvent for many lipophilic organic compounds and is used to remove caffeine from coffee. Carbon dioxide has attracted attention in the pharmaceutical and other chemical processing industries as a less toxic alternative to more traditional solvents such as organ chlorides.[89]

(c) **Methane (CH_4):** It is the simplest alkane and the main component of natural gas. The relative abundance of methane on Earth makes it an attractive fuel, though capturing and storing it poses challenges due to its gaseous state found at standard conditions for temperature and pressure. Methane is used in industrial chemical processes and may be transported as a refrigerated liquid (liquefied natural gas, or LNG). While leaks from a refrigerated liquid container are initially heavier than air due to the increased density of the cold gas, the gas at ambient temperature is lighter than air. Gas pipelines distribute large amounts of natural gas, of which methane is the principal component. Naturally occurring methane is mainly produced by the process of methanogenesis. This multistep process is used by microorganisms as an energy source. Methane was discovered and isolated by Alessandro Volta between 1776 and 1778 when studying marsh gas from Lake Maggiore. It is the major component of natural gas, about 87 per cent by volume.[90]

(d) **Nitrous oxide (N_2O):**It is an oxide of nitrogen. At room temperature, it is a colourless, non-flammable gas, with a slightly sweet odour and taste. It is used in surgery and dentistry for it's an aesthetic and analgesic effects. It is known as "laughing gas" due to the euphoric effects of inhaling it. Nitrous oxide has been the oxidiser of choice in several hybrid rocket designs (using solid fuel with a liquid or gaseous oxidizer). The major safety hazards of nitrous oxide come from the fact that it is a compressed liquefied gas, an asphyxiation risk, and a dissociative an aesthetic. Exposure to nitrous oxide causes short-term decreases in mental performance, audiovisual ability, and manual dexterity. Nitrous oxide is most commonly prepared by careful heating of ammonium nitrate, which decomposes into nitrous oxide and water vapour.[91]

(e) **Ozone (O_3):** In 1785, Dutch chemist Martinus van Marum was conducting experiments involving electrical sparking above water when he noticed an unusual smell, which he attributed to the electrical reactions, failing to realise he had in fact created ozone. Ozone is a powerful oxidizing agent, far stronger than O_2. It is also unstable at high concentrations, decaying to ordinary diatomic oxygen. It has a varying half-life length, depending upon atmospheric conditions (temperature, humidity, and air movement). In a sealed chamber with a fan that moves the gas, ozone has a half-life of approximately a day at room temperature. The standard way to express total ozone levels in the atmosphere is by using Dobson units. Point measurements are reported as mole fractions in nmol/mol (parts per billion, ppb) or as concentrations in ìg/m^3. The study of ozone concentration in the atmosphere started in the 1920s.[92]

(f) **Chlorofluorocarbons (CFCs):** It is an organic compound that produced as a volatile derivative of methane, ethane, and propane. They are also commonly known by the DuPont brand name Freon. Since the late 1970s, the use of CFCs has been heavily regulated because of their destructive effects on the ozone layer. After the development of his electron capture detector, James Lovelock was the first to detect the widespread presence of CFCs in the air, finding a mole fraction of 60 of CFC-11 over Ireland. CFCs were phased out via the Montreal Protocol due to their part in ozone depletion. The atmospheric impacts of CFCs are not limited to its role as an active ozone reducer. This anthropogenic compound is also a greenhouse

> gas, with a much higher potential to enhance the greenhouse effect than CO_2. Chlorofluorocarbons are anthropogenic compounds that have been released into the atmosphere since the 1930s in various applications such as in air-conditioning, refrigeration, blowing agents in foams, insulations and packing materials, propellants in aerosol cans, and as solvents.[93]

In a greenhouse, energy from the sun passes through the glass as rays of light. This energy is absorbed by the plants, soil, and other objects in the greenhouse. Much of this absorbed energy is converted to heat, which warms the greenhouse. The glass helps keep the greenhouse warm by trapping this heat.[94] The main effect of increases in atmospheric greenhouse gas concentrations is global warming. Carbon dioxide, methane, nitrous oxide and fluorinated gases all help trap heat in the Earth's atmosphere as a part of the greenhouse effect. Greenhouse gas levels have been increasing since the start of the Industrial Revolution, but over the last few decades' growth has been particularly fast. Global warming is harming the environment in several ways including desertification, increased melting of snow and ice, sea level rise, stronger storms and extreme events.[95]

The greenhouse effect is a major factor in keeping the Earth warm because it keeps some of the planet's heat that would otherwise escape from the atmosphere out to space. The greenhouse effect is the process by which radiation from a planet's atmosphere warms the planet's surface to a temperature above what it would be in the absence of its atmosphere. If a planet's atmosphere contains radiative active gases (i.e., greenhouse gases) the atmosphere radiates energy in all directions.

The *greenhouse effect* is the process by which radiation from a planet's atmosphere warms the planet's surface to a temperature above what it would be in the absence of its atmosphere. If a planet's atmosphere contains radiative active gases the atmosphere radiates energy in all directions. However, 97 per cent of climate scientists agree that humans have changed Earth's atmosphere in dramatic ways over the past two centuries, resulting in global warming. To understand global warming, it's first necessary to become familiar with the greenhouse effect, though. The greenhouse effect of the atmosphere is named by analogy to greenhouses which get warmer in sunlight.

The explanation given in most sources for the warmer temperature in an actual greenhouse is that incident solar radiation in the visible, long-wavelength ultraviolet, and short-wavelength infrared range of the spectrum passes through the glass roof and walls and is absorbed by the floor, earth, and contents, which become warmer and re-emit the energy as longer-wavelength infrared radiation.[96]

The greenhouse effect is useful because trapping some energy keeps the temperatures on our planet mild and suitable for living things. Without its atmosphere and the greenhouse effect, the average temperature at the surface of the Earth would be zero degrees Fahrenheit. However, too many greenhouse gases can cause the temperature to increase out of control. Such is the case on Venus where greenhouse gases are abundant and the average temperature at the surface is more than 855 degrees Fahrenheit (457 degrees Celsius).[97] Most greenhouse gases have both natural and human sources. According to the Intergovernmental Panel on Climate Change, human-caused GHG emissions disrupt the natural processes occurring in the atmosphere and are extremely likely to be the dominant cause of the observed warming that has occurred since the mid-twentieth century. Globally, almost 80 per cent of GHG emissions from human sources come from the burning of fossil fuels and industrial processes.[98]

Moreover, these greenhouse gases also have the property to trap heat. So more the greenhouse gases in the atmosphere, the more the Earth heats up. This result in melting of the polar ice caps, affecting the life there, also causing floods and massively affecting human life and causing destruction. Greenhouse gases are dangerous to the environment. The most prevalent greenhouse gas is carbon dioxide. Carbon dioxide and other greenhouse gases are released into the atmosphere by agricultural practices and by the burning of fossil fuels. Greenhouse gases can be seen in populated cities throughout the world, when a car is started and smoke is emitted from the muffler, and industries burning toxins in which they create. All of these gases are harmful to the environment.[99]

The greenhouse effect is a natural process that warms the Earth's surface. When the Sun's energy reaches the Earth's atmosphere, some of it is reflected back to space and the rest is absorbed and re-radiated by greenhouse gases. Greenhouse gases include water vapour, carbon dioxide, methane, nitrous oxide, ozone and some artificial chemicals such as chlorofluorocarbons. The absorbed energy warms the atmosphere and the surface of the Earth.[100] Several factors determine how strongly a particular greenhouse gas will affect the Earth's climate. One factor is the length of time that the gas remains in the atmosphere. A second factor is each gas's unique ability to absorb energy. By considering both of these factors, scientists calculate a gas's global warming potential, as compared to an equivalent mass of carbon dioxide.[101]

Predicting the consequences of global warming is one of the most difficult tasks for the world's climate researchers. This is because the natural processes that cause rain, hail and snow storms, increases in sea level and other expected effects of global warming are dependent on many different factors. When the weather gets warmer, evaporation from both land and sea increases. This can cause drought in areas of the world where the increased evaporation is not compensated for by more precipitation. Worldwide, glaciers are shrinking rapidly at present. Ice appears to be melting faster than previously estimated. In areas that are dependent on melt water from mountain areas, this can cause drought and lack of domestic water supply.[102]

The most recent report of the Intergovernmental Panel on Climate Change concluded that: "Our ability to quantify the human influence on global climate is currently limited because the expected signal is still emerging from the noise of natural variability, and because there are uncertainties in key factors. These include the magnitudes and patterns of long-term variability and the time-evolving pattern of forcing by, and response to, changes in concentrations of greenhouse gases and aerosols, and land surface changes. Nevertheless, the balance of evidence suggests that there is a discernible human influence on global climate."[103]

References

1. Brainy Quote, Available at http://www.brainyquote.com/quotes/keywords/environment.html
2. Natural environment (https://en.wikipedia.org/wiki/Natural_environment)
3. Environment (https://simple.wikipedia.org/wiki/Environment)
4. Environmental law (2015) (https://en.wikipedia.org/wiki/Environmental_law)
5. Environmental laws of India (http://www.environmentallawsofindia.com/the-environment-definitions-and-acts.html)
6. *Ibid.*
7. The National forest policy of India (http://www.vajiramandravi.in/the-national-forest-policy-of-india.html)
8. National Forest Policy (1988): New direction in forest management (http://sch.sagepub.com/content/33/2-3/192.abstract)
9. National Forest Policy, 1988 (http://www.moef.gov.in/sites/default/files/introduction-nfp.pdf)
10. See http://iced.cag.gov.in/?page_id=1034
11. National Conservation Strategy and Policy Statement on Environment and Development, 1992, (http://iced.cag.gov.in/?page_id=1030)
12. See http://www.un.org/esa/agenda21/natlinfo/countr/india/inst.htm
13. The Water (Prevention and Control of Pollution) Act, 1974 (http://www.indiawaterportal.org/articles/water-prevention-and-control-pollution-act-1974)
14. See http://envfor.nic.in/division/water-pollution
15. See http://ces.iisc.ernet.in/biodiversity/legis/wateract1.htm
16. Puja Mondal (2014). Summary on Air Prevention and Control of Pollution Act (1981) of India (http://www.yourarticlelibrary.com/law/acts/summary-on-air-prevention-and-control-of-pollution-act-1981-of-india/30191/)
17. Environment Protection Act, 1986 (https://en.wikipedia.org/wiki/ Environment _Protection_Act,_1986)
18. See http://www.cpcb.nic.in/Hazardous_waste.php
19. See http://www.mppcb.nic.in/MSIH.htm
20. See http://www.vanashakti.in/resources_law2.html
21. Wildlife Protection Act, 1972 (https://en.wikipedia.org/wiki/ild life _ Protection _Act,_1972)

22. National Environment Tribunal Act, 1995 (http://lawyerslaw.org/the-national-environment-tribunal-act-1995/)
23. Manju Menon, National Environment Appellate Authority: Puppet of the MoEF? (http://infochangeindia.org/environment/analysis/national-environment-appellate-authority-puppet-of-the-moef.html)
24. Puja Mondal, Environmental Studies: Meaning, Objectives, Scope and Importance of Environmental Studies (http://www.yourarticlelibrary.com/environment/environmental-studies-meaning-objectives-scope-and-importance-of-environmental-studies/12295/)
25. Sabarish Kumar, Essay on the Importance of Environmental Studies (http://www.preservearticles.com/2012042331066/essay-on-the-importance-of-environmental-studies.html)
26. Boyowa A. Chokor, Government policy and environmental protection in the developing world: The example of Nigeria, Environmental Management, Jan/Feb 1993, Volume 17, Issue 1, pp. 15-30.
27. Environmental policy (https://en.wikipedia.org/wiki/Environmental_policy)
28. Environmental protection (https://en.wikipedia.org/wiki/Environmental_protection)
29. Information taken from official website of Ministry of Environment, Forest and Climate Change (http://envfor.nic.in/about-ministry/about-ministry)
30. Models for Protecting the Environment for Future Generations (http://www.sehn.org/pdf/Models_for_Protecting_the_Environment_ for_Future_Generations.pdf)
31. See http://www.epa.wa.gov.au/POLICIES_GUIDELINES/ENVPROTECPOL/Pages/SiteLanding.aspx
32. See http://www.brighthub.com/environment/science-environmental/articles/91133.aspx
33. Seehttp://www.answers.com/Q/What_is_the_need_and_importance_of_afforestation
34. Chapter 1 Environment for Development (http://www.unep.org/geo/geo4/report/01_Environment_for_Development.pdf)
35. From official website of United Nations ESCAP (Economic and Social Commission for Asia and the Pacific).
36. See http://www.desd.org/desdcd/India.pdf
37. Theodore Panayotou, Economic growth and environment, chapter 2 (http://www.unece.org/fileadmin/DAM/ead/pub/032/032_c2.pdf)
38. Growth vs. environment (http://www.thehindu.com/opinion/op-ed/growth-versus-environment/article1200312.ece)
39. *University of Calgary,* Economic Growth and the Environment: A Review of theory and empirics (http://works.bepress.com/taylor/36/)
40. What is sustainable development? (http://www.sd-commission.org.uk/pages/what-is-sustainable-development.html)
41. Seehttp://www.hks.harvard.edu/sustsci/ists/docs/whatisSD_env_kates_0504.pdf

42. Sustainable development (https://en.wikipedia.org/wiki/Sustainable_development)
43. Official website of European Union (http://ec.europa.eu/environment/eussd/)
44. Rachel Emas, Brief for GSDR 2015 The Concept of Sustainable Development: Definition and Defining Principles,https://sustainabledevelopment.un.org/content/documents/5839GSDR%202015_SD_concept_definiton_rev.pdf
45. Our Common Future, Chapter 2: Towards Sustainable Development (http://www.un-documents.net/ocf-02.htm)
46. Sman-Elasha, Climate change impacts, adaptation and links to sustainable development in Africa (http://www.fao.org/docrep/011/i0670e/i0670e03.htm)
47. See http://www.unfpa.org/world-population-trends
48. Causes and Effects of Population Growth in India (http://www.nptel.ac.in/courses/109103022/13)
49. Population growth rate (http://www.eoearth.org/view/article/155312/)
50. Puja Monda, Population Explosion: Definition and Causes of Rapid Population Growth (http://www.yourarticlelibrary.com/essay/population-explosion-definition-and-causes-of-rapid-population-growth/29330/)
51. See http://www.howmany.org/big_picture.php
52. How Global Population Growth is Creating Serious Environmental Problems (http://environment.about.com/od/biodiversityconservation/a/population_grow.htm)
53. See http://www.conserve-energy-future.com/causes-effects-solutions-of-overpopulation.php
54. Rumani Saikia Phukan, Overpopulation in India: Causes, effecs and how to control it? (http://www.mapsofindia.com/my-india/india/overpopulation-in-india-causes-effects-and-how-to-control-it)
55. Puja Mondal- Population Growth: Causes, Characteristics and Explosion of Population Growth (http://www.yourarticlelibrary.com/population/population-growth-causes-characteristics-and-explosion-of-population-growth/9968/)
56. See http://www.tradingeconomics.com/india/population
57. See http://indianexpress.com/article/india/by-2050-india-to-have-the-worlds-largest-muslim-population-study/
58. http://www.un.org/en/globalissues/population/
59. Carolyn Kinder- The Population Explosion: Causes and Consequences (http://www.yale.edu/ynhti/curriculum/units/1998/7/98.07.02.x.html)
60. Puja Mondal- Population: Reasons of Population Explosion and it's Consequences (http://www.yourarticlelibrary.com/population/population-reasons-of-population-explosion-and-its-consequences/11916/)
61. Global warming FAQ (http://www.nmsea.org/Curriculum/Primer/Global_Warming/fossil_fuels_and_global_warming.htm)
62. See http://listovative.com/top-12-main-causes-reasons-of-global-warming/
63. Global Warming: News, Facts, Causes & Effects (http://www.livescience.com/topics/global-warming/

64. Global Warming Causes (http://www.climatehotmap.org/about/global-warming-causes.html)
65. Global Warming Effects and Causes: A Top 10 List (http://planetsave.com/2009/06/07/global-warming-effects-and-causes-a-top-10-list/)
66. Causes of global warming (http://www.wmo.int/pages/themes/climate/causes_of_global_warming.php)
67. Effects of global warming (https://en.wikipedia.org/wiki/Effects_of_global_warming)
68. See http://www.ucsusa.org/our-work/global-warming/science-and-impacts/global-warming-impacts#.VcR1A_mqpHw
69. See http://www.nytimes.com/2014/03/29/world/asia/facing-rising-seas-bangladesh-confronts-the-consequences-of-climate-change.html?_r=0
70. See http://www.conserve-energy-future.com/GlobalWarmingCauses.php
71. Sophie Johnson, How Are Greenhouse Gases Bad for the Earth? (http://classroom.synonym.com/greenhouse-gases-bad-earth-23688.html)
72. Climate change: Causes and evidence- An overview from the Royal Society and the US National Academy of Sciences (http://dels.nas.edu/resources/static-assets/exec-office-other/climate-change-full.pdf)
73. Climate Change - effects on animals, birdlife and plants (http://www.climateandweather.net/global-warming/climate-change-and-animals.html)
74. A blanket around the Earth (http://climate.nasa.gov/causes/)
75. Climate change: Impacts, vulnerabilities and adaptation in developing countries (http://unfccc.int/resource/docs/publications/impacts.pdf)
76. Causes of climate change (http://www.climatechange.gc.ca/default.asp?lang=en&n=65CD73F4-1)
77. See http://www.greenpeace.org/india/en/What-We-Do/Stop-Climate-Change/Climate-Impacts/
78. See http://www.c2es.org/docUploads/101_Science_Impacts.pdf
79. See http://www.nature.org/ourinitiatives/urgentissues/global-warming-climate-change/threats-impacts/changing-landscapes.xml
80. Climate change impacts: Higher temperature (http://www.nature.org/ourinitiatives/urgentissues/global-warming-climate-change/threats-impacts/higher-temperatures.xml)
81. Climate change impacts:Changing Landscapes (http://www.nature.org/ourinitiatives/urgentissues/global-warming-climate-change/threats-impacts/changing-landscapes.xml)
82. Climate change impacts:Wildlife at risk (http://www.nature.org/ourinitiatives/urgentissues/global-warming-climate-change/threats-impacts/wildlife-at-risk.xml)
83. Climate change impacts:Rising Seas (http://www.nature.org/ourinitiatives/urgentissues/global-warming-climate-change/threats-impacts/rising-seas.xml)
84. Climate change effects: Increased Risk of Drought, Fire, and Floods (http://www.nature.org/ourinitiatives/urgentissues/global-warming-climate-change/threats-impacts/drought-fire-floods.xml)

85. Climate change effects: Stronger Storms and Hurricanes (http://www.nature.org/ourinitiatives/urgentissues/global-warming-climate-change/threats-impacts/stronger-storms.xml)
86. Climate change effects:Heat-Related Illness and Disease (http://www.nature.org/ourinitiatives/urgentissues/global-warming-climate-change/threats-impacts/human-health.xml)
87. Climate change effects: Economic Loss and Damage (http://www.nature.org/ourinitiatives/urgentissues/global-warming-climate-change/threats-impacts/economic-loss-and-damage.xml)
88. Water vapor (https://en.wikipedia.org/wiki/Water_vapor)
89. Carbon dioxide (https://en.wikipedia.org/wiki/Carbon_dioxide)
90. Methane (https://en.wikipedia.org/wiki/Methane)
91. Nitrous oxide (https://en.wikipedia.org/wiki/Nitrous_oxide)
92. Ozone (https://en.wikipedia.org/wiki/Ozone)
93. Chlorofluorocarbons (https://en.wikipedia.org/wiki/Chlorofluorocarbon)
94. The green house effects (http://www.climatechange.gc.ca/default.asp?lang=en&n=1A0305D5-1)
95. What are the effects of increased greenhouse gas levels? (http://whatsyourimpact.org/effects-increased-greenhouse-gas-levels)
96. Green House Effect (https://en.wikipedia.org/wiki/Greenhouse_effect)
97. The Greenhouse Effect and Greenhouse Gasses (https://eo.ucar.edu/kids/green/warming4.htm)
98. Drivers and Impacts of Greenhouse Gas Emissions (https://mail.google.com/mail/u/0/?tab=wm#inbox)
99. See http://www.quora.com/What-are-the-harmful-effects-of-green-house-gases-on-Earth
100. Greenhouse effects (http://www.environment.gov.au/climate-change/climate-science/greenhouse-effect)
101. Climate Change Indicators in the United States (http://www.epa.gov/climate/climatechange/science/indicators/ghg/index.html)
102. Consequences of greenhouse-effect temperature rises (http://www.bgs.ac.uk/discoveringGeology/climateChange/CCS/consequencesOfTemperatureIncrease.html
103. The Greenhouse Gas Effect (http://www.infoplease.com/ipa/A0004686.html)

Chapter - 8

Resource

"Healthy people are those who live in healthy homes on a healthy diet; in an environment equally fit for birth, growth work, healing, and dying... Healthy people need no bureaucratic interference to mate, give birth, share the human condition and die."

—***Ivan Illich***[1]

Natural Resources are all that exists without the actions of humankind. Natural resources are materials and components that can be found within the environment. Some natural resources such as sunlight and air can be found everywhere, and are known as ubiquitous resources. However, most resources only occur in small sporadic areas, and are referred to as localised resources. There are various methods of categorising natural resources, these include source of origin, stage of development, and by their renewability. Resource extraction involves any activity that withdraws resources from nature. This can range in scale from the traditional use of preindustrial societies, to global industry.[2]

Natural resources are useful raw materials that we get from the Earth. They occur naturally, which means that humans cannot make natural resources. Instead, we use and modify natural resources in ways that are beneficial to us. There are several ways to classify natural resources, including where they come from and if they are renewable or not. If natural resources come from living things or organic materials, then they are considered biotic resources.[3]

Natural resources are useful materials from the Earth, such as coal, oil, natural gas, and trees. People use natural resources as raw materials to manufacture or create a range of modern conveniences. People use an abundance of resources to survive in a continually developing world. Globally, some people live simpler lifestyles than others and therefore use fewer resources. Increasing demands for natural resources have spurred new methods for conserving existing resources. More and more companies are developing new and innovative technologies that use recycled materials as raw materials in the manufacture of products.[4]

Definition of Resource

Resource is a source or supply from which benefit is produced. Typically, resources are materials, energy, services, staff, knowledge, or other assets that are transformed to produce benefit and in the process may be consumed or made unavailable. In economics a resource is defined as a service or other asset used to produce goods and services that meet human needs and wants. In biology and ecology, a resource is defined as a substance that is required by a living organism for normal growth, maintenance, and reproduction.

Resources have three main characteristics: utility, limited availability, and potential for depletion or consumption. Natural resources are derived from the environment. Many natural resources are essential for human survival, while others are used for satisfying human desire.[5]

Classification of Resource

Natural resources are naturally occurring substances that are considered valuable in their relatively unmodified form. It is mostly classified into renewable and non-renewable resources.

1. Renewable resources are generally living resources (fish, reindeer, coffee, and forests, for example), which can restock (renew) themselves if they are not over-harvested but used sustainably.
2. A non-renewable resource is a natural resource that exists in a fixed amount that cannot be re-made, re-grown or regenerated as fast as it is consumed and used up. Fossil fuels, for example, take millions of years to form and so are not practically considered 'renewable'.

Resources can also be classified on the basis of their origin as biotic and abiotic. Biotic resources are derived from living organisms. Abiotic resources are derived from the non-living world (e.g., land, water and air).[6]

Renewable Resource

Renewable resource is an organic natural resource which can replenish to overcome usage and consumption, either through biological reproduction or other naturally recurring processes. Renewable resources are a part of Earth's natural environment and the largest components of its ecosphere. In 1962 Paul Alfred Weiss defined Renewable Resources as: "The total range of living organisms providing man with food, fibres, drugs, etc..." Renewable resources are endangered by non-regulated industrial developments and growth. They must be carefully managed to avoid exceeding the natural world's capacity to replenish them.[7]

Most renewable energy comes either directly or indirectly from the sun. Sunlight, or solar energy, can be used directly for heating and lighting homes and other buildings, for generating electricity, and for hot water heating, solar cooling, and a variety of commercial and industrial uses. Renewable energy is plentiful, and the technologies are improving all the time. There are many ways to use renewable energy. Demand for energy and associated services, to meet social and economic development and improve human welfare and health, is increasing. All societies require energy services to meet basic human needs (e.g., lighting, cooking, space comfort, mobility and communication) and to serve productive processes.[8]All renewable energies are inexhaustible sources, meaning humans would never run out of these renewable energies to create power.

Hydropower

Hydropower plants convert the energy in flowing water into electricity. The most common form of hydropower uses a dam on a river to retain a large reservoir of water. Water is released through turbines to generate power. Hydropower plants produce no air emissions but can affect water quality and wildlife habitats. Hydroelectric power comes from water at work, water in motion. It can be seen as a form of solar energy, as the sun powers the hydrologic cycle which gives the earth its water. In the hydrologic cycle, atmospheric water reaches the earth's surface as precipitation.

It is power derived from the energy of falling water or running water, which may be harnessed for useful purposes. Since ancient times, hydropower from many kinds of watermills has been used as a renewable energy source for irrigation and the operation of various mechanical devices. International institutions such as the World Bank view hydropower as a means for economic development without adding substantial amounts of carbon to the atmosphere. Hydraulic power networks used pipes to carrying pressurised water and transmit mechanical power from the source to end users. The power source was normally a head of water, which could also be assisted by a pump. Where there is a plentiful head of water it can be made to generate compressed air directly without moving parts.[9]

Small-scale hydropower is one of the most cost-effective and reliable energy technologies to be considered for providing clean electricity generation. The objective of a hydropower scheme is to convert the potential energy of a mass of water, flowing in a stream with a certain fall, into electric energy at the lower end of the scheme, where the powerhouse is located. Hydro-turbines convert water pressure into mechanical shaft power, which can be used to drive an electricity generator, or other machinery. The power available is proportional to the product of head and flow rate. The main component of a small hydropower plant is the hydro turbine.

The planning plays important role in the growth and development of hydropower. The amount of achievable hydropower at any given site is a function of turbine head and the corresponding flow rate. The remote sensing technology is an effective tool for the identification of suitable sites for locating new hydropower projects especially in the inaccessible areas where the water recourse potential is high. The only resource needed for a small/micro hydro power plant is flowing water available at a gradient.[10]

There are various challenges before hydropower projects. Construction and operation of hydropower dams can significantly affect natural river systems as well as fish and wildlife populations. Hydropower projects often require forest areas for their implementation and compensatory afforestation on non-forest lands. Progress of many projects has been affected on account of delay and non-clearance on environment and forest aspects. Hydropower projects are capital-intensive and financing them, by finding an optimum balance between bankability and affordability, is often a challenge.

Techno economic viability of hydropower projects depends on the geology, topography, hydrology and accessibility of the project site. A number of hydropower projects are located in remote sites in states which do not have adequate demand for electricity. This creates the requirement for developing enabling infrastructure for power evacuation. Hydropower projects also require the development of associated infrastructure such as roads and bridges in the area. Inclusion of the cost of development of such associated infrastructure increases the cost of power generated affecting project viability and sustainability.[11]

Water power offers a number of advantages to the communities that they serve. Some of them are: (a) Hydropower is fuelled by water, so it's a clean fuel source, meaning it won't pollute the air like power plants that burn fossil fuels, such as coal or natural gas; (b) Hydroelectric power is a domestic source of energy, allowing each state to produce their own energy without being reliant on international fuel sources; (c) The energy generated through hydropower relies on the water cycle, which is driven by the sun, making it a renewable power source; (d) hydropower efforts produce a number of benefits, such as flood control, irrigation, and water supply.[12]

India was the sixth largest producer of hydroelectric power in 2008 after Norway: 114 TWh and 3.5 per cent the world total in 2008. The present installed capacity as on September 30, 2013 is approximately 39,788.40 MW which is 17.39 per cent of total electricity generation in India.The public sector has a predominant share of 97 per cent in this sector. National Hydroelectric Power Corporation, Northeast Electric Power Company (NEEPCO), Satluj Jal Vidyut Nigam (SJVNL), THDC, NTPC-Hydro is a few public sector companies engaged in development of Hydroelectric Power in India.[13]

From a regional perspective, over 93 per cent of the total potential in the north-eastern region is yet to be tapped, primarily in parts of the Brahmaputra river basin. The scenario is in sharp contrast to the southern and the western regions where more than 65 per cent of the potential has already been harnessed. The government of India has, over the years, taken a number of initiatives to prioritize hydropower development and to attract investments in the sector. Accordingly, in the Eleventh Five Year Plan, the target for hydropower capacity addition was placed at 16.5 GW, which was almost half of the total installed capacity then. However, the achievement, at around 5400 MW, was well short of the target. Various factors such as environmental concerns, R&R issues, land acquisition problems, long clearance and approval procedures, capability of developers, etc. have contributed to the slow pace of hydropower development in the past. Though private participation in the hydropower sector has gained momentum in the recent past, it still faces impediments in the execution of projects across various stages of the project implementation cycle.[14]

India was one of the pioneering countries in establishing hydro-electric power plants. The power plant at Darjeeling and Shimsha was established in 1898 and 1902 respectively and is one of the first in Asia. The installed capacity as on 31st March 2011 was approximately 37567.40 MW i.e. 21.64 per cent. The hydroelectric power plant, also called as dam or hydropower plant, is used for generation of electricity from water on large scale basis. The dam is built across the large river that has sufficient quantity of water throughout the river. Dams are structures built over rivers to stop the water flow and form a reservoir. The reservoir stores the water flowing down the river. This water is diverted to turbines in power stations.[15]

Bio-energy

Bio-energy is the energy derived from biomass (organic matter), such as plants. If you have ever burned wood in a fireplace or campfire, you have used bio-energy. Biomass can be converted directly into liquid fuels, called bio-fuels. Because bio-fuels are easy to transport and possess high energy density, they are favoured to fuel vehicles and sometimes stationary power generation.

According to the definition given by Directive 2009/28/CE, biomass is "the biodegradable fraction of products, waste and residues from biological origin from agriculture (including vegetal and animal substances), forestry and related industries including fisheries and aquaculture, as well as the biodegradable fraction of industrial and municipal waste." The use of bioenerg is related to the impact on land use. 'Renewable', 'Low greenhouse gas emission' and 'Sustainable' are not synonymous terms and must be considered one by one, in the biomass projects. Biomass considered as an energy resource is fandamentally different from carbon free energy sources (i.e. wind). It could generate energy and material products similar to the traditional ones produced by existing fossil fuel uses.

The benefits of biofuels over traditional fuels include greater energy security, reduced environmental impact, foreign exchange savings and socioeconomic issues related to the rural sector. The overwhelming majority of biomass available for bioenergy is derived from plant material also that from animal products. The biomass represented by energy crops is obviously coming by agricultural and forestal sectors.[16]

Geothermal Energy

The adjective geothermal originates from the Greek roots geo, meaning earth, and thermos, meaning heat. Geothermal energy is thermal energy generated and stored in the Earth. Thermal energy is energy that determines the temperature of matter. It ranges from the shallow ground to hot water and hot rock found a few miles beneath the Earth's surface, and down even deeper to the extremely high temperatures of molten rock called magma. It is the thermal energy contained in the rock and fluid in the earth's crust. Calculations show that the earth, originating from a completely molten state, would have cooled and become completely solid many thousands of years ago without an energy input in addition to that of the sun. It is believed that the ultimate source of geothermal energy is radioactive decay occurring deep within the earth.

Geothermal power plants use hydrothermal resources that have two common ingredients: water (hydro) and heat (thermal). Geothermal plants require high temperature (300°F to 700°F) hydrothermal resources that may come from either dry steam wells or hot water wells. We can use these resources by drilling wells into the Earth and piping the steam or hot water to the surface. Geothermal wells are typically one to two miles deep. Enhanced Geothermal Systems, also sometimes called engineered geothermal systems, offer great potential for dramatically expanding the use of geothermal energy.[17] Geothermal energy is generated in the earth's core, almost 4,000 miles beneath the earth's surface. The double-layered core is made up of very hot magma (melted rock) surrounding a solid iron centre. There is more than one type of geothermal energy, but only one kind is widely used to make electricity. It is called hydrothermal energy. Currently, hydrothermal energy is being commercially used for electricity generation and for meeting thermal energy requirements.[18]

Geo-thermal energy is one of the rare forms of energy which is not directly or indirectly from solar energy. In areas where hot springs are found, hot springs baths are very common and enjoyable form of recreation. To harness this geothermal energy, two holes are dug deep into the earth and cold water is pumped through the first one and steam comes out through the second-long pipe which helps in generating electricity.[19]

Various advantages of geothermal energy are (a) there is no wastage or generation of by-products; (b) unlike solar energy, it is not dependent on the weather conditions; (c) maintenance cost of geothermal power plants is very less; (d) it can use directly; (e) Government of various countries are investing hugely in creation of geothermal energy which on other hand has created more jobs for the local people. Some disadvantages of such energy are (a) Only few sites have the potential of Geothermal Energy; (b) most of the sites, where geothermal energy is produced, are far from markets or cities, where it needs to be consumed; (c) there is no guarantee that the amount of energy which is produced will justify the capital expenditure and operations costs; (d) There is always a danger of eruption of volcano.[20]

India has reasonably good potential for geothermal; the potential geothermal provinces can produce 10,600 MW of power.Though India has been one of the earliest countries to begin geothermal projects way back in the 1970s, but at present there are no operational geothermal plants in India. There is also no installed geothermal electricity generating capacity as of now and only direct uses have been detailed.[21] After decades of studies and field surveys, India has finally decided to focus on tapping clean and renewable geothermal energy, which is available in abundance but remains largely untapped.Union Ministry of New and Renewable Energy (MNRE) recently drafted a national policy, which seeks to make India a global leader in the sector, generating 1,000 MW in phase-one, ending 2022. Chhattisgarh government has already decided to establish the first geothermal power plant in the country at Tattapani in Balrampur district, along with NTPC. This is the most promising geothermal resource in central India.[22]

In India, exploration and study of geothermal fields started in 1970. The Geological Survey of India has identified 350 geothermal energy locations in the country. The most promising of these is in Puga valley of Ladakh. The estimated potential for geothermal energy in India is about 10000 MW. There are seven geothermal provinces in India: The Himalayas, Sohana, West coast, Cambay, Son-Narmada-Tapi, Godavari, and Mahanadi. Geothermal Atlas of India, prepared by the Geological Survey of India gives information/data for more than 300 geothermal potential sites. This Atlas is being updated by GSI with the support from MNES.[23]

Puga, which is located at a distance of about 180 km from Leh in the Ladakh region of Jammu and Kashmir across the great Himalayan range, is considered to be a good potential of geothermal energy In Puga valley, hot spring temperatures vary from 30°C to 84°C (boiling point at Puga) and discharge up to 300 liters /minute. A total of 34 boreholes ranging in depths from 28.5 m to 384.7 m have been drilled in Puga valley. Chhumathang spring is another geothermal area located about 40 km north of Puga. The thermal water from Chhumathang is quite similar to the thermal waters at Puga except the difference that its water has relatively higher pH and sulphate. Obviously, geothermal energy has great potential as a clean, green and naturally occurring renewable source of energy.[24]

Solar Energy

Solar energy is radiant light and heat from the sun harnessed using a range of ever-evolving technologies. The large magnitude of solar energy available makes it a highly appealing source of electricity. Solar thermal technologies can be used for water heating, space heating, space cooling and process heat generation. In 1897, Frank Shuman, a U.S. inventor, engineer and solar energy pioneer built a small demonstration solar engine that worked by reflecting solar energy onto square boxes filled with ether, which has a lower boiling point than water, and were fitted internally with black pipes which in turn powered a steam engine. Solar hot water systems use sunlight to heat water. In low geographical latitudes (below 40 degrees) from 60 to 70 percent of the domestic hot water use with temperatures up to 60°C can be provided by solar heating systems.

Due to the nature of solar energy, two components are required to have a functional solar energy generator. These two components are a collector and a storage unit. The collector simply collects the radiation that falls on it and converts a fraction of it to other forms of energy. The storage unit is required because of the non-constant nature of solar energy; at certain times only a very small amount of radiation will be received. Methods of collecting and storing solar energy vary depending on the uses planned for the solar generator. In general, there are three types of collectors and many forms of storage units. The three types of collectors are flat-plate collectors, focusing collectors, and passive collectors. Flat-plate collectors are the more commonly used type of collector today. They are arrays of solar panels arranged in a simple plane. Focusing collectors are essentially flat-plane collectors with optical devices arranged to maximize the radiation falling on the focus of the collector. Passive collectors are completely different from the other two types of collectors.

In the United States, heating, ventilation and air conditioning systems account for 30 percentof the energy used in commercial buildings and nearly 50 percent of the energy used in residential buildings. Solar cookers use sunlight for cooking, drying and pasteurisation. They can be grouped into three broad categories: box cookers, panel cookers and reflector cookers. Solar concentrating technologies such as parabolic dish, trough and Scheffler reflectors can provide process heat for commercial and industrial applications. Solar distillation can be used to make saline or brackish water potable. The first recorded instance of this was by 16th-century Arab alchemists. Development of a solar-powered car has been an engineering goal since the 1980s. Solar chemical processes use solar energy to drive chemical reactions.[25]

Solar energy is a truly renewable energy source. It can be harnessed in all areas of the world and is available every day. It can be used for diverse purposes. Solar energy systems generally do not require a lot of maintenance. Technology in the solar power industry is constantly advancing and improvements will intensify in the future. Innovations in quantum physics and nanotechnology can potentially increase the effectiveness of solar panels and double, or even triple, the electrical input of the solar power systems.[26]

Solar energy can be used to heat water. Heating water for bathing, dishwashing, and clothes washing is the second largest home energy cost. Installing a solar water heater can reduce your water heating bill by as much as 50 percent. Solar energy can also be used to produce electricity. Two ways to make electricity from solar energy are photovoltaics and solar thermal systems.

There are many advantages of such energy, like as (a) It is free although there is a cost in the building of 'collectors' and other equipment required to convert solar energy into electricity or hot water; (b) It does not cause pollution; (c) It can be used in remote areas where it is too expensive to extend the electricity power grid; (d) It is estimated that the world's oil reserves will last for 30 to 40 years. On the other hand, solar energy is infinite (forever);[27](e) The cost of producing electricity isnot the same at all hours. Electricity supply and demand must match in order for the grid to not go down. As such, a variety of energy sources are used to create electricity for the grid; (f) The possibility of much greater energy security is a major advantage of solar power that many people are not aware of.[28]

There are also some disadvantages of such energy, like as (a) It can only be harnessed when it is daytime and sunny; (b) Solar collectors, panels and cells are relatively expensive to manufacture although prices are falling rapidly; (c) Solar power stations can be built but they do not match the power output of similar sized conventional power stations. They are also very expensive; (d) large areas of land are required to capture the suns energy.[29]

India's government has set a mammoth new goal to build a solar power capacity of 100 GW in an energy-starved-but-hungry country, permitting 100 percent foreign investment and offering a series of tax breaks for the fledgling sector. The government's unprecedented push has already attracted a pack of investors. Japanese telecom multinational SoftBank, India's biggest wireless telecom provider Bharti Enterprises and Taiwan's technology manufacturer Foxconn Technology have together announced a $20 billion joint venture, SBG Cleantech, to bid for contracts to develop solar energy plants across the country. SunEdison, the Missouri, U.S.-based renewable energy firm said it intends to invest $15 billion by 2022.[30]

On 16 May 2011, India's first five MW of installed capacity solar power project was registered under the Clean Development Mechanism. The project is in Sivagangai Village, Sivaganga district, Tamil Nadu. Gujarat has been a leader in solar power generation and contributes 2/3rd of the 900 MW of photovoltaics in the country. The State has commissioned Asia's biggest solar park at Charanka village. The park is already generating 2 MW solar power out of its total planned capacity of 500 MW.Rajasthan is one of the states of India in the field of solar energy. The total photovoltaic capacity has passed 500 MW, reaching 510.25 MW at the end of the 2012-13 fiscal year. The Shri Sai Baba Sansthan Trust has the world's largest solar steam system. It was constructed at the Shirdi shrine at an estimated cost of Rs1.33 crore, Rs58.4 lakh of which was paid as a subsidy by the renewable energy ministry. Solar Radiation Resource Assessment stations (51 nos) have been installed across India by the Ministry of New and Renewable Energy to create database of solar energy potential.

The government of India is promoting the use of solar energy through various strategies. In the latest budget for 2010/11, the government has announced an allocation of 1000 crore towards the Jawaharlal Nehru National Solar Mission and the establishment of a clean energy fund. It is an increase of 380 crores from the previous budget. This new budget has also encouraged private solar companies by reducing customs duty on solar panels by five per cent and exempting excise duty on solar photovoltaic panels. The Mysore City Corporation has decided to set up a mega solar power plant in Mysore with 50 per cent concession from the Government of India. The Maharashtra State Power Generation Company has made plans for setting up more power plants in the state to take up total generation up to 200 MW.[31]

The Jawaharlal Nehru National Solar Mission aims at development and deployment of solar energy technologies in the country to achieve parity with grid power tariff by 2022. The National Solar Mission is a major initiative of the Government of India and State Governments to promote ecologically sustainable growth while addressing India's energy security challenge. It will also constitute a major contribution by India to the global effort to meet the challenges of climate change. The objective of the National Solar Mission is to establish India as a global leader in solar energy, by creating the policy conditions for its diffusion across the country as quickly as possible. The aim would be to protect Government from subsidy exposure in case expected cost reduction does not materialise or is more rapid than expected. The immediate aim of the Mission is to focus on setting up an enabling environment for solar technology penetration in the country both at a centralised and decentralised level.[32]

On December 29th 2010, India's first solar park was inaugurated at Charanaka in Patan district of northern Gujarat. So far, land has been allotted in the solar park for projects worth 176 MW to 16 companies from the first and second phases. The total capacity of the solar park is 500 MW with 30,000 sq. m per MW land allotted to Solar Thermal and 20,000 sq. m per MW of land allotted to PV projects. The solar park has been financed with over Rs 12 billion by financial institutions like the International Finance Corporation, the Asian Development Bank and the Infrastructure Development Finance Corporation.

On April 19th 2011, Government of Rajasthan issued Rajasthan Solar Energy Policy, 2011 to promote solar energy in the state. The policy aims to help Rajasthan, develop as a global hub of solar power for 10000-12000 MW capacity over the next 10 to 12 years to meet energy requirements of Rajasthan and other states of India. Karnataka, a south-western state of India, announced its solar policy on July 1, 2011. Under the solar policy 2011-16, the Karnataka Government proposes to promote solar power as part of renewable energy generation policy in the state.[33]

Wind Energy

Winds are due to the fact that the Earth's equatorial regions receive more solar radiation than the Polar Regions, setting up large-scale convection currents in the atmosphere. The extraction of power from wind began very early in centuries, with wind powered ships, grain mills and threshing machines. Now-a-days, the major applications of wind energy involve electricity generation, with the wind turbines operating in parallel with utility grid systems or, in more remote locations, in parallel with fossil fueled engines. A steady supply of reasonably strong wind is a necessary requirement for utilising the power in the wind. As the wind power depends on the cube of the wind speed, it is evident that the average annual power will vary from site to site. Sites with more high wind speeds will return more power. A wind turbine can be placed almost anywhere in a reasonably open ground. However, a wind farm is a commercial development and must attempt to optimise its profitability.[34]

There are various advantages of such energy, like as (a) wind is free and with modern technology it can be captured efficiently; (b) Once the wind turbine is built the energy it produces does not cause greenhouse gases or other pollutants; (c) Remote areas that are not connected to the electricity power grid can use wind turbines to produce their own supply; (d) Although wind turbines can be very tall each takes up only a small plot of land;[35] (e) Land around wind turbines can be used for other uses, e.g. Farming; (f) Like solar energy and hydropower, wind power taps a natural physical resource; (g) Wind Energy is an inexhaustible source of energy and is virtually a limitless resource.[36]

There are also some disadvantages of such energy, like as (a) noise pollution problem is usually associated with wind mill; (b) It can be a threat to wildlife. Birds do get killed or injured when they fly into turbines; (c) It is unreliable energy source as winds are uncertain and unpredictable; (d) requires large open areas for setting up wind farms; (e) Maintenance cost of wind turbines is high as they have mechanical parts which undergo wear and tear over the time.[37]

Wind energy has the potential to be the cheapest power source in Europe, but like any emerging technology, it faces significant barriers. Today, Europe leads the world in terms of manufacturing and development of wind farms. In 1994, there were 1,683 megawatts of wind energy installed across the EU. By the end of 2005, installed capacity had increased 24 times and some 40 gigawatts of cumulative installed capacity were providing about 2.8 per cent of European electricity consumption. Still, the potential of wind energy is far greater. The industry is optimistic about the potential for wind energy, more than it has ever been. In recent decades, to fuel its development, the wind industry has borrowed materials, systems and products from other sectors: defence, for sensors; aerospace and shipbuilding, for blades; and the mining industry, for gear technology. Wind energy can help the European balance of trade not only by reducing the need for imported energy fuels, but through increased exports.[38]

The development of wind power in India began in the 1990s, and has significantly increased in the last few years. Although a relative newcomer to the wind industry compared with Denmark or the United States, India has the fifth largest installed wind power capacity in the world. The worldwide installed capacity of wind power reached 283 GW by the end of 2012. China (75,564 MW), US (60,007 MW), Germany (31,332 MW) and Spain (22,796 MW) are ahead of India in fifth position. Wind power accounts nearly 8.5 per cent of India's total installed power generation capacity and generated 28,214 million Kwh in the fiscal year 2014-15 which is nearly 2.6 per cent of total electricity generation. The capacity utilisation factor is nearly 15 per cent in the fiscal year 2014-15. 70 per cent of wind generation is during the five months' duration from May to September coinciding with South West monsoon duration. Tamil Nadu's wind power capacity is around 35 per cent of India's total.[39]

Table 1: State-wise Wind Power Installed Capacity in India

Sl. No.	*State*	*Total Capacity (MW) till 31.03.2015*
1.	Andhra Pradesh	1038.15
2.	Gujarat	3642.53
3.	Karnataka	2639.45
4.	Kerala	35.1
5.	Madhya Pradesh	876.7
6.	Maharashtra	4437.9
7.	Rajasthan	3308.15
8.	Tamil Nadu	7456.98
9.	Others	4.3
	Total (All India)	**23439.26**

Source: http://www.inwea.org/aboutwindenergy.htm

Wind in India are influenced by the strong south-west summer monsoon, which starts in May-June, when cool, humid air moves towards the land and the weaker north-east winter monsoon, which starts in October, when cool, dry sir moves towards the ocean. During the period march to August, the winds are uniformly strong over the whole Indian Peninsula, except the eastern peninsular coast.[40]

The government plans to rapidly accelerate wind energy generation, adding an ambitious 10,000 MW every year, or five times the total new capacity that came up in the last fiscal, as the Modi government takes steps to reduce India's dependence on costly energy imports.Wind energy, which had been overshadowed by solar projects in recent years, got a big boost as the government has restored key tax incentives that had helped India emerge as one of the top countries in the world in generating electricity from wind. The government feels that tax incentives coupled with conducive environment will rapidly accelerate wind energy. According to Indian Wind Turbine Manufacturers Association proposed target is achievable as the country has capacity to manufacture close to 9,500 MW of wind turbines and it can be expanded in short period. With installed capacity of over 21,000 MW, India is fifth-largest wind power producer in the world after China, US, Germany and

Spain. According to Centre for Wind Energy Technology India has potential to install over one lakh MW of wind turbines.[41]

The Indian Wind Power Association was set up in 1996 as a non-profit organisation. The Association, which began with 21 members, now has 1,352 members spread all over India. The National Office of the Association is located at Chennai and has regional offices at Ahmedabad, Bangalore, Delhi, Hyderabad, Jaipur and Mumbai. Since its inception it has worked consistently, towards removing barriers to wind power development and creation of an enabling regulatory and policy environment for investments in this sector. The Association is working closely with several national industry bodies such as the Indian Renewable Energy Development Agency, Ministry of New and Renewable Energy, Ministry of Power, Ministry of Environment, CWET, CERC, CEA, Confederation of Indian Industry, State utilities, State Electricity Regulatory Commissions, State Nodal Agencies, World Wind Energy Associati n, Bonn, Germany etc. [42]

Hydrogen

Hydrogen is high in energy, yet its use as a fuel produces water as the only emission. Despite its abundance and simplicity, it doesn't occur naturally as a gas on the Earth. Today, hydrogen fuel cells offer tremendous potential to prouce electrical power for distributed energy systems and vehicles. In the future, hydrogen could join electricity as an important energy carrier: storing, moving, and delivering energy in a usable form to consumers. Hydrogen can store the renewable energy produced until its needed.[43]

Ocean Energy

The ocean can produce two types of energy: thermal energy from the sun's heat, and mechanical energy from the tides and waves. Ocean thermal energy can be used for many applications, including electricity generation. Electricity conversion systems use either the warm surface water or boil the seawater to turn a turbine, which activates a generator.[44] Ocean energy resources include energy from waves, tides, both current and range, ocean currents, temperature gradients and salinity gradient. Oceans are already a well exploited source of energy as they are a major reserve of the world's fossil fuels. There is however also an opportunity to access renewable energy from the oceans.[45]

Ocean Energy is a world leader in Innovative Renewable Energy within the wave energy industry. It is now in a very strong position to commercialise the vast body of research and development it has invested in over the past 10 years. The sea is a limitless source of power and is a challenging environment, so in order to exploit wave energy commercially there are a number of key components required.[46] It is as source of power that comes from the endless march of the waves as they roll into the shore then back out again. Humans harness this power along the coastal regions of the United States, Canada, Scotland, and Australia. Energy that comes from the waves in the ocean sounds like a boundless, harmless supply.

There are many benefits of ocean energy, like as (a) the best thing about wave energy is that it will never run out. There will always be waves crashing upon the shores of nations, near the populated coastal regions; (b) creating power from waves creates no harmful byproducts such as gas, waste, and pollution. The energy from waves can be taken directly into electricity-producing machinery and used to power generators and power plants nearby; (c) this energy is its nearness to places that can use it. Lots of big cities and harbors are next to the ocean and can harness the power of the waves for their use; (d) it is easily predictable and can be used to calculate the amount that it can produce; and (e) Dependence on foreign companies for fossil fuels can be reduced if energy from wave power can be extracted up to its maximum.[47]

Ocean energy would help but there are also some drawbacks to using this type of renewable energy. Some of these disadvantages include (a) If using tidal energy, it can only supply power for about 10 hours a day because of the pattern of the tides; (b) Machines and technologies used to create ocean energy are expensive; (c) If using tidal energy, the technology that is often used is tidal barrages. There are very few locations to build these barrages; and (d) intense waves may result in the damage of some technologies used to create ocean energy.[48]

The European Union has compelling reasons for setting up an enabling framework to promote ocean energy. European Ocean Energy Roadmap sets a long-term vision for this emerging sector. It aims to highlight to policymakers at EU and national levels that the ocean energy sector requires support in order to achieve its potential and demonstrate results and benefits similar to, or better than other renewable energy sectors. The Roadmap for the development of the ocean energy industry in Europe aims to advance development of ocean energy technologies, to enable the exploitation of vast European resources of wave, tidal and osmotic energy, to facilitate grid integration of ocean power, and to enable the industry to reach 3.6 GW of installed capacity by 2020 and close to 188 GW by 2050.

The best ocean energy resources within the European Member States are wave, tidal current and tidal range. Systems developed for harvesting these resources have seen the most technological advancement. Several tidal plants are in the planning phase within the European Union, located at suitable estuaries and tidal lagoons. These tidal barrage installations consist of dams and reservoirs with the same operational principle as conventional hydro-power plants. Energy is essential for Europe to function. All EU Member States face the challenges of climate change, increasing dependence on imported energy and higher energy prices.[49]

There are a number of other potential energy sources in the oceans around Japan. One is the kinetic energy of waves washing against Japans 34000 km of coastlines. A 2010 report on wave-power generation by a panel of the Tokyo Metropolitan Government estimated that at least 300 million to 400 million kilowatts of electricity could be generated by wave power. Another estimate shows that within the range of 30 km from the coastlines, at a depth of 100 meters, there are potential energy sources equivalent to more than 10 nuclear power plants.[50]

The World Energy Council recognised the potential several years ago when it listed Australia's southern coastline as one of the world's best sources of wave energy. The federal government has set a target of 20 per cent renewable electricity generation by 2020. Ocean thermal energy uses the temperature difference between the surface and Deep Ocean. This disparity can be used to condense and vapourise a working fluid to drive a turbine. There are also thousands of kilometers of coastline in Australia where waves dump the concentrated energy of the ocean. Australia has an advantage as an island that borders the Southern Ocean. This plays home to the largest global source of surface waves which are constantly being generated night and day, summer and winter, under its powerful storm system.[51]

Canada continues to explore its wealth of resources and has begun to develop new sources of energy. Until recently, ocean energy exploration and development focused on oil and gas. Now, activities include generating energy from offshore wind, tides and waves. Canada's oceans and offshore areas have major renewable energy potential. Efforts to collect energy from ocean currents, tides, waves and offshore wind are now being explored on Canada's east and west coasts. Renewable energy is energy that comes from sources that do not deplete natural resources, for example, electricity generated from offshore wind, tides and waves. Several demonstration and commercial renewable energy projects are at different stages of development on Canada's east and west coasts.[52]

Non-Renewable

Natural resources are materials or things that people use from the earth. There are two types of natural resources. The first are renewable natural resources. They are called renewable because they can grow again or never run out. The second are called nonrenewable natural resources.[53] The original organic material, with the aid of heat and pressure, becomes a fuel such as oil or gas. Earth minerals and metal ores, fossil fuels (coal, petroleum, natural gas) and groundwater in certain aquifers are all non-renewable resources.

A non-renewable resource is a resource that does not renew itself at a sufficient rate for sustainable economic extraction in meaningful human time-frames. An example is carbon-based, organically-derived fuel. The original organic material, with the aid of heat and pressure, becomes a fuel such as oil or gas. Earth minerals and metal ores are other examples of non-renewable resources. Natural resources such as coal, petroleum (crude oil) and natural gas take thousands of years to form naturally and cannot be replaced as fast as they are being consumed.[54]

Today the greatest attention in the world is devoted to energy resources because their use is usually irreversible, but the supplies of traditional fossil fuels (oil, natural gas) are running out fast. This is why over the last decade's attention is focused on renewable energy resources and ways to increase energy efficiency. Over the last 200 years an ever-increasing proportion of our energy has come from non-renewable sources such as oil and coal. While demand for energy raises these resources are running out and scientists are exploring the potential of renewable sources of energy for the future.[55]

Fossil fuels are nonrenewable, which means that their supplies are limited. Coal, oil, and natural gas are examples of fossil fuels. Fossil fuels are highly effective sources of energy because they are rich in hydrocarbons. When fossil fuels are burned, hydrocarbons combine with oxygen at high temperatures and significant amounts of energy are released. The amount of energy produced by burning oil and natural gas is three times greater than the energy produced by burning wood. Fossil fuels are also subject to dramatic price changes due to varying supply and demand. Relying on fossil fuels also perpetuates our dependency on imported energy.[56]

Coal

Coal is traditionally looked upon as the most typical fossil fuel. Today coal is primarily used for energy and coke production for producing iron and steel. Coal of a lower quality is used in cement and food production as well as in several less important industries. At present, the most thorough assessment was carried out in 2006, stating that coal resources suitable for energy production amount to 1.081 trillion tons - thus, their energy value is equivalent to 4.789 billion barrels of oil. Although coal is considered a widely distributed deposit and found in all continents, extraction is economically grounded and concentrated only in four major countries: the USA (27 per cent), Russia (17 per cent), China (13 per cent) and India (10 per cent). These countries provide ~65 per cent of coal extraction in the world.[57]

The activities involved in generating electricity from coal include mining, transport to power plants, and burning of the coal in power plants. Although power plants are regulated by federal and state laws to protect human health and the environment, there is a wide variation of environmental impacts associated with power generation technologies. When coal is burned, carbon dioxide, sulfur dioxide, nitrogen oxides, and mercury compounds are released. For that reason, coal-fired boilers are required to have control devices to reduce the amount of emissions that are released.[58]

Lignite coal is found close to the Earth surface, making it easy to mine, but it has high Sulphur content. Bituminous coal is the most common coal we burn, and it is less polluting than lignite. Anthracite is the highest quality of coal. It is dark and shiny and found deeper in the Earth. Large volumes of unwanted dirt and rock are removed, which can lead to water pollution, unstable ground and, in many cases, it is not appealing to look at. Working in coal mines can also be very dangerous.[59]

Coal mining in India has a long history of commercial exploitation covering nearly 220 years starting in 1774 with John Sumner and Suetonius Grant Heatly of the East India Company in the Raniganj Coalfield along the Western bank of Damodar River. Coal reserves in India are one of the largest in the world. As on April 1, 2012, India had 293.5 billion metric tons (323.5 billion short tons) of the resource. The production of coal was 532.69 million metric tons (587.19 million short tons) in 2010-11.

The production of lignite was 37.73 million metric tons (41.59 million short tons) in 2010-11. India was ranked third in world coal production in 2011. Unscientific mining practices adopted by some of them and poor working conditions of labour in some of the private coal mines became matters of concern for the government. On account of these reasons, the Central Government took a decision to nationalise the private coal mines. The nationalisation was done in two phases, the first with the coking coal mines in 1971-72 and then with the non-coking coal mines in 1973.[60]

Raniganj Coalfield is the birth place of coal mining in the country. In 1774, first mining operation in the country was started in this Coalfield by Sumner & Healy. In 1820, first Coal Company- M/s. Alexander & Company was established. In 1835, first Indian Enterprise i.e. M/s. Carr & Tagore Company was formed. Area of Raniganj Coalfield is 1530 Sq.Kms spreading over Burdwan, Birbhum, Bankura and Purulia Districts in West Bengal and Dhanbad District in Jharkhand. Heart of Raniganj Coalfield is Burdwan District bounded by Ajoy River in North and Damodar River in South. Total Coal Reserve upto 600 m depth is 23 billion tonnes in West Bengal.[61]

Coal India Limited is an Indian state-controlled coal mining company headquartered in Kolkata, West Bengal, India. It is the largest coal producer company in the world and contributes around 81per cent of the coal production in India. Union Government of India owns 89.65 per cent of the shares in CIL and controls the operations of CIL through Ministry of Coal. To consolidate the businesses of both coking and non-coking coal under one entity, a formal holding company in the form of Coal India Limited was formed in November 1975 to manage both the companies. Government of India held 100 per cent of its shares from 1975 till 2010.[62]

Oil

In nature oil is a liquid that fills in empty spaces, crevices and caverns in rocks, forming deposits in anticlines, folds at plate boundaries and foothills. It can be found in pores or on grains of rocks. Such oil can form oil-saturated sandstone and limestone rocks, or plastic and hard layers of crust, most often called natural asphalt or oil shale. In the Earth liquid oil is usually buried to the depth of 0.3–5 km; when deeper, it can be found only as admixture in deposits of natural gas. Oil is a liquid fossil fuel that can be dark brown, yellow or even green. It is easier to mine once it is found because, as it is a liquid, it will flow through pipes, which makes it easier to transport. It can be difficult to locate. Oil forms in reservoirs and, to find these reservoirs, scientists must study rocks and landforms to find potential drilling sites.[63]

The oil and gas sector is one of the six core industries in India. It is of strategic importance and plays a pivotal role in influencing decisions across other important spheres of the economy. In 1997–98, the New Exploration Licensing Policy was envisioned to deal with the ever-growing gap between demand and supply of gas in India. Two landmark initiatives for energy efficiency–Design Guidelines for Energy Efficient Multi-Storey Residential Buildings and Star Ratings for Diesel Gensets and for Hospital Buildings – were launched by Dharmendra Pradhan, Minister of State with Independent Charge for Petroleum and Natural Gas, Government of India.[64]

India is the world's fourth-largest energy consumer in the world; *oil* and gas account for 37.3 per cent of total energy consumption. With the discovery of the Cambay onshore basin and the Bombay offshore basin, the domestic oil production increased considerably. As a result, in the early 70s, almost 70 per cent of the country's oil requirement was met domestically. At independence, oil exploration and production activities were largely confined to the North-Eastern region, particularly Assam and the daily crude oil production averaged just 5,000 barrels per day. In the downstream sector, the first refinery was set up at Digboi in 1901.[65] In October 1959 an Act of Parliament was passed which gave the state owned Oil and Natural Gas Commission the powers to plan, organise, and implement programmes for the development of oil resources and the sale of petroleum products and also to perform plans sent down from central government.

Over the years India Petroleum Industry has played an influential part in triggering the speedy expansion of the country's economy by contributing 15 per cent in the total gross domestic product. Expansion of Indian petroleum retail market is triggered by the growth in automobile sales that resulted in major foreign investments. The growth is estimated to sustain and the market is likely to expand further by 20 million every year till 2030, placing India at the world map in terms of being the biggest automobile market.[66]

Middle East holds 40 per cent of the world's conventional gas reserves. The distribution of oil fields and reserves is not uniform throughout the Middle East for a variety of reasons, partly because of the size of each country. A more important factor is the location of each country with respect to the optimal petroleum geology of sedimentary basins. Middle East as consisting of ten oil-producing countries in what is geographically South West Asia: Iran, Iraq, Syria, Kuwait, Saudi Arabia, Bahrain, Qatar, United Arab Emirates,

Oman, and Yemen. These countries together cover an area of 5.4 million square kilometres (or about 3.6 per cent of the Earth's land surface) but their significance for the world's oil economy is second to none.[67]

More than 80 per cent of the world's proven oil reserves are concentrated in just 10 countries. Venezuela holds the world's biggest proven oil reserve followed by Saudi Arabia, while Canada and Russia hold the third and the eighth largest oil reserves. Venezuela holds the world's largest proven oil reserves. The country's proven oil reserve as of January 2013 stood at 297.57 billion barrels accounting for about one fifth of the world's total proven oil reserve. Saudi Arabia ranks second biggest holding 265.4 billion barrels of proven oil reserve. The Middle East country held the world's largest oil reserve until 2009, until it was surpassed by Venezuela. Canada's proven oil reserves stand at 173.1 billion barrels, which are the third largest in the world. Iran possesses the fourth largest proven oil reserves in the world and the second largest among Middle East countries. Its proven oil reserves as of December 2012 were estimated at 157 billion barrels.

Iraq, with 140.3 billion barrels of proven oil reserves, has the fifth largest oil reserves in the world and the third largest in the Middle East. Iraq's oil reserves are mainly concentrated in Shiite areas of the south and Kurdish region in the north. Kuwait holds the sixth largest proven oil reserves in the world. Most of Kuwait's territorial oil reserves are concentrated in a few mature oil fields. The Greater Burgan oil field, comprised of the Burgan, Magwa and Ahmadi reservoirs, is the largest oil field in Kuwait.

United Arab Emirates holds the world's seventh biggest oil reserve with 97.8 billion barrels of proven oil reserves. Russia, with 80 billion barrels of proven oil reserves, has the eighth largest oil reserves in the world. The North African country Libya ranks ninth, holding 48.47 billion barrels of proven oil reserve. It has the largest endowment (around 38 per cent) of the total oil reserve in the African continent. Nigeria, a West African country located on the Gulf of Guinea, holds the tenth largest proven oil reserves in the world. The country's oil reserves are mainly concentrated along Niger River Delta and offshore of the Bight of Benin, the Gulf of Guinea and the Bight of Bonny.[68]

Peat

Peat is black, brown or yellowish-brown sedimentary rock which, when dry, consists of over 50 per cent organic substances. It is formed of plant material at different stages of decomposition, having accumulated in extremely wet conditions. According to historical data, peat extraction has fundamentally changed throughout the world in the last century. After that peat extraction became economically unprofitable as oil products and, since the 1980s, also natural gas was cheaper and more easily available. Thus, since the mid-1990s, the world peat extraction has only slightly exceeded the amount extracted in the early years of the twentieth century. Today most peat goes to seed farms to propagate seedlings for forests, parks and gardens.[69]

Natural Gas

In recent years Russia has exported 25 per cent of the world gas reserves, the USA 22 per cent, Canada seven per cent, and United Kingdom four per cent. Algeria and the Netherlands export smaller amounts, while the share of other countries amounts to less than one per cent. It is noteworthy that the USA, Canada and the United Kingdom also are the biggest natural gas importers, which is yet another aspect of globalisation of the modern world.[70]

India had 38 trillion cubic feet of proven natural gas reserves as of January 2007.The total gas production in India was about 31,400 mcm in 2002-03 compared with 2,358 mcm in 1980-81. At this production level, India's reserves are likely to last for around 29 years; that is significantly longer than the 19 years estimated for oil reserves.[71] There are many natural gas companies operating in India. The Reliance Group was founded by Dhirubhai H. Ambani (1932-2002). The group's annual revenues are in excess of US$ 34 billion. Oil India Limited is a premier National oil company, engaged in the business of exploration, production and transportation of crude oil and natural gas. Indian Oil Corporation Ltd. 18th largest petroleum company in the world and has a current turnover of Rs 247,479 crores (US $59.22 billion), and profit of Rs 6963 crores (US $ 1.67 billion) for fiscal 2007. Oil and Natural Gas Corporation Ltd. (ONGC) is engaged in E&P activities both in Onshore and Offshore.

Adani Group has forayed into the Oil and Gas sector and has been awarded two oil and gas blocks in Gujarat and Assam, Gujarat and another block with an area of 95 sq. kms is situated in Assam. Petronet LNG Ltd, one of the fast growing companies in the Indian energy sector, has set up the country's first LNG receiving and regasification terminal at Dahej, Gujarat, and is in the process of building another terminal at Kochi, Kerala. GAIL (India) Limited operates as a natural gas company in India and internationally. The company involves in the exploration, production, processing, transmission, distribution, and marketing of natural gas. Bharat Petroleum Corporation Limited engages in refining, storing, marketing, and distributing petroleum products in India. It also involves in the exploration and production of hydrocarbons.[72]

Natural gas is a scarce resource in India and Government of India plays an important role in its allocation. Historically, gas has been allocated in priority to end-users such as fertilizer producers and power plants. In 2007, the GoI started working on a new Gas Utilisation Policy. Historically, gas markets were entirely serviced by PSU with prices determined by the central government. From 1987 to 2005, production and transport prices were fixed by the Empowered Group of Ministers. In retail, GAIL has also a dominant position, while OIL markets the gas it produces itself for historical and geographic reason. The pricing system in India is relatively complex due to the existence of a dual pricing resulting in two distinct gas markets.[73]

Nuclear Power

As of 2005, nuclear power provided 6.3 per cent of the world's energy and 15 per cent of the world's electricity, with the US, France and Japan together accounting for 56.5 per cent of nuclear generated electricity. The United States produces the most nuclear energy, with nuclear power providing 19 per cent of the electricity it consumes, while France produces the highest per centage of its electrical energy from nuclear reactors—80 per cent as of 2006. In the European Union as a whole, nuclear energy provides 30 per cent of the electricity. The first nuclear reactors were created to produce plutonium for nuclear weapons, and it was only in the mid-1950s that the first projects of nuclear reactors were developed for non-military purposes. The first commercial nuclear power plant came into operation in 1956, and further construction of nuclear power plants and reactors expanded fast until the Chernobyl accident.

Nuclear power is the use of nuclear reactions that release nuclear energy, to generate heat, which most frequently is then used in steam turbines to produce electricity in a nuclear power station. Along with other sustainable energy sources, nuclear fission power is a low carbon power generation method of producing electricity, meaning that it is in the renewable energy family of low associated greenhouse gas emissions, per unit of energy generated. On June 27, 1954, the USSR's Obninsk Nuclear Power Plant became the world's first nuclear power plant to generate electricity for a power grid, and produced around five megawatts of electric power. The world's first commercial nuclear power station, Calder Hall at Wind scale, England, was opened in 1956 with an initial capacity of 50 MW (later 200 MW). Life cycle analysis of carbon dioxide emissions shows nuclear power as comparable to renewable energy sources. Emissions from burning fossil fuels are many times higher. The price of energy inputs and the environmental costs of every nuclear power plant continue long after the facility has finished generating its last useful electricity.[74]

In the European Union countries nuclear power used for electricity generation comprises about one-third of the total amount of energy, but in several member states it constitutes over 60 per cent, and there is no reason to believe that the consumption of nuclear energy might decrease in the future.[75] Compressed Natural Gas (CNG) is quite simply gas that has been compressed such that it can be transported in pressure vessels rather than by pipeline as is the traditional method. It is generally used to fuel transit and fleet vehicles in large cities, as well as in a limited number of personal Natural Gas Vehicles.

Optimum Use of Resources

A business resource is anything of value to successfully operate any company. There are various steps for using resources properly:

1. *Step 1:* Learn everything can about a business resource so that can utilise that resource fully.

2. *Step 2:* Treat human business resources, your employees, with respect, admiration and recognition.
3. *Step 3:* Handle tangible business resources with care to ensure that have them for as long as possible and get maximum use out of each item before having to get a replacement.
4. *Step 4:* Turn off business machines or place them on standby when not in use to increase the operational life of the equipment.
5. *Step 5:* Negotiate all business agreements to get the best price possible and shop around to make optimum use of your company's financial resources.
6. *Step 6:* Analyse how use office supplies as another way to make optimum use of business resources.[76]

There are many strategies can be taken for the best uses of the resources

1. Improve staff productivity by automating routine server management tasks, freeing personnel time for other duties.
2. Reduce costs by reclaiming significant amounts of IT resources currently sitting idle in data centre.
3. Determine whether new applications will function in a shared environment and identify underutilised server resources on which to host them.
4. Avoid over or under-provisioning with capacity planning software that helps determine requirements of new applications.
5. Manage growth proactively with accurate forecasts for hardware investments required to meet business demands.[77]

Pýnar Su seeks to identify environmental factors and, by keeping such factors under control, to minimise the environmental harm which they cause while also continuously improving its own environmental performance. Pýnar Su is aware that people must use the natural resources they need to maintain a good way of life in a sustainable manner. Improvements were achieved in many production lines as a result of efforts to increase productivity.[78]

Land Resources

In economics, land comprises all naturally occurring resources whose supply is inherently fixed. Examples of it are any and all particular geographical locations, mineral deposits, forests, fish stocks, atmospheric quality, geostationary orbits, and portions of the electromagnetic spectrum. Land, particularly geographic locations and mineral deposits, has historically been the cause of much conflict and dispute.[79] It is a productive economic factor in agriculture, forestry, grazing, fishing and mining. It is considered as a foundation of social prestige and is the basis of wealth and political power.

It has many physical forms like mountains, hills, plains, lowlands and valleys. It is characterised by climate from hot to cold and from humid to dry. Land may be defined as a physical environment consisting of relief, soil, hydrology, climate and vegetation in so far as they are determined by the land use. Value of land depends on its size, location, distance from the market and nature of potential use besides productive.[80]

Land is a finite resource. It is subject to competing pressures from urbanisation, infrastructure, increased food, feed, fibre and fuel production and the provision of key ecosystem services.[81] Land resources meet many human needs. In fact, they provide the base for life and are the building blocks for development. Only 30 per cent of the earth's surface is land. Different factors are responsible for the changes in the land use pattern of a country or a region at a given time. The land use, in any part of the world, depends on Physical factors and Human factors. Of all the land resources, soil is our prime resource. The plants that grow on the Earth's land areas could not exist without the thin, loose, surface layer that we call soil.[82]

Changing climate patterns, economic globalisation population growth, increasing use of natural resources and rapid urbanisation are putting pressure on terrestrial ecosystems as never before, and virtually all of them are under stress. Growing demands for food, feed, fuel, fibre and raw materials create local and distant pressures for land-use change.[83] Natural resources occur naturally within environments that exist relatively undisturbed by humanity, in a natural form. Resource extraction involves any activity that withdraws resources from nature. In recent years, the depletion of natural resources has become a major focus of governments and organisations such as the United Nations.[84]

Integrate soil and crop management principles with modern tools to maximise profitability and environmental stewardship in diversified cropping systems. Research opportunities include partnerships with government agencies and private industry to develop cost-effective reclamation methods and to evaluate critical interrelationships within disturbed and reclaimed systems.[85] Degradation of natural resources and environmental pollutions are most concerning subject in present day context among the social scientist as well as the environmentalist. As the population increase day by day the amenities are not improving simultaneously. With the advancement of science and technologies the needs of human beings have been changing rapidly.[86]

Forest Resources

Forest is a large area of land covered with trees or other woody vegetation. It is a biotic community predominantly of trees, shrubs and other woody vegetation, usually with a closed canopy. United Nations Food and Agriculture Organisation definition, forests covered an area of four billion hectares (15 million square miles) or approximately 30 per cent of the world's land area in 2006. Forests provide ecosystem services to humans and serve as tourist attractions. Forests can impose costs, affect people's health, and interfere with tourist enjoyment.[87]

Human are indisputably a part of most forests. With the exception of extremely inaccessible forestlands, all forests present on Earth today have been influenced by human being for tens of thousands of years.[88] Deforestation is the dominant environmental, social and economic issue affecting the forestry sector. The removal of trees has a range of very negative impacts, including increased land and water resource degradation, and the loss of livelihoods from forest ecosystem services.[89] Forest can be classified in various ways:

1. *Tropical Rainforest:* The tropical rainforests contain the greatest diversity of species of all biomes on earth. They are found around the equator, between 23.5 degrees N latitude and 23.5 degrees S latitude.
2. *Temperate Deciduous Forest:* Eastern United States and Canada, Western Europe and parts of Russia, China and Japan. Maple, oak and birch trees are some examples of the deciduous trees that dominate these forests.
3. *Temperate Coniferous Forest:* Temperate coniferous forests are typically found in coastal areas with mild winters and heavy rainfall or in in-land mountainous areas with mild climates. Examples of where these forests are found are Pacific Northwestern United States and Canada, southwestern South America, Southern Japan, New Zealand and small parts of northwestern Europe (Ireland, Scotland, Iceland and Norway).
4. *Boreal (taiga) Forest:* This is the northern most forest type and is found between 50 and 60 degrees N latitude. Boreal forests are found in Canada, northern Asia, Siberia and Scandinavia (Denmark, Norway, Sweden, and Finland).[90]

Forests are important renewable natural resources that contribute substantially to economic development. They provide raw materials to a number of important industries, namely, matchboxes, paper, newsprint, rayon, furniture, construction, tanning etc.[91] Today, people depend on forests more than ever, especially for their economic value, environmental value, and enjoyment value. The science of forestry is concerned with increasing and preserving these values by careful management of forestland.[92] Forests also provides material for industry. Those who build houses get timer for house building and for various other purposes.[93]

The progress of human depends upon the exploitation of different natural resources. The utilisation of soil, water, coal, electricity, oil, gas and nuclear energy is very important for the development of nation.[94] Natural resources are conserved due to economic as their natural beauty and importance to local culture. Preserving biodiversity is essential for ecosystems to respond flexibly to damage or change.[95] Mismanagement and overuse of India's once abundant forests has resulted in desertification, contamination, and soil depletion throughout the sub-continent. This has serious repercussions for the livelihoods of hundreds of millions of Indians that live off the land. In Rajasthan alone, it is approximated that nearly five million tribal people (as of 2004) rely on the collection of forest produce as their only source of income or nourishment.[96]

Forests, the green cover, are the natural resource infrastructure for agriculture/primary production and rural economic growth. India, harbouring 16 major forest types – tropical, temperate, alpine etc., is one of the 17 mega diversity centres and two biodiversity hot spots of the world. Per capita forest area in the country (0.064 ha) is one-tenth of that of the world's average, and 41 per cent of the country's forest cover is degraded.[97] The forests of India cover about one-fifth of the total area of land and supply valuable timber, firewood, resins, essential oils, lac, dyeing material, source of paper pulp and other materials for commerce and industry.[98]

Forests of India are ancient in nature and composition, rich in variety and shelter a wide range of fauna, avifauna and insects. India possesses a distinct identity, not only because of its geography, history and culture but also because of great diversity of its natural ecosystems. Main areas of tropical forest are found in Andaman and Nicobar Islands, Western Ghats, which fringe the Arabian Sea coastline of peninsular India, and greater Assam region in north-east.[99] The important forest legislations in India are:[100]

1. **The Indian Forest Act, 1927:** The Indian Forest Act, 1927 was largely based on previous Indian Forest Acts implemented under the British. The most famous one was the Indian Forest Act of 1878. Both the 1878 act and the 1927 one sought to consolidate and reserve the areas having forest cover, or significant wildlife, to regulate movement and transit of forest produce, and duty leviable on timber and other forest produce. Village Forest is constituted under section 28 of the Indian Forest Act, 1927. The government may assign to any village community the rights over a land which may not be a part of a reserved forest for use of the community. Protected Forest an area or mass of land notified under the provisions of India Forest Act or the State Forest Acts having limited degree of protection. In Protected Forests all activities are permitted unless prohibited. Protected Forest is an area or mass of land, which is a reserved forest, and over which the government has property rights, declared to be so by a State Government under the provisions of the section 29 of the Indian Forest Act, 1927.[101]

2. **The Wildlife Protection Act, 1972:** The Wildlife Protection Act, 1972 is an Act of the Parliament of India enacted for protection of plants and animal species. The Act provides for the protection of wild animals, birds and plants; and for matters connected therewith or ancillary or incidental thereto. It extends to the whole of India, except the State of Jammu and Kashmir which has its own wildlife act. It has six schedules which give varying degrees of protection.[102]
3. **The Forest Conservation Act, 1980**: The Parliament has enacted the Forest (Conservation) Act, 1980, to check further deforestation and conserve forests and to provide for matters connected therewith or ancillary or incidental thereto. The Act was enacted with the twin objectives under Section 2 of restricting the use of forest land for non-forest purposes, and preventing the de-reservation of forests that have been reserved under the Indian Forest Act, 1927. However, in 1988 the Act was further amended to include two new provisions under Section 2, where it sought to restrict leasing of forest land to private individuals, authority, corporations not owned by the government, and to prevent clear felling of naturally grown trees. The Act empowers the Central Government to constitute a committee to advise the government with a grant of approval under Section 2, as also on any other matter connected with the conservation of forest and referred to it by the Central Government.[103]
4. **The Scheduled Tribes and other Traditional Forest Dwellers Act, 2006:**[104] It is a key piece of forest legislation passed in India on 18 December 2006. It has also been called the Forest Rights Act, the Tribal Rights Act, the Tribal Bill, and the Tribal Land Act. The law concerns the rights of forest-dwelling communities to land and other resources, denied to them over decades as a result of the continuance of colonial forest laws in India. The rights which are included in section 3(1)[105] of the Act are:

(a) Right to hold and live in the forest land under the individual or common occupation for habitation or for self-cultivation for livelihood by a member or members of a forest dwelling Scheduled Tribe or other traditional forest dwellers;

(b) Community rights such as *nistar*, by whatever name called, including those used in erstwhile Princely states, Zamindari or such intermediary regimes;

(c) Right of ownership, access to collect, use, and dispose of minor forest produce (includes all non-timber forest produce of plant origin) which has been traditionally collected within or outside village boundaries;

(d) Other community rights of uses of entitlements such as fish and other products of water bodies, grazing (both settled or transhumant) and traditional seasonal resource access of nomadic or pastoralist communities;

(e) Rights including community tenures of habitat and habitation for primitive tribal groups and pre-agriculture communities;

(f) Rights in or over disputed lands under any nomenclature in any State where claims are disputed;

(g) Rights for conversion of Pattas or leases or grants issued by any local council or any State Govt. on forest lands to titles;

(h) Rights of settlement and conversion of all forest villages, old habitation, unsurveyed villages and other villages in forest, whether recorded, notified or not into revenue villages;

(i) Right to protect, regenerate or conserve or manage any community forest resource which they have been traditionally protecting and conserving for sustainable use;

(j) Rights which are recognised under any State law or laws of any Autonomous Dist. Council or Autonomous Regional Council or which are accepted as rights of tribals under any traditional or customary law of the concerned tribes of any State;

(k) Right of access to biodiversity and community right to intellectual property and traditional knowledge related to biodiversity and cultural diversity;

(l) Any other traditional right customarily enjoyed by the forest dwelling Scheduled Tribes or other traditional forest dwellers, as the case may be, which are not mentioned in clauses-1 to 11, but excluding the traditional right of hunting or trapping extracting a part of the body of any species of wild animal (Source: wikipedia).

Social Forestry

Social forestry means the management and protection of forests and afforestation on barren lands with the purpose of helping in the environmental, social and rural development. The term, social forestry, was first used in India in 1976 by The National Commission on Agriculture, Government of India. Social forestry also aims at raising plantations by the common man so as to meet the growing demand for timber, fuel wood, fodder, etc., thereby reducing the pressure on the traditional forest area.[106]

The National Commission for Farmers has determined the following objectives for social forestry -

(1) To cooperate soil conservation and to prevent spoiling the productive capacity of soil.

(2) To increase fuel availability and to increase the food modification by increasing fruit production.

(3) To encourage plantation of large and beautiful trees which provide shadow to enhance the natural beauty and to plant all around the cultivation field to increase production.

(4) To encourage environment conservation by plantation and to create general consciousness regarding environment conservation.

(5) To enhance the natural beauty of the villages and cities by plantation.[107]

Management of Common and Forest Land

Common land is land owned collectively by a number of persons, or by one person, but over which other people have certain traditional rights, such as to allow their livestock to graze upon it, to collect firewood, or to cut turf for fuel. When open habitats are no longer grazed they start to develop scrub and then dense woodland, losing the grassy or heath land vegetation which may have occupied the land continuously for many centuries. The legal position concerning common land has been confused, but recent legislation has sought to remedy this and remove the legal uncertainties so that commons can be better used and protected. Most commons are based on ancient rights, that is to say common law (coincidence of term only), which pre-date statute law laid down by parliament.[108]

Sustainable forest management is the management of forests according to the principles of sustainable development. The "Forest Principles" adopted at The United Nations Conference on Environment and Development in Rio de Janeiro in 1992 captured the general international understanding of sustainable forest management at that time. A definition of Sustainable forest management was developed by the Ministerial Conference on the Protection of Forests in Europe, and has since been adopted by the Food and Agriculture Organisation. It defines sustainable forest management as: The stewardship and use of forests and forest lands in a way, and at a rate, that maintains their biodiversity, productivity, regeneration capacity, vitality and their potential to fulfill, now and in the future, relevant ecological, economic and social functions, at local, national, and global levels, and that does not cause damage to other ecosystems.[109]

Common forest management seems to offer most scope for further development under the following conditions:

- where forests are intimately linked to not yet predominantly commercialised farming systems,

- where management activities allow for early and clearly visible benefits in the form of products to be used either in the household or the farm enterprise (agriculture and livestock), and
- where productivity of the forest (in minor forest products such as fodder, as well as in wood) is sufficiently high or can be relatively easily increased so as to allow for profitable returns to management investments.[110]

A Commoner is a person who occupies land to which Common Rights in the New Forest are attached. A Right of Common is authority for the occupier of a plot of land (to which Rights are attached), to take specified material or products from somebody else's land. Rights of Common of Pasture are attributed to land. It permits depasturing of "commonable" animals on 45,000 acres of Open Forest. Common of Mast is the right to turn out pigs in the Forest during the Pannage season. The Pannage season is a period of not less than 60 days, fixed by the Forestry Commission after consultation with the Verderers. Right of Turbary allows the Commoner to cut turf for fuel; turves were once cut in tens of thousands each year. Right of Fuelwood is to cut wood for fuel. The wood must be burned in the house and the Right applies to the hearth, not land. There are Rights to depasture sheep at very few holdings, principally at Godshill and Beaulieu - lands formerly belonging to monastic properties.[111]

Control over land and natural resources has recently become a subject of heated debate in India, and is, today, one of the central fault lines of Indian politics. No party or political leader can afford not to have a position on questions of land acquisition and displacement; as such issues are now seen as electorally important. While definitions of the terms "common property resources," "common pool resources," and "common lands" vary between analysts, certain shared features are clearly visible. What are generally understood as common lands are those that provide services to a limited (if not always rigidly defined) community. Examples include grazing lands, water bodies, village lands, forests, etc. Forest and common lands are under constant threat.

One major and obvious impact is the loss of livelihoods from the land areas that are taken over. This includes the loss of minor forest produce, the destruction or takeover of shifting cultivation lands, the loss of grazing areas, etc. In several types of land takeover, the consequences extend well beyond forest and common lands and their direct uses. The effects include pollution, damage to the water table, additional resources taken from the surrounding area, changes in the ecosystem and so on.

Indian forest law is centred on the Indian Forest Act of 1927, the third in a series of Forest Acts passed by the colonial administration. The Forest Act defines different regulatory systems for different classes of forest, of which the two most significant are reserved forest and protected forest. In 1980, the

Forest (Conservation) Act was passed, making permission of the Central Government mandatory for use of forest land for "non-forest" purposes. Following mass protests against evictions, in 2006 the Central Government passed the Scheduled Tribes and Other Traditional Forest Dwellers (Recognition of Forest Rights) Act that better known as the Forest Rights Act. For the first time, this legislation provided for explicit recognition of the rights of forest-dwelling communities over common lands and resources, including using land for cultivation, minor forest produce, grazing areas, water bodies, etc.[112]

Energy Efficiency

Energy efficiency is the goal to reduce the amount of energy required to provide products and services. For example, insulating a home allows a building to use less heating and cooling energy to achieve and maintain a comfortable temperature. Energy efficiency and renewable energy are said to be the twin pillars of sustainable energy policy. Energy efficiency has proved to be a cost-effective strategy for building economies without necessarily increasing energy consumption. Installing a clothesline will significantly reduce one's energy consumption as their dryer will be used less.[113]

Energy efficiency is one of the easiest and most cost effective ways to combat climate change clean the air we breathe, improve the competitiveness of our businesses and reduce energy costs for consumers. The Department of Energy is working with universities, businesses and the National Labs to develop new, energy-efficient technologies while boosting the efficiency of current technologies on the market.[114] The International Energy Agency promotes energy efficiency policy and technology in buildings, appliances, transport and industry, as well as end-use applications such as lighting. Its analysis has led to the development of 25 energy efficiency recommendations which identify best-practice, highlighting the opportunities for energy efficiency improvements and policy approaches in each sector to realise the full potential of energy efficiency for our member countries.[115]

Ultra-efficient homes combine state-of-the-art energy-efficient construction, appliances, and lighting with commercially available renewable energy systems, such as solar water heating and solar electricity. By taking advantage of local climate and site conditions, designers can often also incorporate passive solar heating and cooling and energy-efficient landscaping strategies. The intent is to reduce home energy use as cost-effectively as possible, and then meet the reduced load with on-site renewable energy systems.[116]

Social and environmental changes have increased focus on conservation of natural resources and sustainable living. Recent economic changes have also caused consumers to revaluate how they use energy, with new attention being given to maximising efficiency. Employing more efficient building methods in new construction and in renovation could reduce the amount of energy consumed, thereby saving money and reducing electric load growth and air emissions resulting from electric generation. State government could adopt a much larger leadership role in advocating building efficiency and demonstrating its benefits.[117]

According to the website of Ministry of Power, Government of India, The Energy Conservation Act (EC Act) was enacted in 2001 with the goal of reducing energy intensity of Indian economy. Bureau of Energy Efficiency was set up as the statutory body on 1st March 2002 at the central level to facilitate the implementation of the EC Act. The Act provides regulatory mandate for: standards and labeling of equipment and appliances; energy conservation building codes for commercial buildings; and energy consumption norms for energy intensive industries. In addition, the Act enjoins the Central Govt. and the Bureau to take steps to facilitate and promote energy efficiency in all sectors of the economy. The Act also directs states to designate agencies for the implementation of the Act and promotion of energy efficiency in the state. Ministry of Power, through Bureau of Energy Efficiency, has initiated a number of energy efficiency initiatives in the areas of household lighting, commercial buildings, standards and labeling of appliances, demand side management in agriculture/municipalities, SME's and large industries including the initiation of the process for development of energy consumption norms for industrial sub-sectors, capacity building of SDA's etc.

The Energy Conservation Building Code was developed by Govt. of India for new commercial buildings on 27th May 2007. It sets minimum energy standards for new commercial buildings having a connected load of 10 kW or contract demand of 120 KVA and above. In order to tap the energy saving potential, Agriculture Demand Side Management programme was initiated in XI plan by Bureau of Energy Efficiency with an objective to induce energy efficiency in agriculture sector by creating market based framework for implementation of few pilot projects and create awareness among end users and other stakeholders for adoption of energy efficient pump sets. To encourage the energy efficient technologies and operational practices in SME sectors in India, Bureau of Energy Efficiency has initiated the energy efficiency interventions in selected 25 SMEs clusters during the Eleventh Plan.

The State Energy Conservation Fund is an instrument to overcome the major barriers for implementation of energy efficiency projects. The contribution under State Energy Conservation Fund was made to those State Govt. / UT Administration who have created their fund and finalised the rules and regulations to operationalise the same. The potential for improvement of energy efficiency of processes and equipment through awareness creation is vast. A sound policy for creation, retention and upgradation of skills of Human Resources is very crucial for penetration of energy efficient technologies and practices in various sectors. The National Mission for Enhanced Energy Efficiency is one of the eight missions under the National Action Plan on

Climate Change. It aims to strengthen the market for energy efficiency by creating conducive regulatory and policy regime and has envisaged fostering innovative and sustainable business models to the energy efficiency sector.

Environment Energy Taxation

Government is underutilising taxation as a tool to curb the environmental consequences of energy use, foregoing revenue and weakening their attack on the principal source of greenhouse gas emissions responsible for climate change and air pollution, according to new OECD analysis. The OECD says that taxes on energy use provide a transparent policy signal and are one of the most effective tools governments have for reducing the negative side effects of energy use. Taxes on energy use are shown to be low relative to the environmental costs of energy use, both on average and within many countries.[118]

Environmental taxes have been increasingly used to influence the behaviour of economic operators, whether producers or consumers. These taxes also generate revenue that can potentially be used to promote further environmental protection. The total revenue from environmental taxes in the EU-28 in 2013 was EUR 331 billion; this figure equates to 2.5 per cent of gross domestic product and to 6.3 per cent of the total revenues derived from all taxes and social contributions. From 2006 to 2013, the total environmental tax revenue in the EU increased by 1.6 per cent per year (at current prices) on an average.

Energy taxes represented by far the highest share of overall environmental tax revenue, accounting for 75.0 per cent of the EU-28 total in 2013. Transport taxes represented the second most important contribution to total environmental tax revenues, with 20.1 per cent of the EU-28 total in 2013. The implicit tax rate on energy is defined as the ratio of energy tax revenues to final energy consumption calculated for a calendar year. Economic instruments for pollution control and natural resource management are an increasingly important part of environmental policy in the EU Member States. Environmental taxes have been increasingly used to influence the behaviour of economic operators, whether producers or consumers.[119]

Rajiv Gandhi Grameen Vidyutikaran Yojana

The scheme has been launched to fulfill the commitment of the National Common Minimum Programme of completing the household electrification in next five years and modernising the rural electricity infrastructure. The scheme, to be implemented through Rural Electrification Corporation, will provide Ninety per cent of the capital cost of the programme by the Central Government as grant. The scheme provides for free of cost connection to all rural households living below poverty line. Further, there will no discrimination in the hours of supply between rural and urban areas.

The scheme has a target of electrifying 1,25,000 un-electrified villages and giving access to 7.8 crore uncovered rural households in next five years. The Central Government has already approved Rs 5000 crores for providing capital subsidy for this scheme in the remaining period of Tenth Five Year Plan.

Rural Electrification Policy

In compliance with Sections 4 and 5 of the Electricity Act, 2003, the Central Government hereby notifies the Rural Electrification Policy. Rural Electrification is viewed as the key for accelerating rural development. The National Electricity Policy states that the key development objective of the power sector is supply of electricity to all areas including rural areas as mandated in Section 6 of the Electricity Act. Accordingly, the Central Government has launched in April, 2005 an ambitious scheme 'Rajiv Gandhi Grameen Vidhyutikaran Yojana' with the goal of electrifying all un-electrified villages/un-electrified hamlets and providing access to electricity to all households in next five years for fulfillment of the NCMP. The Policy aims at: (a) Provision of access to electricity to all households by year 2009; (b) Quality and reliable power supply at reasonable rates; and (c) Minimum lifeline consumption of 1 unit per household per day as a merit good by year 2012.

The Central Government has reviewed the existing schemes of rural electrification recently and has launched a comprehensive programme RGGVY. Under the scheme, projects could be financed with 90 per cent capital subsidy. Rural Electrification Corporation Limited, a Government of India enterprise under the Ministry of Power, is the nodal agency at Central Government level to implement the rural electrification programme. It is also providing loan assistance for projects of rural electrification. The Gram Panchayat/ Village Council or equivalent shall issue the first Certificate at the time of the village becoming eligible for declaration as electrified.

The State Government should set up a committee at the District level pursuant to Section 166(5) of the Act within three months. The District Committee should be constituted under the Chairmanship of the Chairperson of the Zila Panchayat/Chairperson of the District Planning Committee/ Collector of the district and should inter alia have representations from various concerned district level agencies, consumer associations and other important stakeholders. The Act provides that the District Committees would coordinate and review the extension of electrification in the district, review the quality of power supply and consumer satisfaction and promote energy efficiency and conservation. The District Committee should also facilitate the Rural Electrification projects, both through stand-alone systems and grid extension and local management projects, as may be required. The State Governments should take steps for bringing awareness on electricity related issues including generation, distribution, energy conservation and energy efficiency and energy-water nexus among elected Panchayat representatives.

Government-owned Power Companies

India's Ministry of Power administers central government owned companies involved in the generation of electricity in India, i.e. National Thermal Power Corporation, Damodar Valley Corporation, National Hydroelectric Power Corporation and Nuclear Power Corporation of India. The Power Grid Corporation of India is also administered by the Ministry; it is responsible for the inter-state transmission of electricity and the development of national grid.

National Thermal Power Corporation Limited is an Indian Central Public Sector Undertaking under the Ministry of Power, Government of India. It was founded by Government of India in 1975, which now holds 70 per cent of its equity shares on 13 May 2015. In May 2010, NTPC was conferred Maharatna status by the Union Government of India. NTPC operates from 55 locations in India, one location in Sri Lanka and two locations in Bangladesh. The total installed capacity of the company is 43,803 MW (including JVs) with 17 coal-based and seven gas-based stations, located across the country. In addition, under joint ventures, six stations are coal-based, and another station uses naphtha/LNG as fuel. The headquarters of the company is situated at New Delhi. Corporations core business is generation and sale of electricity to state-owned power distribution companies and State Electricity Boards in India.

Damodar Valley Corporation is public company which operates several power stations in the Damodar River area of West Bengal, India. The company operates both thermal power station and hydel power dams under the Indian Ministry of Power. In March 1948, the Damodar Valley Corporation Act (Act No. XIV of 1948) was passed by the Constituent Assembly, and the Damodar Valley Corporation was officially formed on July 7, 1948. The corporation was jointly formed by the government bodies: Central Government, the Government of West Bengal and the Government of Jharkhand to participate jointly for the purpose of building the Damodar Valley Corporation. Corporation has a network of four dams - Tilaiya and Maithon on river Barakar, Panchet on river Damodar and Konar on river Konar. A joint venture company by DVC and Tata Power has been formed to implement 1050 MW Maithon Right Bank Thermal Power Project for meeting the energy needs of power deficient regions on export basis. Corporation is headquartered in the city of Kolkata, West Bengal, India.

National Hydroelectric Power Corporation is an Indian Hydro Power Generation company that was incorporated in the year 1975. It is listed in National Stock Exchange and Bombay Stock Exchange on September 1, 2009.

At present, corporation is a schedule 'A' Enterprise of the Govt. of India with an authorised share capital of Rs 1,50,000 Million. Presently it is engaged in the construction of nine projects aggregating to a total installed capacity of 4271 MW. Corporation has planned to add 5322 MW during Eleventh Plan Period. Twelve projects of 9651 MW are awaiting clearances/Govt. approval for their implementation. Since its inception in 1975, NHPC has grown to become one of the largest organisations in the field of hydropower development in the country.

The Nuclear Power Corporation of India Limited is a government-owned corporation of India based in the financial capital of India viz Mumbai in the state of Maharashtra. It is wholly owned by the Central Government and is responsible for the generation of nuclear power for electricity. It is administered by the Department of Atomic Energy, Govt. of India. It was created in September 1994 as under the Govt. The head of the Mega project is Mr. Purohit. Act 1956, "with the objective of undertaking the design, construction, operation and maintenance of the atomic power stations for generation of electricity in pursuance of the schemes and programmes of the Government of India under the provision of the Atomic Energy Act 1962."

elangana Power Generation Corporation Limited is a power generating organisation of Telangana. It has ceased to do power trading and has retained with powers of controlling system operations of Power Generation after formation of Telangana state. Telangana Power Generation Corporation Limited has been incorporated under Companies Act, 2013, on 19 May 2014 and commenced its operations from 2nd June 2014. Andhra Pradesh Power Generation Corporation Limited is a power generating organisation in Andhra Pradesh. It undertakes operation and maintenance of the power plants and also setting up new power projects alongside upgrading the project's capacity. The total installed capacity of APGENCO, after the formation of TSGenCo is 4559.6 MW comprising 2810 MW Thermal, 1747.6 MW Hydro and 2 MW Wind power stations.

Tamil Nadu Electricity Board is a power generation and distribution company owned by Government of Tamil Nadu. It was created under section 131 of the Electricity Act (2003) as a successor of the erstwhile Tamil Nadu Electricity Board. It was formed on 1st July 1957 as the Madras State Electricity Board according to the Electricity Supply Act of 1948 as a successor to the erstwhile Electricity Department of the Government of Madras under the authority of the Department of Power.

Maharashtra State Electricity Board is a state-owned electricity regulation board operating within the state of Maharashtra in India. The MSEB was formed on 20 June 1960 under Section 5 of the Electricity (Supply) Act, 1948. Kerala State Electricity Board Ltd is a public sector agency under the Government of Kerala, India that generates, transmits and distributes the electricity supply in the state. Established in 1957, the agency comes under the authority of the Department of Power.

The Gujarat Urja Vikas Nigam Limited is an electrical services umbrella company in the state of Gujarat, India. It was set up in May 1999 and is registered under the Companies Act, 1956. Accordingly, erstwhile Gujarat Electricity Board was reorganised effective from 1st April 2005 into Seven Companies with functional responsibilities of Trading, Generation, Transmission and Distribution etc. Power Finance Corporation Ltd. is an Indian financial institution. Established in 1986, it is the financial backbone of Indian Power Sector. PFC presently has nine subsidiary companies. PFC Consulting Ltd. is a wholly owned subsidiary handling fee based services.

Ministry of Power

The Ministry of Power is an Indian government ministry. The ministry is charged with overseeing electricity production and infrastructure development, including generation, transmission, and delivery, as well as maintenance projects. The ministry acts as a liaison between the central government and state electricity operations, as well as with the private sector. The Ministry of Power became a ministry on July 2, 1992.

The Ministry of Power is mainly responsible for evolving general policy in the field of energy. The main items of work dealt with by the Ministry of Power are: (a) General Policy in the electric power sector and issues relating to energy policy and coordination thereof; (b) All matters relating to hydro-electric power (except small/mini/micro hydel projects of and below 25 MW capacity) and thermal power and transmission and distribution system network; and (c) Research, development and technical assistance relating to hydro-electric and thermal power, transmission system network and distribution systems in the States/UTs; (d) All matters relating to Central Electricity Authority, Central Electricity Board and Central Electricity Regulatory Commission.

According to wikipedia, there are many organisations are working under the ministry, like as:

(a) **Central Electricity Authority:** It is a statutory organisation constituted under Section 3(1) of Electricity Supply Act 1948, which has been superseded by Section 70(1) of the Electricity Act 2003. Under the Electricity Act 2003, CEA prescribes the standards on matters such as construction of electrical plants, electric lines and connectivity to the grid, installation and operation of meters and safety and grid standards.

    The CEA plays a lead role in promoting the integrated operations of the regional power grids and the evolution of a national grid. The eastern, western and north-eastern grids have been integrated and are operating in a synchronous mode. The eastern grid is connected to the northern as well as southern grid through HVDC back to back links. The CEA advises central government, state governments and regulatory commissions on all technical matters relating to generation, transmission and distribution of electricity.

(b) **Appellate Tribunal for Electricity:** According to website of Appellate Tribunal and for Electricity, on 10th June, 2003, the Electricity Act was notified by the Govt. of India. This Act seeks to consolidate the laws relating to generation, transmission, distribution, trading and use of electricity and generally for taking measures conducive to development of electricity industry, promoting competition therein, protecting interest of consumers and supply of electricity to all areas, rationalisation of electricity tariff ensuring transparent policies regarding subsidies, promotion of efficient and environmentally benign policies, constitution of Central Electricity Authority, Regulatory Commissions and establishment of Appellate Tribunal and for matters connected therewith or incidental thereto. The Act extends to the whole of India except the state of Jammu & Kashmir.

According to website of Ministry of Power, Govt. of India, concerns relating to pollution and the disposal of the large amount of ash from coal based power stations, which are the mainstay of India's power generation, are being addressed through strategies to promote environmentally sustainable power development. A Special Purpose Vehicle is being set up jointly by NTPC and other Central Power Sector Undertakings as a Registered Society to take up afforestation and environmental measures in order to reduce the carbon dioxide in the atmosphere. All the coal based power stations put together generate around 90 million tonnes of fly-ash per annum. The Fly Ash Mission of TIFAC has made several useful recommendations for utilisation of fly-ash in the manufacture of cement, bricks, pavement materials, floor tiles, wall panels etc., and in agriculture, road construction, land-filling and back-filling of mines.

To address increasing concerns related to the environment and to improve environmental performance, the services of Tata Energy Research Institute (TERI) have been engaged for providing consultancy services to the Ministry of Power on CDM. Established in November 1975 for nation's Sustainable Power Development, National Thermal Power Corporation Ltd. is India's largest power utility with an installed capacity of 21,749 MW contributing to 26 per cent of total generation in the country, with high availability factor of its power plants. NTPC has plans to double its capacity.

Development of Ultra Mega Power Projects (UMPPs) is very large sized projects, approximately 4000 MW each involving an estimated investment of about 25,000 crores. The projects will substantially reduce power shortages in the country. These projects will meet the power needs of a number of States/ distribution companies located in these States, and are being developed on

Design, Build, Finance, Operate and Transfer basis. Originally nine such projects had been identified to be taken up, four at pithead and five at coastal locations. The Ministry of Power is playing a crucial role for the development of the UMPPs by coordinating between various concerned Ministries/ Agencies of the Central Government, and with various State Governments/ Agencies.

Table 2: The Annual Growth in Power Generation

Year	Growth in Achievement (per cent)
2008-09	2.7
2009-10	6.6
2010-11	5.56
2011-12	8.11
2012-13	4.01
2013-14	6.04
2014-15	8.43

Source: Website of Ministry of Power (http://powermin.nic.in/Overview-0)

The Special Purpose Vehicles are responsible for carrying out various activities on behalf of the procurers. Completion of these activities prior to award of the project is considered necessary to enhance the investor's confidence, reduce risk perception and get a good response to the competitive bidding process. States hosting the UMPPs and the other power procuring States are playing a proactive role. Four UMPPs namely, Sasan in Madhya Pradesh, Mundra in Gujarat, Krishnapatnam in Andhra Pradesh and Tilaiya in Jharkhand have already been awarded to the successful bidders and are at different state of development.

Energy Conservation Act 2001

It extends to the whole of India except the state of Jammu and Kashmir. It shall come into force on such dates as the Central Government may, by notification in the Official Gazette, appoint; and different dates may be appointed for different provisions of this Act and any reference in any such provision to the commencement of this Act shall be construed as a reference to the coming into force of that provision. With effect from such date as the Central Government may, by notification, appoint, there shall be established, for the purposes of this Act, a Bureau to be called the Bureau of Energy Efficiency. The general superintendence, direction and management of the affairs of the Bureau shall vest in the Governing Council which shall consists of not less than twenty, but not exceeding twenty-six members to be appointed by the Central Government.

The Governing Council may exercise all powers and do all acts and things which may be exercised or done by the Bureau. The Governing Council shall meet at such times and places, and shall observe such rules of procedure in regard to the transaction of business as its meetings (including quorum of such meetings) as may be provided by regulations. Subject to any regulations made in this behalf, the Bureau shall, within six months from the date of commencement of this Act, constitute Advisory Committees for the efficient discharge of its functions. Each Advisory Committee shall consist of a Chairperson and such other members as may be determined by regulations.

The Central Government shall, by notification, appoint a Director-General from amongst persons of ability and standing, having adequate knowledge and experience in dealing with the matters relating to energy production, supply and energy management standardisation and efficient use of energy and its conservation. The Central Government shall, by notification appoint any person not below the rank of Deputy Secretary to the Government of India as Secretary of the Bureau. The Director-General shall hold office for a term of three years from the date on which he enters upon his office or until he attains the age of sixty years, whichever is earlier. The salary and allowances payable to the Director-General and other terms and conditions of his service and other terms and conditions of service of the Secretary of the Bureau shall be such as may be prescribed. The Director-General of the Bureau shall exercise and discharge such powers and duties of the Bureau as may be determined by regulations.

The Central Government may appoint such other officers and employees in the Bureau as it considers necessary for the efficient discharge of its functions under this Act. The Bureau shall, effectively co-ordinate with designated consumers, designated agencies and other agencies, recognise and utilise the existing resources and infrastructure, in performing the functions assigned to it by or under this Act. The State Government shall constitute a Fund to be called the State Energy Conservation Fund for the purposes of promotion of efficient use of energy and its conservation within the State. To the Fund shall be credited all grants and loans that may be made by the State Government or, Central Government or any other organisation or individual for the purposes of this Act. The Fund shall be applied for meeting the expenses incurred for implementing the provisions of this Act.

The designated agency may appoint, after the expiry of five years from the date of commencement of this Act, as many inspecting officers as may be necessary for the purpose of ensuring compliance with energy consumption standard specified under clause (a) of section 14 or ensure display of particulars on label on equipment or appliances specified under clause (b) of section 14 or for the purpose of performing such other functions as may be assigned to them. The Central Government or the State Government may, in the exercise of its powers and performance of its functions under this Act and for efficient use of energy and its conservation, issue such directions in writing as it deems fit for the purposes of this Act to any person, officer, authority or any designated consumer and such person, officer or authority or any designated consumer shall be bound to comply with such directions.

The Central Government may, after due appropriation made by Parliament by law in this behalf, make to the Bureau or to the State Government grants and loans of such sums or money as the Central Government may consider necessary. The Bureau may, with the consent of the Central Government or in accordance with the terms of any general or special authority given to it by the Central Government borrow money from any source as it may deem fit for discharging all or any of its functions under this Act. The Bureau shall prepare, in such form and at such time in each financial year as may be prescribed, its budget for the next financial year, showing the estimated receipts and expenditure of the Bureau and forward the same to the Central Government. The Bureau shall prepare, in such form and at such time in each financial year as may be prescribed, its annual report, giving full account of its activities during the previous financial year, and submit a copy thereof to the Central Government.

The Bureau shall maintain proper accounts and other relevant records and prepare an annual statement of accounts in such form as may be prescribed by the Central Government in consultation with the Comptroller and Auditor-General of India. The accounts of the Bureau shall be audited by the Comptroller and Auditor-General of India at such intervals as may be specified by him and any expenditure incurred in connection with such audit shall be payable by the Bureau to the Comptroller and Auditor-General. The Comptroller and Auditor-General of India and any other person appointed by him in connection with the audit of the accounts of the Bureau shall have the same rights and privileges and authority in connection with such audit as the Comptroller and Auditor-General generally has in connection with the audit of the Government accounts and in particular, shall have the right to demand the production of books, accounts, connected vouchers and other documents and papers and to inspect any of the offices of the Bureau. The accounts of the Bureau as certified by the Comptroller and Auditor-General of India or any other person appointed by him in this behalf together with the audit report thereon shall forward annually to the Central Government and that Government shall cause the same to be laid before each House of Parliament.

The Central Government shall, by notification, establish an Appellate Tribunal to be known as the Appellate Tribunal for Energy Conservation to hear appeals against the orders of the adjudicating officer or the Central Government or the State Government or any other authority under this Act. Any person aggrieved, by an order made by an adjudicating officer or the Central Government or the State Government or any other authority under this Act, may prefer an appeal to the Appellate Tribunal for Energy Conservation: Provided that any person appealing against the order of the adjudicating officer levying any penalty, shall while filing the appeal, deposit the amount of such penalty: Provided further that where in any particular case, the Appellate Tribunal is of the opinion that the deposit of such penalty would cause undue hardship to such person, the Appellate Tribunal may dispense with such deposit subject to such conditions as it may deem fit to impose so as to safeguard the realisation of penalty.

The Appellate Tribunal may, for the purpose of examining the legality, propriety or correctness of any order made by the adjudicating officer or the Central Government or the State Government or any other authority under this Act, as the case may be in relation to any proceeding, on its own motion or otherwise, call for the records of such proceedings and make such order in the case as it thinks fit. The Appellate Tribunal shall consist of a Chairperson and such number of Members not exceeding four, as the Central Government may deem fit.

The Chairperson or a Member of the Appellate Tribunal may, by notice in writing under his hand addressed to the Central Government, resign his office: Provided that the Chairperson of the Appellate Tribunal or a Member of the Appellate Tribunal shall, unless he is permitted by the Central Government to relinquish his office sooner, continue to hold office until the expiry of three months from the date of receipt of such notice or until a person duly appointed as his successor enters upon his office or until the expiry of term of office, whichever is the earliest. The Chairperson of the Appellate Tribunal or a Member of the Appellate Tribunal shall not be removed from his office except by an order by the Central Government on the ground of proved misbehaviour or incapacity after an inquiry made by such persons as the President may appoint for this purpose in which the Chairperson or a Member of the Appellate Tribunal concerned has been informed of the charges against him and given a reasonable opportunity of being heard in respect of such charges.

In the event of the occurrence of vacancy in the office of the Chairperson of the Appellate Tribunal by reason of his death, resignation or otherwise, the senior-most member of the Appellate Tribunal shall act as the Chairperson of the Appellate Tribunal until the date on which a new Chairperson appointed in accordance with the provisions of this Act to fill such vacancy enters upon his office. When the Chairperson of the Appellate Tribunal is unable to discharge his functions owing to his absence, illness or any other cause, the senior most Member of the Appellate Tribunal shall discharge the functions of the Chairperson of the Appellate Tribunal until the date on which the Chairperson of the Appellate Tribunal resumes his duties. The Central Government shall provide the Appellate Tribunal with such officers and employees as it may deem fit. The officers and employees of the Appellate Tribunal shall discharge their functions under the general superintendence of the Chairperson of the Appellate Tribunal as the case may be. The salaries and allowances and other conditions of service of the officers and employees of the Appellate Tribunal shall be such as may be prescribed.

The Appellate Tribunal shall not be bound by the procedure laid down by the Code of Civil Procedure, 1908 but shall be guided by the principles of natural justice and subject to the other provisions of this Act, the Appellate Tribunal shall have powers to regulate its own procedure. The Appellate

Tribunal shall have, for the purposes of discharging its functions under this Act, the same powers as are vested in the civil court under the Code of Civil Procedure 1908. An order made by the Appellate Tribunal under this Act shall be executable by the Appellate Tribunal as a decree of civil court and, for this purpose, the Appellate Tribunal shall have all the powers of a civil court. All proceedings before the Appellate Tribunal shall be deemed to be judicial proceedings within the meaning of Sections 193 and 228 of the Indian Penal Code and the Appellate Tribunal shall be deemed to be civil court for the purposes of Sections 345 and 346 of the Code of Criminal Procedure, 1973.

A person preferring an appeal to the Appellate Tribunal under this Act may either appear in person or take assistance of a legal practitioner or an accredited energy auditor of his choice to present his case before the Appellate Tribunal, as the case may be. The Central Government or the State Government may authorise one or more legal practitioners or any of its officers to act as presenting officers and every person so authorised may present the case with respect to any appeal before the Appellate Tribunal as the case may be. Any person aggrieved by any decision or order of the Appellate Tribunal may, file an appeal to the Supreme Court within sixty days from the date of communication of the decision or order of the Appellate Tribunal to him, on any one or more of the ground specified in Section 100 of the Code of Civil Procedure, 1908: Provided that the Supreme Court may, if it is satisfied that the appellant was prevented by the sufficient cause from the filing the appeal within the said period, allow it to be filed within a further period of not exceeding sixty days.

Every rule made by the Central Government and every regulation made under this Act shall be laid, as soon as may be after it is made, before each House of Parliament while it is in session, for a total period of thirty days which may be comprised in one session or in two or more successive session, and if, before the expiry of the session immediately following the session or the successive sessions aforesaid, both Houses agree in making any modification in the rule or regulation, or both Houses agree that the rule or regulation should not be made, the rule or regulation shall thereafter have effect only in such modified form or be of no effect, as the case may be; so however that any such modification or annulment shall be without prejudice to the validity of anything previously done under that rule or regulation. The provisions of this Act shall be in addition to, and not in derogation of, the provisions of any other law for the time being in force.

The provisions of this Act shall not apply to the Ministry or Department of the Central Government dealing with Defence, Atomic Energy or such other similar Ministries or Departments undertakings or Boards or institutions under the control of such Ministries or Departments as may be notified by the Central Government. If any difficulty arises in giving effect to the provisions of this Act, the Central Government may, by order, published in the Official Gazette, make such provisions not inconsistent with the provisions of this

Act as may appear to be necessary for removing the difficulty: Provided that no such order shall be made under this section after the expiry of two years from the date of commencement of this Act.

Problems of Indian Power Sector

All central power generation companies like NTPC are highly profitable as bulk power prices are fixed by the regulator providing guaranteed returns. On the other hand, most state run power distribution companies are loss making machines as raising consumer tariffs is politically sensitive. India's electricity sector faces many issues. Inadequate last mile connectivity is the main problem to supply electricity for all users. Despite abundant reserves of coal, India is facing a severe shortage of coal. The country isn't producing enough to feed its power plants. Some plants do not have reserve coal supplies to last a day of operations. Poor pipeline connectivity and infrastructure to harness India's abundant coal bed methane and shale gas potential. Hydroelectric power projects in India's mountainous north and north-east regions have been slowed down by ecological, environmental and rehabilitation controversies, coupled with public interest litigation. India's nuclear power generation potential has been stymied by political activism since the Fukushima disaster in Japan.

The commissioning of new power projects has been delayed for too long. The main reason behind this is the lack of financing and long route of money flow from the departments. India is abundantly gifted with variety of renewable energy sources, not all States are endowed with same level of renewable energy sources. While some States have very high renewable energy potential, some States have very little renewable energy potential. Land Acquisition poses an increasingly significant challenge in the Indian Power sector. Power plants and utilities face major constraints and delays regarding the availability of land and obtaining the requisite environment and other clearances for the projects. The new Bill relating to land acquisition has continued to face political opposition.

The current power generating capacity of India is approximately 210 GW. When analysing the major problems in Indian Power sector, the first thing comes into mind is **fuel (coal, gas) problem. In transmission there are some issues like frequency disturbance and Long term power purchase agreement.** The power sector faces multiple challenges including high subsidy for state utilities and uncertainty over tariff compensation to power producers. The dependence on government subsidy for state utilities is likely to increase by 17 per cent to Rs 72,000 crore in 2014-15 compared to 2013-14, thus posing a challenge for the power sector. In Jammu & Kashmir, the subsidy burden is projected to increase by 51 per cent due to continuous support for funding the high transmission and distribution losses.

As high as 45 MW are lost because of inefficient transmission and distribution (T&D) for every 100 MW of electricity generated in India.

Increasing energy efficiency of electrical appliances is another way to save electricity. Power Sector in India has grown significantly since independence both in the installed electricity generating capacity and transmission and distribution (T&D) system. The total power generating capacity of (utilities and non-utilities) has increased from meagre 1362 MW in 1947 to 267 GW at the end of March; 2015.The per capita electricity consumption which was mere 16.3 kWh in 1947 has increased to 1010 KWh in 2014-15.

References

1. Brainy Quote, Available at http://www.brainyquote.com/quotes/keywords/environment.html
2. Natural Resources, Available at https://en.wikipedia.org/wiki/Natural_resource
3. What Are Natural Resources? - Definition, Lesson and Quiz, Available at http://study.com/academy/lesson/what-are-natural-resources-definition-lesson-quiz.html
4. Natural Resources, Available at http://www.epa.gov/wastes/education/quest/pdfs/unit1/chap1/u1_natresources.pdf
5. Resource (2015) (Available at https://en.wikipedia.org/wiki/Resource)
6. Rashid Faridi (2008), Natural Resources: Definition and Classification (Available at http://rashidfaridi.com/2008/02/26/natural-resources-definition-and-classification/)
7. Renewable resources (Available at https://en.wikipedia.org/wiki/Renewable_resource)
8. Summary for Policymakers, This Summary for Policymakers was formally approved at the 11th Session of Working Group III of the IPCC, Abu Dhabi, United Arab Emirates. 5-8 May 2011. (http://www.se4all.org/wp-content/uploads/2013/09/IPCC_Summary_for_Policy_Makers.pdf)
9. Hydropower (Available at https://en.wikipedia.org/wiki/Hydropower)
10. Prof. Giovanni Riva, Prof. Ester Foppapedretti, Carla de Carolis and Mr Eleftherios Giakoumelos, Handbook on Renewable Energy Sources, for more information on the project you are invited to consult the project website: www.enersupply.eu where you can find also the link for the e-learning platform.
11. Hydropower in India: Key enablers for a better tomorrow (Available at https://www.pwc.in/en_IN/in/assets/pdfs/publications/2014/hydropower-in-india-key-enablers-for-better-tomorrow.pdf)
12. Benefits of Hydropower (Available at http://energy.gov/eere/water/benefits-hydropower)
13. Hydroelectric power in India (Available at https://en.wikipedia.org/wiki/Hydroelectric_power_in_India)
14. Hydropower in India: Key enablers for a better tomorrow (Available at https://www.pwc.in/en_IN/in/assets/pdfs/publications/2014/hydropower-in-india-key-enablers-for-better-tomorrow.pdf)
15. See http://indianpowersector.com/power-station/hydro-power-plant/

16. Prof. Giovanni Riva, Prof. Ester Foppapedretti, Carla de Carolis and Mr Eleftherios Giakoumelos, Handbook on Renewable Energy Sources, For more information on the project you are invited to consult the project website: www.enersupply.eu where you can find also the link for the e-learning platform.
17. See http://www.geothermal.org/what.html
18. See http://indianpowersector.com/home/renewable-energy/geothermal/
19. See http://www.ianswer4u.com/2012/02/geothermal-energy-advantages-and.html#axzz3ibLl5DIy
20. Penna Sparrow, Geothermal Energy: Advantages and Disadvantages (http://www.ianswer4u.com/2012/02/geothermal-energy-advantages-and.html#axzz3ibLl5DIy)
21. See http://indianpowersector.com/home/renewable-energy/geothermal/
22. See http://www.dnaindia.com/india/report-govt-exploring-1000-mw-from-beneath-earth-to-power-rural-india-2059335
23. India energy portal- Geothermal (http://www.indiaenergyportal.org/subthemes_link.php?text=geothermal&themeid=13)
24. Geothermal energy and its potential in India (http://mnre.gov.in/file-manager/akshay-urja/july-august-2013/EN/14-18.pdf)
25. Solar energy (https://en.wikipedia.org/wiki/Solar_energy)
26. 5 Advantages and 5 Disadvantages of Solar Energy (http://www.greenmatch.co.uk/blog/2014/08/5-advantages-and-5-disadvantages-of-solar-energy)
27. V. Ryan (2009), Advantages and disadvantages of solar energy (http://www.technologystudent.com/energy1/solar7.htm)
28. See http://cleantechnica.com/2014/09/22/solar-energy-advantages-vs-disadvantages/
29. V. Ryan (2009), Advantages and disadvantages of solar energy (http://www.technologystudent.com/energy1/solar7.htm)
30. Saritha Rai (2015), For Investors, India's Solar Push Could Signal A Gold Rush (http://www.forbes.com/sites/saritharai/2015/07/07/for-investors-indias-solar-push-could-signal-a-gold-rush/)
31. Solar power in India (https://en.wikipedia.org/wiki/Solar_power_in_India)
32. Swami Prakash Srivastava and Surat Prakash Srivastava, Solar energy and its future role in India economy, International Journal of Environmental Science: Development and Monitoring, Volume 4, No. 3 (2013), pp. 81-88.
33. *Ibid.*
34. Prof. Giovanni Riva, Prof. Ester Foppapedretti, Carla de Carolis & Mr Eleftherios Giakoumelos, Handbook on Renewable Energy Sources, for more information on the project you are invited to consult the project website: www.enersupply.eu where you can find also the link for the e-learning platform
35. See http://www.technologystudent.com/energy1/wind8.htm
36. See http://www.ianswer4u.com/2012/02/wind-energy-advantages-and.html#axzz3ibLl5DIy
37. *Ibid.*

38. Wind Energy: A Vision for Europe in 2030, Prepared by the Advisory Council of the European Wind Energy Technology Platform, September 2006 (http://www.windplatform.eu/fileadmin/ewetp_docs/Structure/061003Vision_final.pdf)
39. Wind power in India (https://en.wikipedia.org/wiki/Wind_power_in_India)
40. Wind Energy Programme in India (http://www.inwea.org/aboutwindenergy.htm)
41. The Economic Times (August 12, 2014), Government aims to add 10,000 MW per year to lift wind energy sector, http://economictimes.indiatimes.com/industry/energy/power/government-aims-to-add-10000-mw-per-year-to-lift-wind-energy-sector/articleshow/40079023.cms
42. From official website of Indian Wind Power Association.
43. Renewable Energy: An overview (http://www.nrel.gov/docs/fy01osti/27955.pdf)
44. *Ibid.*
45. http://urbanearth.co.za/articles/south-africa%E2%80%99s-ocean-energy-potential
46. See http://oceanenergy.ie/
47. Wave Energy (http://www.conserve-energy-future.com/Advantages_Disadvantages_WaveEnergy.php)
48. Renewable oceanic energy (http://oceantidalenergy84.weebly.com/advantagesdisadvantages.html)
49. Oceans of energy; European ocean energy roadmap 2010-2015 (http://www.waveplam.eu/files/newsletter7/European%20Ocean%20Energy%20Roadmap.pdf)
50. Tapping into oceanic energy (http://www.japantimes.co.jp/opinion/2012/03/26/commentary/world-commentary/tapping-into-oceanic-energy/#.VcrnHvmqpHx)
51. Ocean power making waves in Australia's clean energy future (http://theconversation.com/ocean-power-making-waves-in-australias-clean-energy-future-9689)
52. Official website of fisheries and ocean Canada (http://www.dfo-mpo.gc.ca/oceans/industries/oceanenergy-energiemarine/index-eng.htm)
53. Renewable and Nonrenewable Resources (http://extension.psu.edu/publications/uh177)
54. Non-renewable resource (https://en.wikipedia.org/wiki/Non-renewable_resource)
55. See http://www.bbc.co.uk/schools/gcsebitesize/geography/energy_resources/energy_rev1.shtml
56. http://www.y115.org/vimages/shared/vnews/stories/5115515aab7d1/Compare%20&%20Contrast%207th%20 Grade%20Renewable%20&%20NonRenewable % 20Energy.pdf
57. http://www.geo.lu.lv/fileadmin/user_upload/lu_portal/projekti/gzzf/videunilgtspejigaattistiba/VidZ1000/7.LECTURE-Energy_resources.pdf
58. Coal, Website http://www.epa.gov/cleanenergy/energy-and-you/affect/coal.html
59. See http://sciencelearn.org.nz/Contexts/Future-Fuels/Science-Ideas-and-Concepts/Non-renewable-energy-sources
60. Coal mining in India, Website https://en.wikipedia.org/wiki/Coal_mining_in_India
61. Mines, Website http://bardhaman.nic.in/mines/mines.htm

62. Coal India Limited, Website https://en.wikipedia.org/wiki/Coal_India
63. http://vectorschools.co.nz/renewable-and-non-renewable-resources
64. Oil and Gas Industry in India, http://www.ibef.org/industry/oil-gas-india.aspx
65. Evolution of Indian oil and gas industry, https://www.dnb.co.in/IndiasEnergy Sector/GasIndustry.asp
66. India Petroleum Industry, http://business.mapsofindia.com/india-petroleum-industry/
67. http://www.geoexpro.com/articles/2014/02/how-much-oil-in-the-middle-east
68. Countries with the biggest oil reserves, http://www.hydrocarbons-technology.com/features/feature-countries-with-the-biggest-oil-reserves/
69. Renewable resources and nonrenewable resources, http://www.geo.lu.lv/fileadmin/user_upload/lu_portal/projekti/gzzf/videunilgtspejigaattistiba/VidZ1000/7.LECTURE-Energy_resources.pdf
70. http://www.geo.lu.lv/fileadmin/user_upload/lu_portal/projekti/gzzf/videunilgtspejigaattistiba/VidZ1000/7.LECTURE-Energy_resources.pdf
71. See http://www.eai.in/ref/fe/nag/nag.html
72. See http://www.eai.in/ref/fe/nag/nag.html
73. Natural Gas in India, https://www.iea.org/publications/freepublications/publication/natural_gas_india_2010.pdf
74. Nuclear power, https://en.wikipedia.org/wiki/Nuclear_power
75. http://www.geo.lu.lv/fileadmin/user_upload/lu_portal/projekti/gzzf/videunilgtspejigaattistiba/VidZ1000/7.LECTURE-Energy_resources.pdf
76. Louise Balle, http://smallbusiness.chron.com/make-optimum-use-business-resources-5019.html
77. Team quest, http://www.teamquest.com/files/7914/2049/9759/limited-resources-solution-brief.pdf
78. Making optimum use of natural resources and minimizing environmental pollution, http://www.pinar.com.tr/pdf/su/pinarsu/pdf/en9.pdf
79. Land (economics), https://en.wikipedia.org/wiki/Land_(economics)
80. Land resources: Use for prosperity, save for posterity, See http://www.krvp.org/NCSC/NCSC_2010-11_Activity_Guide_Eng.pdf
81. Land as a resource, http://ec.europa.eu/environment/land_use/index_en.htm
82. Unit-I, Land uses, http://www.cbse-international.com/cbse-ipotal/documents/upload/22f23fs23fs/level-4/l-4_c-27_1332764002597.pdf
83. Carol Hunsberger and Tom P. Evans, Land, http://www.unep.org/geo/pdfs/geo5/GEO5_report_C3.pdf
84. Natural resources, In recent years, the depletion of natural resources has become a major focus of governments and organisations such as the United Nations.
85. Land Resources and Environmental Science, http://ag.montana.edu/departments/lresbrochure.pdf
86. Lakhimi Gogoi, Degradation of Natural Resources and its Impact on Environment: a Study in Guwahati City, Assam, India, International Journal of Scientific and Research Publications, Volume 3, Issue 12, December 2013, p.1.

87. Forest, https://en.wikipedia.org/wiki/Forest
88. Puja Mondal, Forest Resources in India: Use, Over Exploitation, Causes and Effects.
89. Forest resources, http://postconflict.unep.ch/publications/sudan/09_forests.pdf
90. Types of forest, http://www.defenders.org/forest/types-forests
91. Akash, 864 words essay on Natural Resources, http://www.preservearticles.com/201107048726/essay-on-natural-resources.html
92. The importance of forest, http://forestry-learning.blogspot.in/2010/10/importance-of-forests.html
93. Short Essay on Importance of Forests in India, http://www.importantindia.com/16058/short-essay-on-importance-of-forests-in-india/
94. Manali Sa, Short essay on natural resources, http://www.publishyourarticles.net/knowledge-hub/essay/short-essay-on-natural-resources/3102/
95. Manali Sa, Short essay on the conservation of natural resources, http://www.publishyourarticles.net/knowledge-hub/essay/short-essay-on-the-conservation-of-natural-resources/3109/
96. Environmental Sustainability Issues in India, http://www.fsdinternational.org/country/india/envissues
97. Report of the Working Group on Natural Resources Management Eleventh Five Year Plan (2007-2012) (http://planningcommission.nic.in/aboutus/committee/wrkgrp11/wg11_agnrm.pdf)
98. Bharti Preeti, Short essay on forests in India, http://www.preservearticles.com/2011121318392/short-essay-on-forests-in-india.html
99. Darshan Kadu, Essay on the Indian forest, http://www.shareyouressays.com/111495/essay-on-the-indian-forest
100. Darshan Kadu, Essay on the Indian forest, http://www.shareyouressays.com/111495/essay-on-the-indian-forest
101. Indian Forest Act, 1927, https://en.wikipedia.org/wiki/Indian_Forest_Act,_1927
102. Wildlife Protection Act, 1972, https://en.wikipedia.org/wiki/Wildlife_Protection_Act,_1972
103. Resources, http://www.vanashakti.in/resources_law2.html
104. Read more at Law Teacher: http://www.lawteacher.net/free-law-essays/international-law/the-indian-forest-and-wildlife-acts-international-law-essay.php#ixzz3jF9caIrS
105. Scheduled Tribes and Other Traditional Forest Dwellers (Recognition of Forest Rights) Act, 2006, https://en.wikipedia.org/wiki/The_Scheduled_Tribes_and_Other_Traditional_Forest_Dwellers_(Recognition_of_Forest_Rights)_Act,_2006
106. Social forestry in India, https://en.wikipedia.org/wiki/Social_forestry_in_India
107. Shanti, what is the meaning and aim of Social Forestry? http://www.preservearticles.com/2012032829046/what-is-the-meaning-and-aim-of-social-forestry.html
108. Common land, https://en.wikipedia.org/wiki/Common_land

109. Sustainable forest management, https://en.wikipedia.org/wiki/Sustainable_forest_management
110. See http://www.fao.org/docrep/006/u9040e/U9040E07.htm
111. See http://www.newforest.hampshire.org.uk/today1.html
112. Shankar Gopala Krishnan (2012). Undemocratic and Arbitrary, Control, Regulation and Expropriation of India's Forest and Common Lands.
113. Efficient energy use, https://en.wikipedia.org/wiki/Efficient_energy_use
114. See http://www.energy.gov/science-innovation/energy-efficiency
115. See http://www.iea.org/
116. Energy-Efficient Home Design, http://www.energy.gov/energysaver/articles/energy-efficient-home-design
117. D. Todd Littlefield, Taylor Moore, Pam Thomas, and Eric Kennedy (2009). http://www.lrc.ky.gov/lrcpubs/rm503.pdf
118. Energy taxes misaligned with environmental impacts of energy use, http://www.oecd.org/tax/energy-taxes-misaligned-with-environmental-impacts-of-energy-use.htm
119. Environmental tax statistics, http://ec.europa.eu/eurostat/statistics-explained/index.php/Environmental_tax_statistics
120. Rajiv Gandhi Grameen Vidyutikaran Yojana, http://powermin.nic.in/upload/pdf/Rajiv_gandhi.pdf
121. Extraordinary Part-I, Section 1, Published by Authority, Ministry of Power, Available at http://powermin.nic.in/upload/pdf/RE%20Policy.pdf
122. Official website of Ministry of Power, Available at http://powermin.nic.in/Energy-Efficiency
123. The Energy Conservation Act, 2001, Available at http://powermin.nic.in/upload/pdf/ecact2001.pdf
124. Ministry of Power, Govt. of India (http://powermin.nic.in/)

Chapter - 9

Environmental Education

"Look at the bark of a redwood, and you see moss. If you peer beneath the bits and pieces of the moss, you'll see toads, small insects, a whole host of life that prospers in that miniature environment. A lumberman will look at a forest and see so many board feet of lumber. I see a living city."

***—Sylvia Earle*[1]**

Plato founded the Academy in Athens, the first institution of higher learning in Europe. Formal education occurs in a structured environment whose explicit purpose is teaching students. Usually, formal education takes place in a school environment with classrooms of multiple students learning together with a trained, certified teacher of the subject. Preschools provide education from ages approximately three to seven, depending on the country, when children enter primary education. Primary education consists of the first five to seven years of formal, structured education. In general, primary education consists of six to eight years of schooling starting at the age of five or six, although this varies between, and sometimes within, countries. In most contemporary educational systems of the world, secondary education comprises the formal education that occurs during adolescence. Higher education is the non-compulsory educational level that follows the completion of a school such as a high school or secondary school.[2]

The second goal in the United Nations Millennium Development Goal is to achieve Universal Primary Education. Universal Primary Education is one of the eight international Millennium Development Goals, towards which progress has been made in the past decade, though barriers still remain. Since 1999, there has been great progress towards achieving universal primary enrollment due in large part to a pursuit of the Millennium Development Goals (MDGs) and the Education for All (EFA) goal. UNICEF believes that in treating education as a basic human right, it will address the basic inequalities in our society, especially gender inequalities. The Millennium Development Goals are the eight international development goals that were established following the Millennium Summit of the United Nations in 2000, following the adoption of the United Nations Millennium Declaration. There are eight goals with 21 targets, and a series of measurable health indicators and economic indicators for each target (wikipedia).

Definition of Environmental Education

Education is the process of facilitating learning. Knowledge, skills, values, beliefs, and habits of a group of people are transferred to other people, through storytelling, discussion, teaching, training, or research. Education began in prehistory, as adults trained the young in the knowledge and skills deemed necessary in their society. It is commonly and formally divided into stages such as preschool, primary school, secondary school and then college, university or apprenticeship. The methodology of teaching is called pedagogy.[3]

According to the dictionary an education is "the act or process of imparting or acquiring general knowledge, developing the powers of reasoning and judgment, and generally of preparing oneself or others intellectually for mature life." Environmental education is a process that allows individuals to explore environmental issues, engage in problem solving, and take action to improve the environment. Significant environmental benefits gained by adopting energy efficient technologies and processes include: lowering the demand for natural resources, reducing the emission of air pollutants, improving water quality.

Environmental education may best be defined as a process directed at creating awareness and understanding about environmental issues that leads to responsible individual and group actions.Environmental education utilises processes that involve students in observing, measuring, classifying, experimenting, and other data gathering techniques. It is a methodology in which people pick up familiarity with their surroundings and secure learning, abilities, values, experiences, and passion, all of which will empower them to act.

Environmental education may best be defined as a process directed at creating awareness and understanding about environmental issues that leads to responsible individual and group actions. It is a process in which individuals gain awareness of their environment and acquire knowledge, skills, values, experiences, and also the determination, which will enable them to act - individually and collectively - to solve present and future environmental problems. It refers to organised efforts to teach how natural environments function, and particularly, how human beings can manage behaviour and ecosystems to live sustainably.

Importance of Environmental Education

Environmentalism is an ideology that evokes the necessity and responsibility of humans to respect, protect, and preserve the natural world from its anthropogenic (caused by humans) afflictions. Environmental conservation is an umbrella term that defines anything we do to protect our planet and conserve its natural resources so that every living thing can have an improved quality of life. Environmental stewardship refers to responsible use and protection of the natural environment through conservation and sustainable practices. Aldo Leopold (1887–1949) championed environmental stewardship based on a land ethic "dealing with man's relation to land and to the animals and plants which grow upon it."

With an ever-evolving outlook on the planet's wellbeing UNESCO's science educational activities in Environment strive to better understand the Earth as well as spread this understanding. UNESCO's actions in Water Education inspire a more responsible attitude towards the planet's most important resource.

Economics of Environmental Education

Economics of education is the study of economic issues relating to education, including the demand for education and the financing and provision of education. Economics is a powerful research and policy tool for scholars and educational practitioners who wish to develop a better understanding of educational institutions and decisions.[4] The basic tools of economics provide a framework to evaluate education policies including early childhood interventions, K-12 school finance, and college choice and financial aid.[5]

Environmental Education is a process in which individuals gain awareness of their environment and acquire knowledge, skills, values, experiences, and also the determination, which will enable them to act - individually and collectively - to solve present and future environmental problems.It is the teaching of individuals, and communities, in transitioning to a society that is knowledgeable of the environment and its associated problems, aware of the solutions to these problems, and motivated to solve them. The goal of environmental education is to develop a world population that is aware of, and concerned about, the environment and its associated problems, and which has the knowledge, skills, attitudes, motivations, and commitment to work individually and collectively towards solutions of current problems.

Being well educated never only means to earn certificates and good salary from the recognised and reputed organisation companies or institutions however it also means to be a good and social person in the life. It helps to determine whether something is good or bad for us and other persons related to us.[6] Education plays a very important role in your life. For living a luxurious life or for living a better life, you should be educated. Education is that which transforms a person to live a better life and even in a social wellbeing. Education plays a vital role in your success in the personal growth. A person who gets good education will become good citizen, more dependable worker.[7]

An education is something that one can keep for a lifetime. Acquiring a good education can affect one's personal life, one's community, and one's entire generation. Scientific education is important to this world due to the effects of it. Science teaches people important factors of certain subjects, and those can be further developed and expanded into new ideas. Getting a science education in the twenty-first century can be very beneficial to children of all ages. Science is what makes up the world and the only way you would be able to know that would be by getting a real education in the studies of science.[8]

Expenditure on Education

Expenditure on education may help foster economic growth, enhance productivity, contribute to people's personal and social development, and help reduce social inequalities. Expenditure on education is an investment that can foster economic growth, enhance productivity, contribute to personal and social development and reduce social inequality. In principle, public expenditure includes both direct expenditure on educational institutions and educational-related public subsidies to households administered by educational institutions.[9]

Public expenditure on education in the EU-28 in 2011 was equivalent to an estimated 5.3 per cent of gross domestic product, while the expenditure of both public and private sources of funds on educational institutions amounted to 6.0 per cent of GDP. The highest public spending on education relative to GDP was observed in Denmark (8.8 per cent of GDP), while Malta (8.0 per cent), Cyprus (7.9 per cent), Sweden, Finland (both 6.8 per cent) and Belgium (6.6 per cent) also recorded relatively high proportions.[10]

Table 1: Overview of Education Policies related to Financing of Education in India

Education Policy / Committee	*Year*	*Recommendations*
Kher Committee	1948-49	A fixed per centage of Central (10 per cent) and Provincial (20 per cent) revenues should bear marked for education and that around 70 per cent of the total expenditure on education should come from the local bodies and provinces.
Kothari Commission	1964-66	(a) Public expenditure on education should reach the level of 6 per cent of GNP by 1986. (b)Vocationalization of secondary education. (c) Strengthening of cenres of advanced study and setting up of small number of major universities of international standard.
National Education Policy	1968	(a) Investment on education to be gradually increased to reach a level of six per cent of national income as early as possible. (b) Focus on science & technology and agriculture. Provision of food and effective

(Contd...)

		education at primary level (on a free and compulsory basis). (c) Equality in education for rich and poor: common 10+2+3 education structure throughout India and eventually free schooling till class 10.
Secondary Education Commission	1972	(a) To assume certain direct responsibility for reorganisation of secondary education and give financial aid for the purpose. (b) Encourage private contribution through tax exemptions (income tax, property tax and custom duties). (c) Industrial education cess should be levied for furtherance of Technical and vocational education at secondary stage
42nd Constitutional amendment	1976	Education transferred from list to concurrent list (School education under jurisdiction of both, the Centre and the State)
National Education Policy	1986 (with revisions in 1992)	(a) Resource support for implementing programmes of educational transformation, reducing disparities, universalisation of elementary education, adult literacy, scientific and technological research, etc.will be provided. For this actual requirements will be computed at regular intervals and outlay on education will be stepped up so that more than six per cent of national income is allocated from eighth plan onwards. (b) While the role and responsibility of the States in regard to education will remain essentially unchanged, the Union Government would accept a larger responsibility to reinforce the national and integrative character of education, to maintain quality and standards (including those of the teaching profession at all levels) and to study and monitor the educational requirements of the country. Additional resources to be raised by mobilizing donations, asking beneficiary communities to maintain school buildings, raise fees at higher levels of education and effecting savings through efficient use of resources.
73rd and 74th constitutional amendment	1992	Statutory recognition of local governments, and inclusion of school education in the list of its responsibilities. Local bodies to play an important role in financing and implementing education programmes.
Saikia Committee	1996	Need for an expenditure of 6 per cent of GNP on education with 50 per cent of it earmarked for primary education. Recommended additional expenditure of Rs 40000 crores over next five years on elementary education.

(Contd...)

Tapas Majumdar Committee	1999	Estimated additional fund requirements for UEE – it was in the range of 137000 crores over the following 10 years.
86th Constitutional Amendment	2002	Provide free and compulsory education of children between age 6 to 14 years, and provision of early childhood care and education for children below six years.
National Common Minimum Programme of UPA Government	2004	(a) Raise public spending in education to at least 6 per cent of the GDP with at least half this amount be presenting spent on primary and secondary sectors. This will be done in a phased manner. (b) A Cess of two per cent on all central taxes to finance the commitment to universalize access to quality basic education. (c) A national cooked nutritious mid-May-meal scheme, funded mainly by the Central Government, will be introduced in primary and secondary school. (d) The Integrated Child Development Services (ICDS) scheme will be universalised to provide a functional Anganwadi in every settlement and ensure full coverage for all children. (e) All northeastern States will be given special assistance to upgrade and expand infrastructure. (a) The additional financial requirement for universalising secondary education as per cent of GDP works out to be around 0.18 per cent in 2003-04 and to 0.86 per cent 2019-20. (b) With 6 per cent of GDP earmarked for education, the shares of elementary, secondary and higher secondary (as per cent of GDP) will be 3, 2 and 1 respectively.

Source: From MHRD website; Relevant committee reports

The total amount of budget provisions on the revenue account made for education for the year 2012-13 by education departments for the States/UTs and the Centre works out to Rs 323849.98 crore (Rs 249810.14 crore in State Sector and Rs 74039.84 crore in the Central sector) which is 14.49 per cent more than the revised estimates of Rs 282852.09 crore for 2011-12. The total budget provisions (Revenue Account) for 2012-13 made by the departments other than Education works out to Rs 79386.53 crore. The States/UTs are contributing about 72.91 per cent of the total revenue expenditure on education in the country while centre contributes about 27.09 per cent to the education sector as a whole.

About 82.94 per cent of the Central expenditure on education is under plan whereas in the case of States/UTs it is only 19.26 per cent in the year

2012-13. The following table indicates the Sector-wise Expenditure on Education by Education Department incurred by both Centre and States.

The difference in trends in public expenditure by the Centre and the States over the past fifteen years highlights the increasingly important role played by the Centre in States' finance, particularly in elementary education. A large proportion of transfers from the Centre are allotted to the States for implementing Centrally Sponsored Schemes (CSS). These schemes are formulated by the Centre which also funds a major part of their implementing costs. States, which are the implementing agencies, fund the remaining portion. As a mode of transfer of resources direct central assistance is advantageous to the states from autonomy point of view.[11]

Table 2: Sector-wise Expenditure (Plan and Non Plan) on Education by Education Department (Revenue Account) with per centage Centre and States/UTs 2012-13 (BE) (Rs in crore)

Areas	*Plan Expenditure*	*Plan Percentage share*	*Non-Plan Expenditure*	*Non-Plan Percentage Share*	*Total Expenditure*	*Total Percentage Share*
Elementary Education	64717.68	59.09	98386.12	45.90	163103.80	50.36
Secondary Education	21437.08	19.57	75839.12	35.38	97276.20	30.04
Adult Education	915.87	0.84	272.60	0.13	1188.47	0.37
Language Development	295.11	0.27	844.56	0.39	1139.67	0.35
University and Hr.Education	11117.33	10.15	31387.28	14.65	42504.61	13.12
Technical Education	9949.68	9.09	6300.29	2.94	10249.97	5.02
General Education	1083.23	0.99	1304.03	0.61	2387.26	0.74
Total Education	**109515.98**	**100.00**	**214334.00**	**100.00**	**323849.98**	**100.00**

Source: Analyzing of Budgeted Expenditure on Education 2010-11 to 2012-13, Government of India, p. 3.

Elementary Education accounted for 50.36 per cent of the total expenditure on education in 2012-13, followed by Secondary Education, which was 30.04 per cent. The share of University and Higher Education and Technical Education was 13.1 per cent and. 5.02 per cent respectively.[12]

Almost the entire allocation in the budget for education by the central government is spent through different schemes. These range from large system-wide interventions, such as SSA, to particular organisations and institutions such as the Kendriya Vidyalaya Sangathan (KVS), to targeted scholarship schemes for girl students. Most schemes have a particular motivation, a funding structure and a delivery mechanism. During the Eleventh Plan, education financing by the central government has reflected the focus on increasing enrolment and reducing dropouts. Institutional grants for higher education, either directly or through the UGC, have shown significant increase in allocations. The Public–Private Partnership (PPP) strategy, therefore, is a combination of projecting demand for different levels of education, separation of public goods (equity, non-discrimination, knowledge creation, research and development, etc.) from private goods (private school education, technical and professional courses, employment-oriented skill formation, etc.), and adhering to quality standards for both.[13]

The Ninth Plan looks at education as the most vital and crucial investment in human development. The Special Action Plan (SAP) of the Prime Minister gave an emphasis to total eradication of illiteracy, equal access to and opportunity of education up to the school leaving stage, improvement in the quality of education at all levels from primary schools to universities and the need for expansion and improvement of social infrastructure facilities for education. The Government has accorded high priority to education sector in the Ninth Plan and has allocated, Rs 24908.38 crore against an expenditure of Rs 8521.89 crore in the Eighth Five Year Plan, representing a nearly threefold increase in the funds available to the Union Department of Education. During the first three years of the Ninth Five Year Plan expenditure is likely to be of the order of Rs 12012 crores which is about 50 per cent of the Ninth Five Year Plan outlay.

The Programme of Minimum Levels of Learning (MLL) has been introduced in most States. The Programme aims at specifying competency levels which children are required to attain in language, mathematics and in the environmental studies, in classes 1 to 5 and to reorient the teaching learning process to facilitate achievement of these. The Mid-Day Meal Programme has acquired all India coverage in 1997-98. The number of children covered under the Programme has risen from 3.4 crores in about 3.22 lakh schools in 1995-96 to 9.85 crore in about 6.88 lakh schools in 1998-99. The programme of Non-Formal Education i.e. education for out of school children has been expanded and consolidated.

The Scheme of Operation Blackboard which aimed at improving class room environment by providing infrastructural facilities, additional teachers and teaching learning material to primary schools and by provision of a third teacher to such schools where the enrolment figure exceeded 100 has been extended to upper primary schools. The National Literacy Mission (NLM) was set up in 1988 with the target of making 100 million persons in the age group of 15-35 literate in a phased manner.[14]

The Tenth Plan laid emphasis on Universalisation of Elementary Education (UEE) guided by five parameters: (i) Universal Access, (ii) Universal Enrolment, (iii) Universal Retention, (iv) Universal Achievement, and (v) Equity. The major schemes of elementary education sector during the Tenth Plan included SSA, District Primary Education Programme (DPEP), National Programme of

Nutritional Support to Primary Education, commonly known as Mid-Day Meal Scheme (MDMS), Teacher Education Scheme, and Kasturba Gandhi Balika Vidyalaya Scheme (KGBVS).

The Tenth Plan outlay for Elementary Education and Literacy was Rs 30000 crores. The actual expenditure has been Rs 48201 crores, out of which SSA (Rs 28077 crore) and MDMS (Rs 13827 crore) account for 88 per cent. Prarambhik Shiksha Kosh, a non-lapsable fund for crediting the education cess proceeds, has been set up. The States of UP (19 per cent), MP (10 per cent), Rajasthan and Bihar (7 per cent each), Maharashtra and WB (6 per cent each), Andhra Pradesh, Tamil Nadu, and Karnataka (5 per cent each) accounted for 70 per cent of the total expenditure incurred by the Central and State Governments under SSA during the Tenth Plan.

The Constitution of India was amended in 2002 to make elementary education a justiciable Fundamental Right. In the Eleventh Plan additional madarsas maktabs will be supported for modernisation under AIE component and it should be possible to cover all the 12000 odd Madarsas during the Plan period. The Central Government is managing and fully funding four types of schools viz., KVs, Navodaya Vidyalayas (NVs), Central Tibetan Schools (CTSs), and National Institute of Open Schooling (NIOS). There are 972 KVs with an enrolment of 9.54 lakh and staff strength of about 46000. During the Eleventh Plan, the thrust of the Open Schooling system will be on (i) developing NIOS as a potential Resource Organisation in Open Schooling at the national and international level, besides offering courses of study, (ii) up-scaling programmes of the existing 10 State Open Schools (SOSs), and (iii) setting up SOSs in the remaining 19 States.[15]

The Sarva Shiksha Abhiyan (SSA) is intended for the enlargement and growth mainly in the primary education. The aim of this flagship programme was to attain universalisation of primary schooling at an acceptable level by 2010. It is being implemented in partnership with State Governments to cover the entire country and address the needs of 192 million children in 1.2 million habitations. The present rules of SSA have been modified recently by putting into practice the "Right of Children to Free and Compulsory Education" which has been enforced from April 1, 2010 onwards.

Scheme of Infrastructure Development in Minority Institutions has been operationalised to augment infrastructure in private aided/unaided minority schools/ institutions in order to enhance quality of education to minority children. Programme for Nutritional Support to Primary Education commonly known as the Mid-Day Meal Scheme was launched as a Centrally Sponsored Scheme on 15th August 1995 covering all children studying in Classes I-VIII. Saakshar Bharat was launched in 8th September, 2009 aiming to accelerate Adult Education, especially for women in the age group of 15 years and above. It targets to raise literacy rate to 80 per cent by 2012 and reduce gender gap to half by the same period. Rashtriya Madhyamik Shiksha Abhiyan (RMSA) launched in March, 2009 is the flagship programme in secondary education for universalising access to secondary education and improving its quality, while ensuring equity.[16]

Productivity of Education

Increasing educational productivity by doing more with less will not be easy. It will mean graduating a significantly greater number of students at a lower cost per outcome. This will require leaders at every level to work together to rethink the policies, processes, tools, business models, and funding structures that have been ingrained in our education system for decades.[17]

Researchers have examined many aspects of education, mainly by trying to decompose individual parts of an increasingly complicated system and examining their functioning through research. Johnson (2008) states that "the idea of a school as a complex system in which developmental processes and outcomes emerge from a complex interaction among systemic layers is consistent with what seems to be intuitively known by many educators – that the rate of academic achievement is not a simple monotonic function that increases toward absolute proficiency. Instead, any mathematical model for expected rate of change in academic achievement of a particular school must build the ecological systems of the school into the equation as parameters."[18]

The Return of Education

Individuals are willing to take more years of schooling partly because they can earn more and get better jobs, on average, with more schooling. The link between education and economic growth in some of the early work on the economics of education was based on the argument that a major effect of more education is that an improved labor force has an increased capacity to produce. The frequent observation that individuals with more education have higher earnings is another indication that education contributes to growth.[19]

Although it is difficult to determine the monetary return to education, it is practically impossible to quantify the numerous nonmonetary returns. Studies have shown that "experiences and skills acquired in school reverberate throughout life, not just through higher earnings. Schooling also affects the degree one enjoys work and the likelihood of being unemployed. It leads individuals to make better decisions about health, marriage and parenting. It also improves patience, making individuals more goal-oriented and less likely to engage in risky behaviour."[20]

Human-Capital

The idea that human capital plays an important role in explaining income differences have been present in economists' thinking for a long time. By some accounts, it can even be traced to the work of Adam Smith and Alfred Marshall, although it was not until the middle of the twentieth century that Gary Becker and others developed a theory of human capital.[21]

Adam Smith defined human capital as follows: "Fourthly, of the acquired and useful abilities of all the inhabitants or members of the society. The acquisition of such talents, by the maintenance of the acquirer during his education, study, or apprenticeship, always costs a real expense, which is a capital fixed and realised, as it were, in his person. Those talents, as they make a part of his fortune, so do they likewise that of the society to which he belongs. The improved dexterity of a workman may be considered in the same light as a machine or instrument of trade which facilitates and abridges labour, and which, though it costs a certain expense, repays that expense with a profit."

Justin Slay defined four types of fixed capital. The four types were: (a) useful machines, instruments of the trade; (b) buildings as the means of procuring revenue; (c) improvements of land; (4) the acquired and useful abilities of all the inhabitants or members of the society. The idea of "human capital" is similar to Karl Marx's concept of labour power: he thought in capitalism workers sold their labour power in order to receive income (wages and salaries).[22]

Human capital is the stock of knowledge, habits, social and personality attributes, including creativity, embodied in the ability to perform labour so as to produce economic value.The focus on human capital as a driver of economic growth for developing countries has led to undue attention on school attainment.[23] Human capital is the sum total of a person's knowledge and skills that the company can use to further its goals. Human resource management is involved in acquiring, cultivating, and retaining human capital.[24]

Physical Capital

In economics, physical capital is a factor of production, consisting of machinery, buildings, computers, and the like. In economic theory, physical capital is one of the three primary factors of production, also known as inputs in the production function. The others are natural resources (including land), and labour.[25]

Physical capital is part of the production process; what economists call a factor of production. It includes things like buildings, machinery, equipment and computers. It is the machinery, buildings and computers that helped turn the raw materials into finished products or services.[26] Manufacturing plants that contain all production equipment and facilities, warehouses that contain finished or work in progress products, and even buildings used for administration, accounting, sales, etc. are also referred to as physical capital. Vehicles are also considered physical capital.[27]

Both physical and human capital directly impact on the productive capacity of an economy. More human capital may itself affect the rate of growth of physical capital. If human and physical capitals are complements, then increasing human capital raises the rate of return on physical capital.[28]

The effective use of both types of capital requires that employees have the resources on hand to accomplish the tasks associated with their jobs. The proper combination of physical and human capital will vary, based on the type of business operation involved. Essentially, human capital has to do with the resources that employees bring to the workplace, while physical capital focuses on physical assets such as facilities or equipment that are used in the business operation.[29] The right human capital can enhance the value of physical capital, and without the right physical capital human capital cannot contribute to its full extent.[30]

Educational Reforms

India has over a third of the world's children (6–11 year olds) out of school—around 40 million. Six states of India account for three-fourths of its children out of school (Andhra Pradesh, Bihar, Madhya Pradesh, Rajasthan, Uttar Pradesh and West Bengal).[31] In the nearly six decades since achieving Independence, the infrastructure for higher education in India has grown significantly. By some estimates, India has the third largest higher education system in the world, comprising of some 330 university-level institutions, about 16,000 colleges with approx. 10 million students and 350,000 teachers. India is home to one of the world's largest technical manpower pools with over five million scientists, engineers and technicians. Unfortunately, in India, the structure of our human resources is in the form of an hourglass. There are a huge number of mid and top level professionals such as doctors, engineers and lawyers of an indifferent quality that the society cannot accommodate or put to productive use.[32]

Teacher Education reforms in India has been a significant concern taken up by various Education commissions and reform committees since independence. The Education Commission (1964-66) dwelt at length on various issues related to teacher education. It recommended professionalisation of teacher education, development of integrated programmes, comprehensive colleges of education and internship. The National Commission on Teachers (1983-85) recommended five-year integrated courses and internship.[33]

The post-liberalisation scenario has added a few new challenges for the education system to address. The pressures of the emerging economic order to reduce subsidies of all kind have resulted in increasing the cost recovery rates. Diminishing role of the State in social and educational sector has led to the emergence of a private sector in higher education also.[34] *Reforming Education* focuses on *education* in *India* and across the globe generally and suggests *reforms* for its improvement. The University Grants Commission (UGC) has taken various measures for educational reforms, such as the introduction of the semester system, the regular updating of curricula and

Choice Based Credit Systems, etc. The UGC has issued the UGC Minimum Qualifications for Appointment of Teachers and other Academic Staff in Universities and Colleges and Measures for the Maintenance of Standards in Higher Education, Regulation, 2010 for improving the standard of teaching in Indian universities.[35]

The complexity of the Indian higher education system gets further compounded due to large number of regulatory bodies who sometimes have overlapping scope of work resulting in power struggle and additional confusion for stakeholders. Consider the recent example of conflict between UGC and All India Council for Technical Education or AICTE on the regulatory jurisdiction for management programmes in India.[36]

National Knowledge Commission has underlined the over-regulation but under-governed nature of regulatory regime at present in India. The present system is presided over by a University Grants Commission-UGC (which is very tightly controlled by the Government) and a plethora of distinct segregated bodies like All India Council of Technical Education, Medical Council of India etc. NKC perceiving confusion and overlap in mandates of multiplicity of regulatory agencies has recommended establishment of an Independent Regulatory Authority for Higher Education which should be at an arm's length from all stake holders including Government of India.[37]

Right to Education Bill came into force on the 1st of April 2010 RTE will provide compulsory and free education for all children between 6 to 14 years of age. FDI allowed in Education Sector as India becomes an attractive economy. To facilitate students avail quality learning in competitive world. Government was abolishment of compulsory CBSE board exam for class X from 2010-11 and introduction of grading system to de-traumatize education. Comprehensive Compulsory Evaluation in place of examination.

Privatisation of higher education is apparently a fledgling but welcome trend: Higher education requires it to maintain creativity, adaptability and quality. The economic trail of liberalisation and globalisation demands it. Considering the chronic paucity of resources, gradually unburdening itself of the additional responsibility for higher education may be advisable for the government. Privatisation of higher education, however, is not without social costs. In a polity such as India's, where structured inequalities have been entrenched, privatisation is sure to reinforce existing inequalities and to foster inegalitarian tendencies. Privatisation of higher education is apparently a fledgling but welcome trend: Higher education requires it to maintain creativity, adaptability and quality.[38]

The 73rd Constitutional amendment provides for transfer of the responsibility for primary and secondary school education to the elected bodies. Consequently, there is no uniformity in the manner in which local bodies have been involved in school education across the states. While in several states a vast gamut of functions is assigned to PRIs at every level, in practice the PRIs, especially Taluk and Gram Panchayats, discharge few education-related tasks.[39]

The National Commission for Higher Education and Research Bill, 2010 is an act to provide for the determination, co-ordination, maintenance of standards in, and promotion of, higher education and research, including university education, technical and professional education other than agricultural [and medical] education, and for that purpose, to establish the National Commission for Higher Education and Research. This act further to promote the autonomy of higher educational institutions for the free pursuit of knowledge and innovation, and for facilitating access, inclusion and opportunities to all, and providing for comprehensive and holistic growth of higher education and research in a competitive global environment through reforms and renovation; and to provide for an advisory mechanism of eminent peers in academia.

The Central Government shall, by notification, establish, for the purposes of this Act, a Commission to be called the "National Commission for Higher Education and Research". The Commission shall be a body corporate by the name aforesaid, having perpetual succession and a common seal, with power, subject to the provisions of this Act, to acquire, hold and dispose off property, both movable and immovable, and to contract, and shall, by the said name, sue or be sued.

Distance education council was an organisation based in New Delhi, India responsible for the promotion and coordination of the Open University and distance education system and for determination of its standards in India. The Council was constituted under the Indira Gandhi National Open University Act (1985). The Distance Education Council is an apex body for the Open and Distance Learning (ODL) system in the country. It is empowered, under Statute 28 of the IGNOU Act, to act as an apex body for the ODL system. In June 2013, University Grants Commission has taken over DEC, by establishing Distance Education Bureau which will govern the distance education programmes in India. The UGC has constituted a Committee to examine the pending proposals of programme-wise recognition to the institutions.[40]

Right of Education Act[41]

The Right of Children to Free and Compulsory Education Act or Right to Education Act (RTE) is an Act of the Parliament of India enacted on 4 August 2009, which describes the modalities of the importance of free and compulsory education for children between 6 and 14 in India under Article 21A of the Indian Constitution. India became one of 135 countries to make education a fundamental right of every child when the act came into force on 1 April 2010. The bill was approved by the cabinet on 2 July 2009. Rajya Sabha passed the bill on 20 July 2009 and the Lok Sabha on 4 August 2009. It received Presidential assent and was notified as law on 26 August 2009 as The Children's Right to Free and Compulsory Education Act.

The law came into effect in the whole of India except the state of Jammu and Kashmir from 1 April 2010, the first time in the history of India a law was brought into force by a speech by the Prime Minister. In his speech, Manmohan Singh, former Prime Minister of India stated that, "We are committed to ensuring that all children, irrespective of gender and social category, have access to education, education that enables them to acquire the skills, knowledge, values and attitudes necessary to become responsible and active citizens of India."

The RTE Act provides for the: Right of children to free and compulsory education till completion of elementary education in a neighbourhood school. It clarifies that 'compulsory education' means obligation of the appropriate government to provide free elementary education and ensure compulsory admission, attendance and completion of elementary education to every child in the six to fourteen age group. 'Free' means that no child shall be liable to pay any kind of fee or charges or expenses which may prevent him or her from pursuing and completing elementary education. It makes provisions for a non-admitted child to be admitted to an age appropriate class. It specifies the duties and responsibilities of appropriate Governments, local authority and parents in providing free and compulsory education, and sharing of financial and other responsibilities between the Central and State Governments.

The Act makes education a fundamental right of every child between the ages of 6 and 14 and specifies minimum norms in elementary schools. It requires all private schools (except the minority institutions) to reserve 25 per cent of seats for the poor and other categories of children (to be reimbursed by the state as part of the public-private partnership plan). Children are admitted in to private schools based on caste based reservations. The Act also provides that no child shall be held back, expelled, or required to pass a board examination until the completion of elementary education. There is also a provision for special training of school drop-outs to bring them up to par with students of the same age.

According the Website of Ministry of Human Resource Development, Government of India, The RTE Act provides for the:[42]

(1) Right of children to free and compulsory education till completion of elementary education in a neighbourhood school.

(2) It clarifies that 'compulsory education' means obligation of the appropriate government to provide free elementary education and ensure compulsory admission, attendance and completion of elementary education to every child in the six to fourteen age group. 'Free' means that no child shall be liable to pay any kind of fee or charges or expenses which may prevent him or her from pursuing and completing elementary education.

(3) It makes provisions for a non-admitted child to be admitted to an age appropriate class.

(4) It specifies the duties and responsibilities of appropriate Governments, local authority and parents in providing free and compulsory education, and sharing of financial and other responsibilities between the Central and State Governments.

(5) It lays down the norms and standards relating inter alia to Pupil Teacher Ratios (PTRs), buildings and infrastructure, school-working days, teacher-working hours.

(6) It provides for rational deployment of teachers by ensuring that the specified pupil teacher ratio is maintained for each school, rather than just as an average for the State or District or Block, thus ensuring that there is no urban-rural imbalance in teacher postings. It also provides for prohibition of deployment of teachers for non-educational work, other than decennial census, elections to local authority, state legislatures and parliament, and disaster relief.

(7) It provides for appointment of appropriately trained teachers, i.e. teachers with the requisite entry and academic qualifications.

(8) It prohibits (a) physical punishment and mental harassment; (b) screening procedures for admission of children; (c) capitation fee; (d) private tuition by teachers and (e) running of schools without recognition,

(9) It provides for development of curriculum in consonance with the values enshrined in the Constitution, and which would ensure the all-round development of the child, building on the child's knowledge, potentiality and talent and making the child free of fear, trauma and anxiety through a system of child friendly and child centred learning.

References

1. Brainy Quote, Available at http://www.brainyquote.com/quotes/keywords/environment.html
2. Education, Available at https://en.wikipedia.org/wiki/Education
3. *Ibid.*
4. See http://www.tc.columbia.edu/epsa/economics/
5. Maria D. Fitzpatrick, Economics of education, Available at https://economics.stanford.edu/files/Econ%20146%20syll_spr11.pdf
6. Importance of education speech, http://www.indiacelebrating.com/speech/importance-of-education/
7. Importance of education, Available at https://myeducationservices.wordpress.com/2011/04/13/importance-of-education-%E2%80%93-why-it-is-important-in-life/
8. See http://www.123helpme.com/search.asp?text=importance+ of+education
9. Education expenditure, Available at http://www.oecd-ilibrary.org/sites/factbook-2011-en/10/02/04/index.html?contentType=% 2Fns%2 FStatisticalPublication%

2C%2Fns%2FChapter&itemId=%2Fcontent% 2F chapter%2 Ffactbook-2011-89-en&mimeType=text%2Fhtml &containerItemId=%2 Fcontent%2Fserial% 2F18147364 &accessItemIds=

10. Educational expenditure statistics, Available at http://ec.europa.eu/eurostat/statistics-explained/index.php/Educational_expenditure _ statistics
11. Anuradha De and Tanuka Endow, Public Expenditure on Education in India: Recent Trends and Outcomes, http://ceid.educ.cam.ac.uk/publications/WP18-ADfin.pdf
12. http://mhrd.gov.in/sites/upload_files/mhrd/files/statistics/ABE_2010-13.pdf
13. Anit N. Mukherjee and Satadru Sikdar, Public Expenditure on Education in India by the Union Government and Roadmap for the Future, http://www.idfc.com/pdf/report/2012/Chapter_2.pdf
14. http://planningcommission.nic.in/plans/mta/mta-9702/mta-ch12.pdf
15. See http://mhrd.gov.in/sites/upload_files/mhrd/files/document-reports/XIPlandocument_1.pdf
16. D. Sampath Kumar, Recent reforms in education in India: Achievements and unfinished tasks, International Journal of Social Science & Interdisciplinary Research, Vol.1 Issue 8, August 2012, pp. 82-90.
17. From official website of U.S. Department of Education, http://www.ed.gov/oii-news/increasing-educational-productivity
18. Kieran M. Killeen, Educational Productivity and Opportunities to Learn: An overview of concepts and discussion points, https://www.uvm.edu/~jeffords/reports/pdfs/Issue%20Brief_ Educational %20Productivity% 20and%20Opportunities%20to%20Learn.pdf
19. Economic Returns to Investment in Education, http://siteresources.worldbank.org/INTMENA/Resources/EDU_02-Chap02-Education.pdf
20. Natalia A. Kolesnikova, The return to education cannot calculated easily,https://www.stlouisfed.org/publications/regional-economist/january-2010/the-return-to-education-isnt-calculated-easily
21. The Importance of Human Capital for Economic Growth, Available at http://www.iwim.uni-bremen.de/publikationen/pdf/W027.pdf
22. Human capital, Available at https://en.wikipedia.org/wiki/Human_capital
23. See http://hanushek.stanford.edu/publications/economic-growth-developing-countries-role-human-capital
24. See http://study.com/academy/lesson/what-is-human-capital-importance-to-an-organisation.html
25. Physical capital, Available at https://en.wikipedia.org/wiki/Physical_capital
26. Physical Capital: Definition and Effects on Productivity, Available at http://study.com/academy/lesson/physical-capital-definition-and-effects-on-productivity.html
27. Difference Between Human Capital and Physical Capital, Available at http://www.differencebetween.com/difference-between-human-capital-and-vs-physical-capital/

28. http://www.evancarmichael.com/African-Accounts/1665/The-role-of-human-and-physical-capital-in-growth-The-Effects-of-Human-Capital-on-Economic-Development.html
29. What is the difference between human and physical capital? Available at http://www.wisegeek.com/what-is-the-difference-between-physical-and-human-capital.htm
30. Difference Between Human Capital and Physical Capital, Available at http://www.differencebetween.com/difference-between-human-capital-and-vs-physical-capital/
31. Santosh Mehrotra, Reforming elementary education in India: A menu of options, Available at http://birbhum.nic.in/DPSC/reference/78.pdf
32. Dr Jayaprakash Narayan (2005), Reforming Higher Education in India, Available at http://ap.loksatta.org/documents/advocacy/highedu.pdf
33. Dr. Jyoti Sharma, Pre-service teacher education reforms in India and Pakistan: Challenges and possibility, International Journal of Research, Vol. 2 (Iss.2): November, 2014, pp.1-13.
34. Sushma Berlia, Educational Reforms in India, Available at http://www.aserf.org.in/articles/Educational%20Reforms% 20in%20 India.pdf
35. Qualitative reforms in Higher education, available at http://mhrd.gov.in/sites/upload_files/mhrd/files/ru2388.pdf
36. Rahul Choudaha, Three Solutions for Reforming Indian Higher Education, Available at http://higheredsig.org/cihe/Number05-19.pdf
37. Suman Sharma, Higher Education: Recent Reform Initiatives in India, Available at http://www.napsipag.org/pdf/suman-sharma.pdf
38. N. Jayaram, Higher Education Reform in India: Prospects and Challenges, Available at http://www.cshe.nagoya-u.ac.jp/seminar/kokusai/jayaram.pdf
39. http://www.ncert.nic.in/rightside/links/pdf/focus_group/Systemic_ reforms_final.pdf
40. Distance Education Council, Available at https://en.wikipedia.org/wiki/Distance_Education_Council
41. Right of Children to Free and Compulsory Education Act or Right to Education Act, Available at https://en.wikipedia.org/wiki/Right_of_Children_to_Free_and_Compulsory_Education_Act
42. From the website of Ministry of Human Resource Development, Government of India, Available at http://mhrd.gov.in/rte

Chapter - 10

Climate Changes and Health Impact

"Being in control of your life and having realistic expectations about your day-to-day challenges are the keys to stress management, which is perhaps the most important ingredient to living a happy, healthy and rewarding life."

—***Marilu Henner***[1]

The four primary components that are important to improved physical health are as follows: Cardio respiratory capacity is the ability of the body to take in oxygen (respiration), deliver it to the cells (circulation), and use it at the cellular level to create energy (bioenergetics) for physical work (activity). Muscular capacity refers to the spectrum of muscular capability. This includes muscular endurance; muscular strength; and muscular power. Flexibility is the range of movement or amount of motion that a joint is capable of performing. Body composition is the proportion of fat-free mass (muscle, bone, blood, organs, and fluids) to fat mass.[2]

For the common man, health is merely an absence of sickness and ailments. This view is narrow and one-sided. The term 'health' is much more comprehensive. Good health is the state of all-round physical, social and mental wellbeing of a person, which enables him to live and work normally and to resist the negative impact of his environment.[3] Many people do not realise, and often underestimate, the importance of good health. Health, as they say, is wealth. Good health is necessary to carry out daily tasks. When discussing healthy, many people would consider the condition of their bodies and forget about the condition of their minds,[4] The common saying Health is Wealth fits to everyone's life. Good health is the real wealth means money which has capability to help us always. Good health is most important part of our life without which we are incomplete and living unhealthy life. Good health is really better than wealth and other things in this whole world.

Definition of Health

Health is the level of functional or metabolic efficiency of a living organism. The World Health Organisation defined health in its broader sense in its 1948 constitution as "a state of complete physical, mental, and social well-being and not merely the absence of disease or infirmity." According to the World Health Organisation, the main determinants of health include the social and economic environment, the physical environment, and the person's individual characteristics and behaviours.

The World Health Organisation describes mental health as "a state of well-being in which the individual realises his or her own abilities, can cope with the normal stresses of life, can work productively and fruitfully, and is able to make a contribution to his or her community". Achieving and maintaining health is an ongoing process, shaped by both the evolution of healthcare knowledge and practices as well as personal strategies and organised interventions for staying healthy.[5] Good nutrition is an important part of leading a healthy lifestyle. The link between good nutrition and healthy weight, reduced chronic disease risk, and overall health is too important to ignore.[6]

Determination of Healthcare

Healthcare is the diagnosis, treatment, and prevention of disease, illness, injury, and other physical and mental impairments in human beings. Access to healthcare varies across countries, groups, and individuals, largely influenced by social and economic conditions as well as the health policies in place. Better health is central to human happiness and well-being. It also makes an important contribution to economic progress, as healthy populations live longer, are more productive, and save more.[7] The delivery of modern health-care depends on groups of trained professionals and paraprofessionals coming together as interdisciplinary teams.

Health care extends beyond the delivery of services to patients, encompassing many related sectors, and set within a bigger picture of financing and governance structures. Primary care refers to the work of health professionals who act as a first point of consultation for all patients within the health care system. Secondary care is the health care services provided by medical specialists and other health professionals who generally do not have first contact with patients, for example, cardiologists, urologists and dermatologists. Tertiary care is specialised consultative health care, usually for inpatients and on referral from a primary or secondary health professional.[8]

Many factors combine together to affect the health of individuals and communities. The determinants of health include: (a) the social and economic environment, (b) the physical environment, and (c) the person's individual characteristics and behaviours.[9] Many things in the environment can affect our health. Hazardous substances found in the air, soil and water can originate from a variety of sources, such as agricultural and industrial activities, mining operations, landfills and leaky underground storage tanks.[10]

Malnutrition

Malnutrition is a condition that results from eating a diet in which nutrients are either not enough or are too much such that the diet causes health problems. Malnutrition is often used specifically to refer to under nutrition where there is not enough a calorie, protein, or micronutrients. It is caused by eating a diet in which nutrients are not enough or are too much such that it causes health problems. Malnutrition increases the risk of infection and infectious disease, and moderate malnutrition weakens every part of the immune system.[11]

Malnutrition is estimated to contribute to more than one third of all child deaths, although it is rarely listed as the direct cause. Lack of access to highly nutritious foods, especially in the present context of rising food prices, is a common cause of malnutrition.[12] Malnutrition continues to be a major public health problem throughout the developing world, particularly in southern Asia and sub-Saharan Africa.[13]

The World Bank estimates that India is one of the highest ranking countries in the world for the number of children suffering from malnutrition. One of the major causes for malnutrition in India is gender inequality. Due to the low social status of Indian women, their diet often lacks in both quality and quantity. Women who suffer malnutrition are less likely to have healthy babies. Under-nutrition is more prevalent in rural areas, again mainly due to low socio-economic status. Anaemia for both men and women is only slightly higher in rural areas than in urban areas. Children of Muslim households and those belonging to scheduled castes or tribes also face higher rates of malnourishment.[14]

Malnutrition, unhealthy diets deficient in micronutrients, and micronutrient imbalances can disrupt the function of various immune system components. This weakens immune defence, decreasing its effectiveness in the elimination of pathogens and making us vulnerable to various diseases. Malnutrition is not always synonymous with the state of starvation seen in many places in the world. Most often, malnutrition is caused by an inadequate or imbalanced diet and unhealthy lifestyle common in the developing world, as well as among apparently well-nourished people living in western economies.[15]

The Midday Meal Scheme is a school meal programme of the government of India designed to improve the nutritional status of school-age children nationwide. The roots of the programme can be traced back to the Pre-Independence era, when a mid-day meal programme was introduced in 1925 in Madras Corporation by the British administration. A mid-day meal programme was introduced in the Union Territory of Puducherry by the French administration in 1930. The Government of India initiated the National Programme of Nutritional Support to Primary Education on 15 August 1995.

The objective of the scheme is to help improve the effectiveness of primary education by improving the nutritional status of primary school children.

Initially, the scheme was implemented in 2,408 blocks of the country to provide food to students in classes one through five of government, government-aided and local body run schools. The central and state governments share the cost of the Midday Meal Scheme, with the centre providing 75 per cent and the states 25 per cent.[16] The objectives of the Mid-Day Meal Scheme are:

(1) Improving the nutritional status of children in classes I-V in Government, Local Body and Government aided schools, and EGS and AIE centres.

(2) Encouraging poor children, belonging to disadvantaged sections, to attend school more regularly and help them concentrate on classroom activities.

(3) Providing nutritional support to children of primary stage in drought affected areas during summer vacation.[17]

The programme envisaged the provision of cooked meals/ processed food of calorific value equivalent to 100 g of wheat /rice for children studying in classes IV in all Government, local body and government aided primary schools free of cost. This recommendation was based on a study done by NNMB (1990-92) on dietary consumption patterns of rural children using a one-day 24-hour recall method. The programme which started in August 1995 has seen all India coverage in 1997-98 and the coverage of children under the programme has increased from 3.4 crores in 1995-96 to 10.5 crores in 2003-04 in about the same number of schools. In May 2004 a new coalition government was formed at the centre, which promised universal provision of cooked meals fully funded by the centre. This 'promise' made in the Common Minimum Programme was followed by enhanced financial support to the states for cooking and building sufficient infrastructure.[18]

Despite the broad-based efforts of the central government for more than a decade and a half and a few pioneering efforts earlier on, the problem of malnutrition, anemia, deficiency in vitamin A and Iodine is very common among children in India. Today, 94 per cent of children in the age group of six to nine are mildly, moderately, or severely underweight. About 67.5 per cent of children under five years and 69 per cent of adolescent girls suffer from anemia due to iron and folic acid deficiency.

In the post-independence era, Gujarat was the first state to start school lunch programme in 1984. However, it was only in 1995 that the National Programme of Nutritional Support to Primary Education (NP-NSPE) was launched at the national level [GOI, 1995]. The then union territory of Delhi followed suit immediately. The objective of this programme was to give boost to universalisation of primary education and to impact the nutritional intake of students in primary classes.[19]

With a view to enhancing enrollment, retention and attendance and simultaneously improving nutritional levels among children, the National Programme of Nutritional Support to Primary Education (NP-NSPE) was launched as a Centrally Sponsored Scheme on 15th August 1995, initially in 2408 blocks in the country. In September 2004 the scheme was revised to provide cooked mid-day meal with 300 calories and 8-12 grams of protein to all children studying in classes I-V in government and aided schools and EGS/ AIE centres.

In July 2006 the scheme was further revised to provide assistance for cooking cost at the rate of (a) Rs 1.80 per child/school day for States in the North Eastern Region, provided the NER states contribute Rs 0.20 per child/ school day, and (b) Rs 1.50 per child/school day for other States and UTs, provided that these States and UTs contribute Re 0.50 per child/school day. The Department of School Education and Literacy, Ministry of Human Resource Development has prescribed a comprehensive and elaborate mechanism for monitoring and supervision of the Mid-Day Meal Scheme. The Finance Minister has announced in the Union Budget 2007-08 that the Mid-Day Meal Scheme will be extended to cover children in Upper Primary Classes in 3427 Educationally Backwards Blocks (EBBs) in 2007-08. A Budget provision of Rs 7324 crores has been made for this purpose, representing 37 per cent increase over the budget for 2006-07.[20]

The Mid-Day Meal Scheme is the world's biggest school lunch programme and is being implemented all over India for primary and upper primary school students. However, nutrition and hygiene are now among the main challenges it faces. Out of 876 test reports of mid-day meal samples in Delhi from 1 January 2012 to 31 March 2013, more than 90 per cent failed to meet the standard of 12 gms of protein and 450 calories. A number of loopholes in the scheme need to be plugged if nutritious food, not just something cooked, is to reach the plates of poor students.[21]

Ocean Acidification

Recent reports on global climatic change suggest significant global warming trends over the past 30 years associated with continuously increasing greenhouse gas concentrations. The ecosystem is affected by: (i) increasing sea temperature, (ii) irradiance, (iii) ocean acidification, (iv) frequency of intense tropical storms and (v) altered rainfall and river flood plumes. Coral reefs are found in only a small per centage of global oceans, between 0.08 and 0.16 per cent, but they shelter about one-third of the marine species known today. Long-term changes in Earth's atmosphere and oceans exert considerable control over biotic turnover and evolution through a number of variables, including sea surface temperature, sea level, and mineral saturation state.

Coral reefs represent some of the most biologically diverse ecosystems on Earth, providing critical habitat to approximately 25 per cent of marine species. In addition, these ecosystems provide economic benefits through tourism and fisheries. One recent estimate valued the annual net economic benefits of the world's coral reefs at $30 billion. Coral reefs have been identified as an endangered ecosystem because they are subject to multiple natural, man-made and man-mediated stresses.

Macroalgae is a collective term used for seaweeds and other benthic marine algae that are generally visible to the naked eye. Larger macroalgae are also referred to as seaweeds. The macroalgae of the Great Barrier Reef are a very diverse and complex assemblage of species and forms. They occupy a wide variety of habitats, including shallow and deep coral reefs, deep inter-reef areas, sandy bottoms, seagrass beds, mangroves roots, and rocky intertidal zones.

Changes to the greenhouse gas content (principally CO_2 and methane) have driven changes to the average temperature of the planet, which have in turn driven changes to the temperature of the upper layers of the ocean. The upper layers of the ocean are now 0.7°C warmer than they were was 100 years ago. The primary impact of elevated temperature on coral reefs is manifested as a phenomenon known as "coral bleaching", and the primary impact of increased ocean acidity is on the calcium carbonate deposition and dissolution processes of corals and other calcareous organisms that form the structure of coral reefs.

Coral reefs are among the most biologically diverse and economically important ecosystems on the planet, providing ecosystem services that are vital to human societies and industries through fisheries, coastal protection, building materials, new biochemical compounds, and tourism. Increasing concentrations of CO_2 lower the pH of seawater, which reduces the capacity of corals and many other marine organisms to make calcium carbonate skeletons because of a coincident decrease in the concentration of carbonate ions. Even though coral reefs are critically important to many island economies, they are among the most threatened ecosystems on the planet. The abundance of coral reefs has declined by as much as 50 per cent on and Western Pacific coral reefs and is continuing to decline at the rate of 1–2 per cent per year.

Since the 1980s the frequency of warming events has intensified and simultaneously widespread coral bleaching and enhanced coral mortality have been observed. Yet, it remains unpredictable how tropical coral reef. Global climate change is feared to lead to the collapse of living coral reefs, whose component organisms can respond in but three ways: migration, adaptation, and extinction. Because ancient reefs have been exposed to multiple episodes of environmental change, the fossil record provides an important resource for understanding the range of responses of coral reefs to climate change.

The earth appears to possess an amazingly effective meteorological "ThermoSolarStat" that jumps into operation to suppress the intensity of solar radiation to which corals are exposed whenever dangerously-high water temperatures are approached. While extreme increases in ocean temperatures may cause extensive bleaching and mortality of corals, even moderate increases in temperature may have important demographic consequences for corals, moderating growth and/or reproduction. Human dependence on reefs for food, materials, and income (tourism or exports) is high and growing. The threat posed by rising sea levels is a special case for the inhabitants of low coral reef islands and coastal plains, since human use and habitation of reef islands and structures may become impossible, even though the surrounding reefs are unaffected and remain healthy.

Ocean warming and acidification from increasing levels of atmospheric CO_2 represent major global threats to coral reefs, and are in many regions exacerbated by local-scale disturbances such as overfishing and nutrient enrichment. The increased mortality of coral polyps and the bleaching of coral reefs are consequences of sustained periods of elevated water temperature. The impact on coral reefs from a rapid rise in sea level cannot be envisaged by considering the response of corals to sea-level change in isolation from other influences that presently govern coral growth.

Health Issues of Neem Tree

Plants play a pivotal role in the survival and development of human civilisation. The use of traditional medicine and medicinal plants in most developing countries, as a normative basis for the maintenance of good health, has been widely observed. Neem commonly known as 'Indian lilac' or 'Margosa' is a native tree to India. It is an evergreen deciduous tree. The people of India have long revered the neem tree; for centuries, millions have cleaned their teeth with neem twigs, smeared skin disorders with neem-leaf juice, taken neem tea as a tonic, and placed neem leaves in their beds, books, grain bins, cupboards, and closets to keep away troublesome bugs.

The many uses of the neem tree include various health, pesticide, and soil amending applications. A native to east India and Burma, it grows in much of South East Asia and West Africa, and more recently Caribbean and South and Central America. Neem has been indispensable herb in ayurveda, unani and other traditional medicine therapies since prehistoric times. A number of bioactive components have been isolated from various parts of the neem tree.

Neem oil is extracted from the seeds of the neem tree and has insecticidal and medicinal properties due to which it has been used in pest control in rice cultivation. Neem leaves are used as green leaf manure and also in preparation of litter compost. Neem leaves are used in storage of grains. Neem bark and roots also have medicinal properties. Neem seed cake performs the dual function of both fertilizer and pesticide. Neem cake is used to manufacture high quality organic or natural manure, which does not have any aftermaths on plants, soil and other living organisms. Neem fumigants are ecofriendly, do not harm other microorganisms, are nontoxic, and do not contaminate terrestrial and aquatic environment.

Neem leaves are excellent source of some minerals and they contain adequate quantity of trace minerals except Zinc, for which the recommended requirement is 40 ppm. During the past five decades' intensive investigations on the diverse properties of Neem have been carried out. Neem trees show considerable variability in the azadirachtin content of their seeds, irrespective of the habitat. India has encouraged scientific investigations of Neem tree as a part of its program to revitalize Indian tradition and also to increase commercial interest on Neem.

Table 1: Pharmacological activity of various parts of Neem

Part used	***Medicinal properties***
Leaves	Leprosy, eye problem, epistaxis, intestinal worms, anorexia, biliousness, skin ulcer
Barks	Analgesic, alternative and curative fever
Flowers	Bile suppression, elimination of intestinal worms and phlegm
Fruits	Piles, intestinal worms, urinary disorder, epistaxis, phlegm, eye problem, diabetes, wounds and leprosy
Twings	Cough, asthma, piles, phantom tumor, intestinal worms, sperma torrhoea, obstinate urinary disorder, diabetes
Gum	Scabies, wounds, ulcers, skin diseases
Seeds	Leprosy and intestinal worms
Oil	Leprosy and intestinal worms

Source: Astif, M. (2013). A Review on Spermicidal Activities of Azadirachta indica, Journal of Pharmacognosy and Phytochemistry, 1 (5), p. 62.

The neem derivatives have shown their insecticidal properties on a broad range of insect pests. Almost all parts of the neem tree have been used as traditional Ayurvedic, unani and sidhha medicine in India. The aqueous extract of neem bark and leaf also possesses anticomplement and immunostimulant activity (Asif, 2013). Neem is effective in treating skin problems, infections and inflammations such as acne, boils, eczema, psoriasis, yeast infections and warts. Neem root has antihyperglycemic and hypoglycemic activity.

Table 2: Chemicals found in Neem and Their Pharmacological Actions

Chemicals	***Pharmacological***
Gedunin	Vasodilator, antifungal
Nimbidin	Antibacterial and analgesic
Quercetin	Anti-protozoal, antioxidant
Salanin	Repellant, anti-feedant

During the last five decades, apart from the chemistry of the neem compounds, considerable progress has been achieved regarding the biological activity and medicinal applications of neem. It is now considered as a valuable source of unique natural products for development of medicines against various diseases and also for the development of industrial products (Biswas, 2002). Neem provides shade, ornamental look, shelterbelt, fuel wood and construction material, and also helps in degraded land reclamation and soil conservation activities (Mishra, 2012). Extracts of leaf, oil and seed kernels are effective against certain human (Pandey *et. al.,* 2014). Neem seed is a part of Neem tree which has high concentration of oil.

Neem has rightly been called sarvaroghari. Since time immemorial, Indians have learnt and made use of neem in a variety of ways both for personal and community health by way of environmental amelioration. Neem is recognised today as a natural product which has much to offer in solving global agricultural, environmental and public health problems. Researchers worldwide are now focusing on the importance of neem in the agricultural industry. Neem, correctly stated as "Tree for Solving Global Problems" is one of the most precious gift by nature to us. It is indeed a 'Green Gold', which we should nourish and cherish for centuries to come.

Hepatitis B Virus

Hepatitis B virus is a species of the genus Orthohepadnavirus, which is likewise a part of the Hepadnaviridae family of viruses. This virus causes the disease hepatitis B. The life cycle of hepatitis B virus is complex. Hepatitis B is one of a few known non-retroviral viruses which use reverse transcription as a part of its replication process. HBV is a noncytopathic virus. This means that the virus itself does not cause direct damage to liver cells. Hepatitis C virus is a major cause of liver disease worldwide and a potential cause of substantial morbidity and mortality in the future. Hepatitis A, B, C and E viruses cause more than 80 per cent of viral hepatitis. In the remaining 15-20 per cent cases, the etiology of hepatitis remains uncertain and cannot be attributed to any of the known infectious and non-infectious causes of hepatitis.

Hepatitis B is an infectious disease caused by the hepatitis B virus which affects the liver. It can cause both acute and chronic infections. It may take 30 to 180 days for symptoms to begin. Transmission of hepatitis B virus results from exposure to infectious blood or body fluids containing blood. Several professional societies like the American Association for the Study of Liver Diseases, the European Association for the Study of the Liver and Asian Pacific Association for the Study of the Liver have developed guidelines to assist physicians in the management of CHB patients.

HBV infection leads to a wide spectrum of liver disease ranging from acute (including fulminant hepatic failure) to chronic hepatitis, cirrhosis, and hepatocellular carcinoma. Most people infected with hepatitis B as adults recover fully, even if their signs and symptoms are severe. Infants and children are more likely to develop a chronic hepatitis B infection. A vaccine can prevent hepatitis B, but there's no cure if you have it. If you are infected, taking certain precautions can help prevent spreading HBV to others.

In 1995, the population of India was reported to be around 900 million. The average estimated carrier rate of hepatitis B virus is four per cent, placing India in the intermediate range for hepatitis B endemicity and giving an approximate total of 36 million carriers. Hepatitis B remains a significant public health problem in India and will continue to do so as long as commercial blood banks remain operational and until appropriate nationwide vaccination programmes and other control measures are established. Spread of HBV infection in many South Asian countries is attributed to unsafe blood supply, reuse of contaminated syringes, lack of maternal screening to prevent perinatal transmission and delay in the introduction of hepatitis B vaccine.

It is spread through contact with the blood and body fluids of an infected person. Any person may get hepatitis B if: (a) Have sex with an infected person without using a condom; (b) Share needles (used for injecting drugs) with an infected person; (c) Get a tattoo or piercing with tools that weren't sterilised; and (d) Share personal items like razors or toothbrushes with an infected person. In acute hepatitis, it takes about one to six months from the time of infection for the disease to manifest itself. Early symptoms include nausea and vomiting, loss of appetite, fatigue, and muscle and joint aches. Jaundice, together with dark urine and light stools, follows.

Most people do not experience any symptoms during the acute infection phase. However, some people have acute illness with symptoms that last several weeks, including yellowing of the skin and eyes (jaundice), dark urine, extreme fatigue, nausea, vomiting and abdominal pain. A small subset of persons with acute hepatitis can develop acute liver failure which can lead to death. In some people, the hepatitis B virus can also cause a chronic liver infection that can later develop into cirrhosis of the liver or liver cancer.

The physical examination findings in hepatitis B disease vary from minimal to impressive (in patients with hepatic decompensation), according to the stage of the disease. Hepatitis B is preventable through vaccination. All children should receive the vaccine. In addition, adults at high risk for hepatitis B should be. Liver transplantation should be considered for patients with impending liver failure due to acute (initial) infection or advanced cirrhosis. Chronic Hepatitis B can lead to serious health issues, like cirrhosis or liver cancer. The best way to prevent Hepatitis B is by getting vaccinated.

Chronic hepatitis B is not curable, but it is treatable. The goal of therapy is to reduce the risk of complications, including premature death. Treatment can help to prevent cirrhosis, liver failure and liver cancer. Many experts anticipate that medications to cure hepatitis B virus will be available, perhaps as early as a few years from now. Treatment for hepatitis B is used to manage the effects of the infection but is not a cure. In general, people who are chronically infected but do not have any signs of current liver damage will not need treatment.

The primary treatment goals for patients with hepatitis B infection are to prevent progression of the disease, particularly to cirrhosis, liver failure, and hepatocellular carcinoma. Several antiviral medications- including lamivudine, adefovir, telbivudine and entecavir can help fight the virus and slow its ability to damage your liver. During a liver transplant, the surgeon removes your damaged liver and replaces it with a healthy liver. Most transplanted livers come from deceased donors, though a small number come from living donors who donate a portion of their livers.

Hepatitis B is a liver infection caused by the Hepatitis B virus. Hepatitis B is transmitted when blood, semen, or another body fluid from a person infected with the Hepatitis B virus enters the body of someone who is not infected. This can happen through sexual contact; sharing needles, syringes, or other drug-injection equipment; or from mother to baby at birth. People who have not been infected with HBV can be vaccinated against the virus to prevent infection.

With improvement in economic and living conditions of the communities, the age of acquiring hepatitis A virus (HAV) infection is shifting from early childhood to adolescence and young adulthood. Such epidemiological shift leads to an increased incidence of symptomatic HAV infection, including heightened risk of liver failure. One of the important factors for this decrease could be attributed to the improvement in living conditions, hygiene and sanitation in these countries.

Human Life

The meaning of life as we perceive it is derived from our philosophical and religious contemplation of, and scientific inquiries about existence, social ties, consciousness, and happiness. Every living being other than humans have a purpose, they maintain the food chain at the least and do not destroy earth's valuable resources. Scientific contributions focus primarily on describing related empirical facts about the universe, exploring the context and parameters concerning the 'how' of life. The philosophical perspectives on the meaning of life are those ideologies which explain life in terms of ideals or abstractions defined by humans. The religious perspectives on the meaning of life are those ideologies which explain life in terms of an implicit purpose not defined by humans.[22]

Christianity teaches that the universe was created through love by an intelligent power, namely the God of the Bible. Creation was purposeful, not arbitrary, and therefore the universe is not morally neutral, but fundamentally good. God created human beings in the divine image, enabling humans to have some understanding of God and of God's vast and complex design. The purpose of life is to love and serve God in order to help bring about God's glorious plan for creation. The Christian concept of sin originates in the story of Adam and Eve found in Chapters 2-3 of the Book of Genesis, a story that has central importance for Christians. The story relates the creation by God of the first humans, a man and woman.[23]

The Bible makes it abundantly clear that God created man and that He created him for His glory (see Isaiah 43:7). The ultimate purpose of man, according to the Bible, is simply to glorify God.[24] The purpose of man's life on earth is a question which many have pondered about for thousands of years but the answer to which has often become elusive. The purpose of life according to our prevailing belief is to just live as best we can and accumulate material wealth, get married and have children and if possible have as many earthly honours as possible and if we are successful in these then our purpose has been achieved.[25]

The phenomenon of a sustained increased in the real per capita income of a country over a period of time is known as economic growth. Till 1960 the term 'economic development' was often used as a synonym of 'economic growth' in economic literature. But now the entire concept of economic development has changed. According to UNO economic development concerns not only man's material needs, but also the improvement of social conditions of his life. As per the World Bank reports, economic development means 'the improvement in quality of life.

Measures of Quality Changes

- *Physical Quality of Life Index (PQLI):* It is developed by Morris.D. Moris in 1979. He uses three important variablesLike Life expectancy at age 1, Infant Mortality Rate and adult literacy. A country's rank in PQLI is based on its performance in the above three areas. The Overseas Development Council (ODC), a US based research council is the nodal agency to construct the PQLI.
- *Human Development Index (HDI):* HDI was developed in 1990 by Pakistan economist Mahabub-ul-Haq and Indian economist Amartya Sen. It has three important variables such as life expectancy, literacy, education and standard of living for countries worldwide. It is used to measure the impact of economic policies on quality of life. It is prepared by UNDP in every year in its Human Development Report (HDR).
- *Gender Development Index (GDI):* GDI is same as HDI, but adjusted to reflect gender in equalities. It is also a comparative measure of longitivity, literacy and standard of living. But while calculating GDI separate index for each of the dimension are separately calculated for men and women and then two are club together to calculate the GDI.
- *Gender Empowerment Measure (GEM):* GEM measures the opportunities available to a woman in a society the capability of political participation and decision making, economic participation and decision making and command over resources.
- *Human Poverty Index (HPI):* It tell us the extent of deprivation in a society, i.e. What per centage of the population is deprived of a longer life, literate life and decent standard of living.

Inequalities in Health - Class and Gender

Gender inequality refers to unequal treatment or perceptions of individuals based on their gender. Wage discrimination exists when workers are equally qualified and perform the same work but one group of workers is paid more than another. Historically, wage discrimination has favoured men over similarly qualified women. Gender inequality is a result of the persistent discrimination of one group of people based upon gender and it manifests itself differently according to race, culture, politics, country, and economic situation. Gender inequality and discrimination is argued to cause and perpetuate poverty and vulnerability in society as a whole.[26]

Gender inequality in India refers to health, education, economic and political inequalities between men and women in India. Since its independence, India has made significant strides in addressing gender inequalities, especially in the areas of political participation, education, and legal rights. Policies and legal reforms to address gender inequalities have been pursued by the government of India. Men and women have equal rights within marriage under Indian law, with the exception of Muslim men who are allowed to unilaterally divorce their wife.

The dowry system in India contributes to gender inequalities by influencing the perception that girls are a burden on families. While women express a strong preference for having at least one son, the evidence of discrimination against girls after they are born is mixed. A key factor driving gender inequality is the preference for sons, as they are deemed more useful than girls. The causes of gender inequalities are complex, but a number of cultural factors in India can explain how son preference, a key driver of daughter neglect, is so prevalent.[27]

Gender inequality remains a major barrier to human development. Girls and women have made major strides since 1990, but they have not yet gained gender equity. The disadvantages facing women and girls are a major source of inequality.[28] Gender equality is a human right. Women are entitled to live with dignity and with freedom from want and from fear. Gender equality is also a precondition for advancing development and reducing poverty: Empowered women contribute to the health and productivity of whole families and communities, and they improve prospects for the next generation.[29]

Gender inequalities in health have been a major area of sociological research interest since the early 1970s. Gender related social change as reflected in patterns of employment, education, family and household structure, leisure and consumption at the societal level, and in the everyday experience of individual men and women, has been high on the policy agenda and a topic of widespread academic interest among social scientists since the mid-1980s.[30]

Health inequalities have become recently one of the major concerns of European health policy. Observed differences in health status of men and women are also frequently discussed within this framework, and are becoming a subject of growing interest of researchers. Clinical and epidemiological researches document male-female health differences, trying to explain them within bio-medical model.[31] The inequity in health persists from before birth and throughout the life span in both men and women. For instance, low birth weight is a marker for conditions encountered in the womb, and thus for mother's health, which is strongly associated with socioeconomic deprivation.[32]

Human Development Index

The Human Development Index (HDI) is a summary measure of average achievement in key dimensions of human development: a long and healthy life, being knowledgeable and have a decent standard of living. It is the geometric mean of normalised indices for each of the three dimensions. The health dimension is assessed by life expectancy at birth component of the HDI is calculated using a minimum value of 20 years and maximum value of 85 years. The education component of the HDI is measured by mean of years of schooling for adults aged 25 years and expected years of schooling for children of school entering age.[33]

It was developed by Pakistani economist Mahbub ul Haq, is anchored in the Nobel laureate Amartya Sen's work on human capabilities. The origins of the HDI are found in the annual Development Reports of the United Nations Development Programme. These were devised and launched by Pakistani economist Mahbub ul Haq in 1990 and had the explicit purpose "to shift the focus of development economics from national income accounting to people-centred policies".[34]

The HDR covers 187 countries across the world and is published annually by the United Nations Development Programme. In the current report, the top five countries ranked in terms of the HDI are Norway, Australia, Switzerland, Netherlands and the US. The bottom five in this ranking is Niger, Democratic Republic of Congo, Central African Republic, Chad and Sierra Leone. India is ranked at 135, among the 'medium development' countries like Egypt, South Africa, Mongolia, Philippines and Indonesia. Among India's neighbours, Bhutan and Bangladesh too figure in this category. Pakistan (ranked 146) and Nepal (145) are in the 'low development' category, while Sri Lanka (73) is in the 'high development' category.[35]

Gender Development Index

The Gender-related Development Index is an index designed to measure of gender equality. It is defined as a distribution-sensitive measure that accounts for the human development impact of existing gender gaps in the three components of the HDI. The HDI and the GDI were created to rival the more traditional general income-based measures of development such as Gross Domestic Product and Gross National Product.[36]

Gender Empowerment Index

The Gender Empowerment Measure is an index designed to measure of gender equality. It is the United Nations Development Programme's attempt to measure the extent of gender inequality across the globe's countries, based on estimates of women's relative economic income. It is determined using three basic indicators: Proportion of seats held by women in national parliaments, per centage of women in economic decision-making positions (incl. administrative, managerial, professional and technical occupations) and female share of income (earned incomes of males vs. females).

This index, developed by the United Nations Development Programme quantitatively measures the empowerment of women on a country-by-country basis. The index measures gender inequality in three key areas: (a) Power over economic resources based on earned income: (b) access to professional opportunities and participation in economic decision-making; and (c) access to political opportunities and participation in political decision-making.[37]

References

1. Brainy Quote, Available at http://www.brainyquote.com/quotes/topics/topic_health.html
2. http://www.essaywow.com/health-and-fitness-essays/essay-health-fitness-importance-good-health.html
3. *Ibid.*
4. *Ibid.*
5. Health, Available at https://en.wikipedia.org/wiki/Health
6. See http://www.fitness.gov/eat-healthy/why-is-it-important/
7. Health and development, Available at http://www.who.int/hdp/en/
8. Health care, Available at https://en.wikipedia.org/wiki/Health_care
9. From official website of World Health Organisation, Available at http://www.who.int/hia/evidence/doh/en/
10. Environmental factors, Available at http://health.mo.gov/living/environment/
11. Malnutrition, Available at https://en.wikipedia.org/wiki/Malnutrition
12. Malnutrition,Available at http://www.who.int/maternal_child_adolescent/topics/child/malnutrition/en/
13. Olaf Müller, Michael Krawinkel, Malnutrition and health in developing countries, Available at http://files.givewell.org/files/DWDA%202009/Interventions/Muller%20and%20Krawinkel.%202005.% 20Malnutrition%20and%20health%20in%20developing%20countries.pdf
14. Malnutrition in India, Available at https://en.wikipedia.org/wiki/Malnutrition_in_India
15. Malnutrition: The Leading Cause of Immune Deficiency Diseases Worldwide, Available at http://www4.dr-rath-foundation.org/nat_vit/PDF-Files/malnutrition_brochure_screen.pdf

16. Midday Meal Scheme, Available at https://en.wikipedia.org/wiki/Midday_Meal_Scheme
17. From official website of Akshaya Patra (http://www.akshayapatra.org/objectives-of-mdm)
18. Sushma Sharma, Santosh Jain Passi, Salila Thomas, Hema S Gopalan (2006), Evaluation of mid-day meal programme in MCD Schools, Available at http://mdm.nic.in/Files/Initiatives%20&%20Case% 20Studies/NUTRITION_%20FOUNDATION_%20OF_%20 INDIA.pdf
19. Satish Y. Deodhar, Sweta Mahandiratta, K.V. Ramani, Dileep Mavalankar, Sandip Ghosh, and Vincent Braganza, An evaluation of midday meal scheme, Available at http://www.iimahd.ernet.in/~satish/MDMJISPEPaper(2).pdf
20. Mid-Day Meal Scheme, Available at http://www.archive.india.gov.in/sectors/education/index.php?id=7
21. Siddheshwar Shukla, Mid-day meal: Nutrition on Paper, Poor Food on the Plate, Vol - XLIX No. 7, February 15, 2014, http://www.epw.in/special-articles/mid-day-meal.html
22. Meaning of life, Available at https://en.wikipedia.org/wiki/Meaning_ of_life
23. http://www.patheos.com/Library/Christianity/Beliefs/Human-Nature-and-the-Purpose-of-Existence
24. What is the purpose of man, according to the Bible?, Available at http://www.gotquestions.org/purpose-of-man.html
25. The Purpose of Man's Life on earth, Available at http://www.kisol. com/man/purposeoflife.htm
26. Gender Inequality, Available at https://en.wikipedia.org/wiki/Gender_inequality
27. Gender inequality in India, Available at https://en.wikipedia.org/wiki/Gender_inequality_in_India
28. Gender inequality index, Available at http://hdr.undp.org/en/content/gender-inequality-index-gii
29. http://www.unfpa.org/gender-equality
30. Ellen Annandale and Kate Hunt, Gender inequalities in Health, Available at https://www.mheducation.co.uk/openup/chapters/0335203647.pdf
31. See http://www.ncbi.nlm.nih.gov/pubmed/22768415
32. See http://www.diva-portal.org/smash/get/diva2:297883/FULLTEXT01.pdf
33. The Human Development Index, Available at http://hdr.undp.org/en/content/human-development-index-hdi
34. Human Development Index, Available at https://en.wikipedia.org/wiki/Human_Development_Index
35. The Times of India (Jul 24, 2014). India ranks 135 in human development index: UNDP, Available at http://timesofindia. india times.com/india/India-ranks-135-in-human-development-index-UNDP/articleshow/38959685.cms
36. Gender-related Development Index, Available at https://en.wikipedia.org/wiki/Gender-related_Development_Index
37. See http://www.sachet.org.pk/web/page.asp?id=443

Chapter - 11

Disaster Management

WHO defines Disaster as "any occurrence that causes damage, ecological disruption, loss of human life, deterioration of health and health services, on a scale sufficient to warrant an extraordinary response from outside the affected community or area". United Nations (UN) defines a disaster as "a serious disruption of the functioning of society, causing widespread human, material or environmental losses which exceed the capacity of the affected society to cope using only its own resources." Disaster management plans are multi-layered and are aimed to address such issues as floods, hurricanes, fires, bombings and even mass failures of utilities or the rapid spread of disease. Developing countries are becoming increasingly aware of the importance of disaster management systems and increasing efforts are being made to streamline preparedness, response and recovery mechanisms at all levels.

Disaster management has emerged as a serious career option with the potential to take workers to all parts of the world. Meanwhile, as the frequency and intensity of disasters escalates catastrophic disasters continue to threaten the lives of millions. Natural disasters have exacted a heavy human toll on nations throughout the Caribbean and Central America, but Cuba is largely an exception to the rule. Cuba's success in saving lives amidst natural disasters reflects joint efforts of the civil defence, meteorologists and public administrators who assign high priority to the value of human life. Some of those most at risk are the cities of Havana, Nuevitas, Baracoa, Manzanillo, Cienfuegos, and Isle of Youth.

The European Commission has a holistic approach to disaster management; this includes prevention, preparedness, response and rehabilitation. These include training programmes and joint exercises for civil protection experts, cooperation projects and transport co-financing.The European Commission manages the Mechanism through its emergency response centre (the Monitoring and Information Centre).The Treaty of Lisbon set out that "the Union shall encourage co-operation between Member States in order to improve the effectiveness of systems for preventing and protecting against natural or man-made disasters." The European Commission Humanitarian Aid Office promotes disaster preparedness as part of an overall Commission Disaster Prevention and Preparedness approach to reduce vulnerability and exposure of people to risks and disasters as well as the economic costs of such disasters.

The Asia Pacific Alliance for Disaster Management is a trans-national disaster aid alliance that works to facilitate cooperation and understanding between governments, private companies and NGOs in the Asia Pacific region. Bangladesh suffers from natural calamities every now and then. Disasters have a particularly severe impact in Bangladesh. The geographical location, land characteristics, multiplicity of rivers and the monsoon climate render Bangladesh highly vulnerable to natural hazards. It is recognised as a country at high risk of recurring natural and human induced hazards with on average 10 million people affected every year. Frequent floods, cyclones, river bank erosion, water-logging, drought and tornadoes significantly disrupt Bangladesh's economy and the lives and livelihoods of its population.

Types of Disaster

There are four main types of disaster.

- *Natural disasters:* These disasters include floods, hurricanes, earthquakes and volcano eruptions that can have immediate impacts on human health, as well as secondary impacts causing further death and suffering from floods causing landslides, earthquakes resulting in fires, tsunamis causing widespread flooding and typhoons sinking ferries.
- *Environmental emergencies:* These emergencies include technological or industrial accidents, usually involving hazardous material and occur where these materials are produced, used or transported. Large forest fires are generally included in this definition because they tend to be caused by humans.
- *Complex emergencies:* These emergencies involve a break-down of authority, looting and attacks on strategic installations. Complex emergencies include conflict situations and war.
- *Pandemic emergencies:* These emergencies involve a sudden onset of a contagious disease that affects health but also disrupts services and businesses, bringing economic and social costs.

Objectives of Disaster Management

The basic objectives of disaster management are:

- To reduces or avoids morbidity, mortality, and economic and physical damages from a hazard. The methods used to achieve this include hazard and vulnerability analysis, preparedness, mitigation and prevention measures, and the use of predictive and warning systems.

- To reduces personal suffering, such as morbidity and emotional stress following a hazard. The methods used to prevent suffering include hazard and vulnerability analysis, preparedness and mitigation and prevention measures.
- The third objective is to speed recovery. The methods to accomplish this objective include effective response mechanisms and the institution of recovery programmes and assistance. Examples of efforts to speed recovery include providing paperwork assistance for insurance claims and grant or loan applications.

Disaster Management in India

Disasters are sometimes classified according to whether they are "natural" disasters, or "human-made" disasters. India has been traditionally vulnerable to natural disasters on account of its unique geo-climatic conditions. At the central or national level, Ministry of Home affairs is entrusted with the nodal responsibility of managing disaster. At the state level, there are state relief commissioners who are incharge of the relief measures in wake of natural disaster in the perspective states. The chief secretary is the overall in charge of the relief operations in the state.

At the national level, the Ministry of Home Affairs is the nodal Ministry for all matters concerning disaster management. The Central Relief Commissioner in the Ministry of Home Affairs is the nodal officer to coordinate relief operations for natural disasters. It receives information relating to forecasting/warning of a natural calamity from India Meteorological Department or from Central Water Commission of Ministry of Water Resources on a continuing basis. At the State level, response, relief and rehabilitation are handled by Departments of Relief and Rehabilitation. The State Crisis Management Committee set up under the Chairmanship of Chief Secretary who is the highest executive functionary in the State. At the State level, as indicated in para disaster management was being handled by the Departments of Relief and Rehabilitation.

The National Disaster Management Authority, which was conceived as the apex planning and supervising body was found ineffective in its functioning in most of the core areas.The States have been advised to set up their own Specialist Teams for responding to disasters. Ministry of Home Affairs will provide assistance for the training of the State trainers. Many States/UTs have initiated action for setting up of specialised SAR units. Fourteen Regional Response Centres are being set up across the country to enable immediate response to floods, cyclones, earthquakes, landslides etc.

Disaster Management Bill, 2005

A committee was constituted on 11 January 2005 by the Government of India to draft the Disaster Management Bill. The Bill was introduced in the Rajya Sabha on the 11 May, 2005. It was referred to the Parliamentary Standing Committee for examination and report. The report was presented to the GoI on 25th August 2005. Rajya Sabha passed the Bill with amendments on 28 November 2005 and Lok Sabha did so on 12 and 13 December 2005. President of India signed the Bill on the 23 December 2005 and the Bill becomes the National Disaster Management Act. The Disaster Management Act, 2005 provides for the constitution of the following institutions at national, state and district levels.

- *National Disaster Management Authority:* The Authority initially created under an administrative order was notified in 2005 under the Disaster Management Act. The Prime Minister is the chairperson of this Authority. The apex body is responsible for laying down policies, plans and guidelines on Disaster Management.
- *State Disaster Management Authorities:* State Disaster Management Authorities have been set up for laying down policies and plans for disaster management in their respective states and are in the process of becoming operational.
- *District Disaster Management Authorities:* District Disaster Management Authorities have been set up as planning, coordinating and implementing bodies for disaster management and to take all measures in the district in accordance with the guidelines laid down by the National and State Authorities.
- *National Institute of Disaster Management:* The National Centre for Disaster Management, established in 1995 was upgraded to the National Institute of Disaster Management after the transfer of the subject of disaster management to the Ministry of Home Affairs. The main responsibility of the institute is human resource development through development and implementation of human resource plans, capacity building and training, research, documentation and policy advocacy in the field of disaster management. It works in tandem with the District Disaster Management Authorities and Central, State and local governments as well as various other stakeholders to build their capacities towards promoting a culture of prevention and preparedness at all levels.
- *National Disaster Response Force:* Ten battalions of National Disaster Response Force comprising 144 specialised teams trained in various types of natural, man-made and non-natural disasters have been set up. All the battalions are being trained to respond to

natural disasters while four of them are being specially trained for handling radiological, nuclear, biological and chemical disasters.

Disaster Management in Bangladesh

Bangladesh having around 160 millions of people is highly vulnerable to climate change and sea level rise. The geographical location and low-lying characteristics of the country makes it more vulnerable and susceptible to different natural and climate-induced disasters. Bangladesh seems to be the worst victim after Tuvalu due its geographical location and for its geographical incompatibility such as flood zones, fault lines etc.The floods in Bangladesh can be divided roughly in four types: (1) By an increase in the amount of water in rivers, (2) By heavy rain and poor drainage systems, (3) Flash flooding types seen in the mountainous areas, and (4) By high tide. It is forecasted that as much as 30 per cent of the current land area of Bangladesh may be inundated as a result of sea level rise and impeded drainage, notably along the coasts and the riverine tracts inland. A number of devastating cyclones hit Bangladesh's coast in 1797, 1822, 1876, 1897, 1901, 1941, 1960, 1961, 1963, 1965, 1969, 1970, 1985, 1991 and 1996, among which cyclones of 1970 and 1991 caused huge loss of lives and assets.

In Bangladesh south west part of the country was affected by Category 4 Cyclone, Cyclone Sidr, in November 2007.The cyclone Aila, which struck on 25 May 2009, caused enormous loss of properties, infrastructure, social and economic disruption, environmental degradation, etc in the coastal areas.The houses, livestock, assets, crops, etc were washed away by the floodwater. Between 1877 and 1995 Bangladesh was hit by 154 cyclones (including 43 severe cyclonic storms, 43 cyclonic storms, 68 tropical depressions). Since 1995, five severe cyclones hit coast of Bangladesh coast in May 1997, September 1997, May 1998, November 2007 and May 2009. On average, a severe cyclone strikes Bangladesh every three years.

Flood management strategies adopted in the country have continuously evolved over the last 50 years, in three distinct phases of their development, and with mixed experiences. The emphasis was on structural measures through the implementation of some large-scale flood control, drainage and irrigation projects.The Flood Forecasting and Warning System was established in the 1970s and modernised in 1996 and then again as of 2000.The Early Warning System evolved historically in Bangladesh Meteorological Department. Bangladesh Meteorological Department is the source of cyclone warning in Bangladesh. It generates the warning and passes this on to public media and preparedness units for dissemination and follow-up action at periodic intervals.There are three committees and three institutions at the apex level namely, National Disaster Management Council, headed by Prime Minister, Inter Ministerial Disaster Management Committee headed by Minister, Ministry of Food, Disaster Management and Relief (MFDMR), National Disaster

Management Advisory Council, MFDMR, Disaster Management Bureau and Directorate of Relief and Rehabilitation.

The most dedicated agency for cyclone disaster information dissemination and mobilisation at the coastal level is the Cyclone Preparedness Programme. It is a mechanism which relies on technical skills and volunteer's commitment for ensuring that all potential victims of an approaching cyclone are given sufficient warning. The Comprehensive Disaster Management Programme of the Government of Bangladesh is implemented by the Ministry of Food and Disaster Management and is supported by UNDP, DFID-B and the European Commission (EC). It is designed to strengthen Bangladesh Disaster Management System and more specifically to achieve a paradigm shift from reactive response to a proactive risk reduction culture. Disaster Management Programme in partnership with United Kingdom Department for International Development and United Nations Development Programme UNDP. About 53 central government organisations and 13 ministries are identified to be involved in water and different stages of flood management, and a National Water Council was set up to coordinate all the various activities of the Agencies and Departments involved in the water sector.

National government Ministry has been conducting community risk assessment and disaster risk reduction action planning with municipal governments across the country, as a part of the country's Comprehensive Disaster Management Programme. Local governments were encouraged to participate and assume the responsibility through a 'learn through doing' approach. The Government of Bangladesh in coordination with non-government organisations, international organisations and bilateral donors has rapidly responded to the flood emergency and assisted the affected population. Many non-government organisations and the International Federation of Red Cross Red Crescent Societies responded rapidly to coordinate relief efforts.The Ministry of Food and Disaster Management has the mandate to coordinate all disaster management activities within the country and supports three operational elements: Disaster Management Bureau, Directorate of Relief and Rehabilitation, and the Directorate of Food.

United Nations Efforts

UN-HABITAT Disaster Management programme helps governments and local authorities rebuild in countries recovering from war or natural disasters. The right to adequate shelter is central to the mandate of UN-HABITAT and expressed through the campaigns on "Urban Governance" and "Shelter for All" and is even more important when addressing the needs of communities affected by disasters. Shelter is often the primary need in the post-disaster phase, but the delivery of immediate shelter needs must be undertaken within a long-term shelter strategy. The agency is working, or has worked in Afghanistan, Angola, Bangladesh, Burundi, the Caribbean, Central Asia, China,

Guatemala, India, Indonesia, Iran, Iraq, Kenya, Kosovo, Malawi, Mozambique, Nepal, Rwanda, Serbia and Montenegro, Sierra Leone, Somalia, Sri Lanka, Sudan, Timor Leste and Vietnam, and Indian Ocean rim countries hit a giant tsunami wave.

The UN Resident Coordinator is responsible for forming and leading the UN Disaster Management Team in each disaster or emergency prone country. Various United Nations organisations involve in disaster management are:

- The Office for the Coordination of Humanitarian Affairs in collaboration with the Inter-Agency Standing Committee is the arm of the United Nations responsible for bringing together national and international humanitarian providers to ensure a coherent response to emergencies. It also ensures that a framework is in place within which each provider can contribute to the overall response effort. It also advocates for people in need, promotes preparedness and prevention and facilitates sustainable solutions.
- The Food and Agriculture Organisation of the UN provides early warning of impending food crises, and assesses global food supply problems.
- Seagate-3FE2A3\Public\Production The International Organisation for Migration is an intergovernmental agency which helps transfer refugees, internally displaced persons and others in need of internal or international migration services.
- The Office of United Nations High Commissioner for Human Rights provides assistance and advice to governments and other actors on human rights issues, sets standards and monitors rights violations.
- The United Nations Development Programme assists disaster-prone countries in contingency planning and with disaster mitigation, prevention and preparedness measures.
- The United Nations High Commission for Refugees provides international protection and assistance for refugees, stateless persons and internally displaced persons, particularly in conflict-related emergencies.
- The United Nations Children's Emergency Fund works to uphold children's rights, survival, development and protection by intervening in health, education, water, sanitation, hygiene and protection.
- The World Food Programme is the principle supplier of relief food aid.

Bibliography

Books/Manuscripts

- Alfred Endres (2011), Environmental Economics: Theory and Policy, Cambridge University Press.
- Barry C. Field (1994), Environmental economics: an introduction, Edition 5, McGraw-Hill.
- Barry C. Field (2008), Natural Resource Economics: An Introduction, Second Edition, Waveland Press.
- Charles D. Kolstad (2000). Environmental Economics, Volume 1, Oxford University Press.
- Gareth Edwards-Jones, Ben Davies, Salman S. Hussain (2000), Ecological Economics: An Introduction, Wiley.
- Herman E. Daly (1999), Ecological Economics and the Ecology of Economics: Essays in Criticism, Edward Elgar.
- Herman E. Daly and Joshua Farley (2011), Ecological Economics, Second Edition: Principles and Applications, Island Press.
- Herman E. Daly, Joshua Farley (2004), Ecological Economics: Principles and Applications, Island Press.
- Jon M. Conrad (2010), Resource Economics, Cambridge University Press.
- Jon M. Conrad, Colin Whitcomb Clark (1987), Natural Resource Economics: Notes and Problems, Cambridge University Press.
- Joshua Farley, Herman E. Daly, Jon D. Erickson (2005), Ecological Economics: A Workbook for Problem-based Learning, Island Press.
- Karl-Goran Maler, Jeffrey R.Vincent (2003), Handbook of Environmental Economics: Environmental Degradation and Institutional Responses, Elsevier.
- Michael S. Common (2009), Environmental and Resource Economics: An Introduction, Edition 2, Longman.
- Mohan Munasinghe (1993), Environmental Economics and Sustainable Development, World Bank Publications.
- Philip A. Neher (1990), Natural Resource Economics, Cambridge University Press.

- Ralf Eriksson, Jan Otto Andersson (2010), Elements of Ecological Economics, Routledge.
- Roger Perman (2010), Natural Resource and Environmental Economics, Pearson Education.
- Roger Perman, Yue Ma, Michael Common, David Maddison, James McGilvray (2011), Natural Resource and Environmental Economics, Edition 4, Pearson Addison Wesley.
- Steven C. Hackett (2010), Environmental and Natural Resources Economics: Theory, Policy, and the Sustainable Society, M.E. Sharpe.
- Tony Prato (1999), Natural Resource and Environmental Economics, Wiley.
- Vincent Kerry Smith, John V. Krutilla (1982), Explorations in Natural Resource Economics, Resources for the Future.

Websites

- Allemand, D. (2016). Coral reefs and climate change, p. 34.
- Amarapurkar, D., Madan, K., and Kapoor, D. (2015). Management of Chronic Hepatitis B Infection in India, Journal of the Association of Physicians of India, 63, p. 43.
- Anand, A. and Puri, P. (2015), Indian Guidelines and Protocols: Hepatitis B, Retrieved from http://www.apiindia.org/medicine_update_2013/chap53.pdf
- Andhra Pradesh Power Generation Corporation Limited, Available at https://en.wikipedia.org/wiki/Andhra_Pradesh_Power_Generation_Corporation
- Anthony, K. (2011). Ocean acidification and warming will lower coral reef resilience, Global Change Biology, 17, p. 1798.
- Astif, M. (2013). A Review on Spermicidal Activities of Azadirachta indica, Journal of Pharmacognosy and Phytochemistry, 1 (5), pp.61-62.
- Biswas, K. (2002). Biological activities and medicinal properties of neem, Current Science, 82 (11), p.1336.
- Buddemeier, R. (2004). Potential Contributions of Climate Change to Stresses on Coral Reef Ecosystems, p. 3.
- Chaturvedi, R., Razdan, M., and Bhojwani, S. (2004). In vitro clonal propagation of an adult tree of neem (Azadirachta indica A. Juss.) by forced axillary branching, Plant Science 166, pp. 501-506.
- Chaurasia, A. (2016). Neem in Oral Diseases - An Update, Journal of Oral Medicine, Oral Surgery, Oral Pathology and Oral Radiology, 2 (1), p. 1.

- Coles, S. (2008). Potential Climate Change Impacts on Corals and Coral Reefs in Melanesia from Bleaching Events and Ocean Acidification, Bishop Museum Technical Report 42(5), p. 3.
- Control of soil pollution, Available at https://www.classle.net/book/control-soil-pollution
- Coral Reefs in Hot Water (2015), Coral Reefs and Global Warming, p.1.
- Damodar Valley Corporation, Available at https://en.wikipedia.org/wiki/Damodar_Valley_Corporation
- Diaz-Pulido, G. (2015). Vulnerability of macroalgae of the Great Barrier Reef to climate change, p.154.
- Done, T. (2003). Global Climate Change and Coral Bleaching on the Great Barrier Reef, p. 2.
- Drabu, S., Khatri, S., & Babu, S. (2012). Neem: Healer of All Ailments, Research Journal of Pharmaceutical, Biological and Chemical Sciences, 3 (1), pp. 121-122.
- Dubey, S. and Kashyap, P. (2014). Azadirachta indica: A Plant with Versatile Potential, RGUHS- Journal of Pharmaceutical Science, 4 (2), p. 45.
- Economics Teacher, Economic growth and development, Available at http://ecoarticles.blogspot.in/2012/05/economic-growth-and-development.html
- Economics Teacher, Pareto optimality, Available at http://ecoarticles.blogspot.in/2012/05/pareto-optimality.html
- Eric W. Brown (1988), An Introduction to Solar Energy, Available at http://www.ccs.neu.edu/home/feneric/Papers/solar.pdf
- Fabricius, K. (2012). Vulnerability of coral reefs of the Great Barrier Reef to climate change, p.1.
- Girish, K. and Bhat, S. (2008). Phomopsis azadirachtae – The Die-Back of Neem Pathogen, Electronic Journal of Biology, 4 (3), p.112.
- Guldberg, H. and Guldberg, H. (2008). The impact of climate change and ocean acidification on the Great Barrier Reef and its tourist industry, Garnaut Climate Change Review, p.7.
- Guldberg, O. (2007). Coral Reefs under Rapid Climate Change and Ocean Acidification, Science, Volume: 318, p. 1737.
- Guldberg, O. (2011). Coral reef ecosystems and anthropogenic climate change, Reg Environ Change, 11, p. 215.
- Hepatitis B (2016), Retrieved from https://en.wikipedia.org/wiki/Hepatitis_B
- Hepatitis B (2016), World Health Organisation, Retrieved from http://www.who.int/mediacentre/factsheets/fs204/en/

- Hepatitis B Guide (2016), Topic overview, Retrieved from http://www.webmd.com/hepatitis/hepb-guide/hepatitis-b-topic-overview#1
- Hepatitis B Treatment (2016), Retrieved from https://www.hepmag.com/basics/hepatitis-b-basics/hepatitis-b-treatment
- Hepatitis B virus (2017). Retrieved from https://en.wikipedia.org/wiki/Hepatitis_B_virus
- HIV and Hepatitis B (2016), Retrieved from https://www.poz.com/basics/hiv-basics/hiv-hepatitis-b-hbv
- Hoey, A. (2016). Recent Advances in Understanding the Effects of Climate Change on Coral Reefs, Diversity, 8 (12), p. 3.
- http://economics.fundamentalfinance.com/positive-externality.php
- http://www.economicshelp.org/blog/glossary/externalities/
- http://www.economicsonline.co.uk/Market_failures/Positive_externalities.html
- http://www.kacee.org/what-environmental-education-0
- Idso, C. (2009). CO_2 global warming and coral reefs: Prospects for the future, Center for the Study of Carbon Dioxide and Global Change & Science and Public Policy Institute, p.10.
- Jones, N., Ridgwel, A., and Hendy, E. (2015). Evaluation of coral reef carbonate production models at a global scale, Biogeosciences, 12, p. 1339.
- Kaur, R. (2015). Ethnobotanical studies of some of the traditionally important medicinal plants of Punjab (India), International Journal of Current Research and Academic Review, 3 (5), p. 262.
- Kleypas, J. and Guldberg, O. (2005). Coral Reefs and Climate Change: Susceptibility and Consequences, Status of Coral Reefs in the Caribbean after Bleaching and Hurricanes of 2005, p. 19.
- Liang, T. (2010). Hepatitis B: The Virus and Disease, Hapatology, 49 (5), p. 13.
- Lokanadhan, S., Muthukrishnan, P., and Jeyaraman, S. (2012). Neem products and their agricultural applications, JBiopest, 5 (Supplementary), pp.72-76.
- Maithani, A. (2011). Azadirachta indica (Neem) leaf: a review, Journal of Pharmacy Research, 4 (6), p. 1824.
- Malhotra, P. (2015). Epidemiological Profile of Hepatitis C Patients at India's New Hub –Haryana, Advance Research Gastroentero Hepato, 1(1), p. 01.
- Mathur, P. and Arora, N. (2008). Epidemiological transition of hepatitis A in India: Issues for vaccination in developing countries, Indian Journal of Medical Research, 128, p. 699.

- Mayo Clinic Staff (2016). Diseases and conditions of Hepatitis B, Retrieved from http://www.mayoclinic.org/diseases-conditions/hepatitis-b/basics/definition/con-20022210
- Mineard, K. (2010). Neem tree assessment for socioeconomic empowerment in rural Burkina Faso, p. 2.
- Mishra, G. (2012). Neem, the wonder tree, under attack: a new major pest, Current Science, 102 (7), p. 969.
- Mondal, E. and Chakraborty, K. (2016). Azadirachta indica - A Tree with Multifaceted Applications: An Overview, Journal of Pharmaceutical Science and Research, Vol. 8(5), p. 299.
- Mulla, M. and Tianyun, T. (1999). Activity and biological effects of neem products against arthropods of medical and veterinary importance, Journal of the American Mosquito Control Association, 15 (2), p.133.
- National Hydroelectric Power Corporation, Available at https://en.wikipedia.org/wiki/NHPC_Limited
- Nettleman, M. (2016). Hepatitis B, http://www.medicinenet.com/hepatitis_b/article.htm
- NTPC Limited, Available at https://en.wikipedia.org/wiki/NTPC_Limited
- Nuclear Power Corporation of India Limited, Available at https://en.wikipedia.org/wiki/Nuclear_Power_Corporation_of_India
- Pandey, G., Verma, K., and Singh, M. (2014). Evaluation of phytochemical, antibacterial and free radical scavenging properties of azadirachta indica (neem) leaves, International Journal of Pharmacy and Pharmaceutical Sciences, 6 (2), p. 444.
- Pandolfi, J. and Kiessling, W. (2014). Gaining insights from past reefs to inform understanding of coral reef response to global climate change, Current Opinion in Environmental Sustainability, 7, p. 52.
- Pandolfi, J., Connolly, S., Marshall, D., and Cohen, A. (2011). Projecting Coral Reef Futures under Global Warming and Ocean Acidification, Science, Vol. 333, p. 418.
- Patil, P. (2013). Antidiabetic Activity of Alcoholic Extract of Neem (Azadirachta Indica) Root Bark, National Journal of Physiology, Pharmacy and Pharmacology, 3 (2), p. 142.
- Peevor, S. and Carey, J. (2014). Effects of sea water rise on coral reefs, Climate change, Human systems and Policy, Volume-II, p. 2.
- Power Finance Corporation, Available at https://en.wikipedia.org/wiki/Power_Finance_Corporation
- Prashanth, G. and Krishnaia, G. (2014). Chemical composition of the leaves of Azadirachta Indica Linn, p. 22.

- Puja Mondal, Soil pollution controlling technologies, Available at http://www.yourarticlelibrary.com/essay/soil-pollution-control-technologies/27482/
- Pyrsopoulos, N. (2016). Hepatitis B Treatment and Management, Retrieved from http://emedicine.medscape.com/article/177632-treatment
- Pyrsopoulos, N. (2016). Hepatitis B, http://emedicine.medscape.com/article/177632-overview
- Rao, N., Patil, A., Patil, S., and Rani, S. (2007). Hepatitis a vaccination in chronic liver disease: is it really required in a tropical country like india?, Indian Journal of Medical Microbiology, 25 (2), p.137.
- Riegl, B. (2003). Climate change and coral reefs: different effects in two high-latitude areas (Arabian Gulf, South Africa), Coral Reefs, 22, p. 434.
- Riegl, B. (2009). Coral Reefs: Threats and Conservation in an Era of Global Change, The Year in Ecology and Conservation Biology, p. 136.
- Rizvi, M. (2011). Leptospirosis: an emerging disease in cryptogenic hepatitis patients in north India, Biology and Medicine, 3 (2), p.98.
- Scheibner, C. and Speijer, R. (2008). Decline of coral reefs during late Paleocene to early Eocene global warming, p.19.
- Shanmugapriyan, R. and Dhanalakshmi, V. (2015). Biological effects of neem on the pupation of Henosepilachna vigintioctopunctata Fab. On bittergourd, Journal of Entomology and Zoology Studies, 3 (1), p.78.
- Soil pollution - Types, effects, sources and control of soil pollution, Available at http://mjcetenvsci.blogspot.in/2013/11/soil-pollution-types-effects-sources.html
- Solar, Available at http://www.need.org/Files/curriculum/infobook/SolarI.pdf
- Tamil Nadu Electricity Board, Available at https://en.wikipedia.org/wiki/TNEB
- Tandon, B., Acharya, S., and Tandon, A. (1996). Epidemiology of hepatitis B virus infection in India, Gut, 36, p. 56.
- Telangana Power Generation Corporation Limited, Available at https://en.wikipedia.org/wiki/Telangana_Power_Generation_Corporation
- Treatment for hepatitis B (2016), Retrieved from http://www.hepatitisaustralia.com/hepatitis-b-facts/treatment-for-hep-b
- Tripathi, A. and Bhatnagar, M. (2014). Physico-Chemical Study of Foliar Chemicals of Neem (Azadirachta Indica A. Juss) in Different

Seasons, around Amarkantak Thermal Power Plant, Chachai (Madhya Pradesh) India, International Journal of Science and Research, 3 (11), pp. 119-120.

- Valenzuela, S. (2007). Neem Tree Morphology and Oil Content, Reprinted from: Issues in new crops and new uses, p. 126.
- Viral Hepatitis (2016). Retrieved from https://www.cdc.gov/hepatitis/hbv/
- What is HBV (2015), http://biology.kenyon.edu/slonc/bio38/scuderi/parti.html
- What is soil pollution? Available at http://www.thebigger.com/biology/pollution/what-is-soil-pollution/
- Wilkinson, C. and Buddemeier, R. (1994). Global Climate Change and Coral Reefs: Implications for People and Reefs, p. 8.
- A.K.M. Sadrul Islam and Mazharul Islam (2005). Status of Renewable Energy Technologies in Bangladesh, Detailed available at http://www.isesco.org.ma/ISESCO_Technology_Vision/NUM01/A.K.M.%20Sadrul%20Islam/A.K.M.%20Sadrul%20Islam.pdf
- A.N.H. Akhtar Hossain. Flood Management, Detailed available http://www.apfm.info/pdf/case_studies/bangladesh.pdf
- Australia leads advances in disaster managemen (2013), Retrieved from http://app.griffith.edu.au/news/2013/01/02/australia-leads-advances-in-disaster-management/
- A.N.H. Akhtar Hossain. Flood Management, Detailed available http://www.apfm.info/pdf/case_studies/bangladesh.pdf
- Aftershocks: Natural Disaster Risk and Economic Development Policy (2005), Detailed available at http://www.odi.org.uk/resources/docs/2596.pdf
- Bangladesh: 2004 Flood, Response, Damage and Recovery Needs, Detailed available at http://www.adb.org/Documents/Economic_Updates/BAN/2004/eco-update-ban.pdf
- Alexandra Matthews (2009), Bangladesh's Climate Change Emergency, Detailed available at http://csis.org/files/publication/sam_136.pdf
- Annex 6: Size doesn't matter: Why the same-sized cyclone had different impacts in Bangladesh and Burma, Detailed available at http://www.ausaid.gov.au/hottopics/pdf/AIDRF_Feasibility_Study_Report_annex6-10.pdf
- Asia Pacific Allibance (2013), Retrieved from http://apadm.org/activity/

- B. E. Aguirre and Joseph E Trainor, Emergency Management in Cuba: Disasters Experienced, Lessons Learned, and Recommendations for the Future.
- Business Standard (April 11, 2013), India, Russia to cooperate in disaster management, Retrieved from http://www.business-standard.com/article/pti-stories/india-russia-to-cooperate-in-disaster-management-113041100446_1.html
- Bishnu Pandey and Kenji Okazaki, Community Based Disaster Management: Empowering Communities to Cope with Disaster Risks, Detailed available at http://unpan1.un.org/intradoc/groups/public/documents/un/unpan020698.pdf
- Bangladesh's Comprehensive Approach to Disaster Management: World Resources Report Case Study, Detailed available at http://www.worldresourcesreport.org/case-studies/bangladeshs-comprehensive-approach-disaster-management
- Bernhard G. Gunter, Atiq Rahman and A. F. M. Ataur Rahman (2008), How Vulnerable are Bangladesh's Indigenous People to Climate Change? Detailed available at http://papers.ssrn.com/sol3/papers.cfm?abstract_id=1126441
- Climate Change Impact and Disaster Vulnerability in the Coastal Areas of Bangladesh, Detailed available at http://www.unisdr.org/files/4032_DisasterBD.pdf
- Cyclone Sidr in Bangladesh: Damage, Loss and Needs Assessment For Disaster Recovery and Reconstruction, Detailed available at Cyclone Sidr in Bangladesh: Damage, Loss and Needs Assessment For Disaster Recovery and Reconstruction, Detailed available at http://www.recoveryplatform.org/outfile.php?id=91&href=http://www.recoveryplatform.org/assets/publication/Cyclone_Sidr_in_Bangladesh.pdf
- Climate Change Impacts and Responses in Bangladesh (2009), http://www.mrfcj.org/news/2011/climate_justice_needed_ in_ bangladesh.html? gclid=CMesjamQ0q0CFcEc6wodsHXykw
- Cyclone Preparedness Programme (CPP) Bangladesh Red Crescent Society, Detailed available at http://www.adrc.asia/publications/TDRM2005/TDRM_Good_Practices/PDF/PDF-2005e/Chapter3_3.1.2-1.pdf
- Charlotte Benson and Edward Clay (2002), Bangladesh: Disasters and Public Finance, Detailed available at http://books.google.co.in/books/about/Bangladesh_disasters_and_public_finance.html?id=DMDZHAAACAAJ&redir_esc=y
- Cyclone Preparedness Programme (CPP) Bangladesh Red Crescent Society, Detailed available at http://www.adrc.asia/publications/

TDRM2005/TDRM_Good_Practices/PDF/PDF-2005e/Chapter3_3.1.2-1.pdf

- Cooperation in disaster management: the European Union and the United States take a major step forward (2011), Retrieved from http://europa.eu/rapid/press-release_IP-11-1365_en.htm
- Chapter 1 Disaster management: An introductory, Retrieved from http://mizoramdmr.nic.in/ATISchoolSafety/Chap1.pdf
- Comprehensive Disaster Management Program (CDMP), Bangladesh (2011), Detailed available at http://www.nset.org.np/nset/html/IK2011/29_CDMP%20Bangladesh.pdf
- Carlie Lawson (2013), The Objectives of Disaster Management, Retrieved from http://www.ehow.com/list_6788890_objectives-disaster-management.html
- Diaster, Nagaland Board of Secondary Education, Retrieved from http://www.nbsenagaland.com/disaster_management.htm
- Disaster Management in India. Retrieved from http://www.unisdr.org/2005/mdgs-drr/national-reports/India-report.pdf
- Disaster management authority not ready for calamities – CAG (2013), Retrieved from http://in.reuters.com/article/2013/04/24/india-disaster-management-audit-cag-idINDEE93N0F420130424
- Disaster management in India: A status report, Government of India, Home affairs, Retrieved from http://www.ndmindia.nic.in/eqprojects/disaster%20management%20in%20india%20-%20a%20status%20report%20-%20august%202004.pdf
- Disaster Risk Management For Coastal Tourism Destinations Responding to Climate Change: A Practical Guide for Decision makers (2008), Detailed available at http://www.unep.fr/shared/publications/pdf/DTIx1048xPA-DisasterRiskManagementforCoastalTourism.pdf
- Dulal Chandra Roy, Vulnerability and population displacements due to climate-induced disasters in coastal Bangladesh, Detailed available at http://www.iisd.ca/download/pdf/sd/ymbvol141num2e.pdf
- Disaster Management in Bangladesh, UNOPS, Detailed available at http://www.unops.org/SiteCollectionDocuments/Factsheets/English/Success%20Stories/GBL_PJFS_CDMP_EN.pdf
- Dulal Chandra Roy, Vulnerability and population displacements due to climate-induced disasters in coastal Bangladesh, Detailed available at http://www.ehs.unu.edu/file/get/5410
- Disaster Management (2013), Retrieved from http://www.studymode.com/essays/Disaster-Management-705538.html

- Disaster Management: Goals and Activities, Retrieved from http://www.uncrd.or.jp/disaster/goal.htm
- Disaster Management (2013), Retrieved from http://www.undp.org.cn/modules.php?op=modload&name=News&file= article&catid= 10&sid=44434
- Disaster Management Bureau Strategic Plan 2005-2006, Turning Strategic in Action, Detailed available at http://unpan1.un.org/intradoc/groups/public/documents/apcity/unpan029418.pdf
- Disaster Management in India (2013), Retrieved from http://www.undp.org/content/india/en/home/library/crisis_prevention_and_recovery/disaster-management-in-india/
- Displaced Populations in Post-Disaster Reconstruction and Rehabilitation (2013), Retrieved from http://www.unhabitat.org/content.asp?typeid=19&catid=286&cid=868
- Dnyanesh Kumar (2013), Short easy on the concept of disaster management in India, Retrieved from http://www.preservearticles.com/2011092714226/short-essay-on-the-concept-of-disaster-management-in-india.html
- Diaster risk management, Retrieved from http://www.adb.org/themes/governance/disaster-risk-management
- Daya Kaul, Md. Ayaz , Lohitkumar S N (2013), Disaster Management In India, Retrieved from http://unpan1.un.org/intradoc/groups/public/documents/apcity/unpan050292.pdf
- Disaster Management (2013), Retrieved from http://www. iwawaterwiki .org/xwiki/bin/view/Articles/DisasterManagement
- Disaster (2013), Retrieved from http://en.wikipedia.org/wiki/Disaster
- Dulal Chandra Roy (2011), Vulnerability and Population Displacements due to Climate-induced Disasters in Coastal Bangladesh, Michelle Leighton, Xiaomeng Shen, and Koko Warner (Eds), Climate Change and Migration: Rethinking Policies for Adaptation and Disaster Risk Reduction, Detailed available athttp://www.ehs.unu.edu/file/get/8468
- Disaster Management in Bangladesh, UNOPS, Detailed available at http://www.unops.org/SiteCollectionDocuments/Factsheets/English/Success%20Stories/GBL_PJFS_CDMP_EN.pdf
- Disaster Management in India-A Status Report (2004), Government of India, Ministry of Home Affairs, National Disaster Management Division, Detailed available at http://www.ndmindia. nic.in/eqprojects/disaster%20management%20in%20india%20-%20a%20status%20report%20-%20august%202004.pdf

- Emergency and Humanitarian Action: Country Report, Detailed available at http://pacificdisastermanagement.kemlu.go.id/Documents/Timor_Leste/Emergency%20Humanitarian%20Action_%20Country%20Report_%20Timor-Leste.pdf
- Earthquake and tsunami in Japan (2013), Retrieved from http://www.ifrc.org/what-we-do/disaster-management/responding/ongoing-operations/japan-earthquake/
- Engendering Disaster Management: A Review of Policy and Practice in Africa, Detailed available at http://www.unhabitat.org/downloads/docs/1270_1921_RGR.pdf
- Environmental Management and Disaster Preparedness: Building a multi-stakeholder partnership, Detailed available at http://www.unep.or.jp/ietc/Publications/DM/wcdr_session_report.pdf
- Final Climate Management Plan (2009), Detailed available at http://www.ambdhaka.um.dk/NR/rdonlyres/3F63B483-5CB5-4654-8020-6D34CB103CF3/0/FINALClimateManagementPlan_Agriculture.pdf
- Factor Analysis of Water-related Disasters in Bangladesh (2007), Detailed available at http://www.icharm.pwri.go.jp/publication/pdf/pdf_0706/bang_e.pdf
- Farid Uddin Ahmed (2000), System and National level experiences for protecting traditional knowledge, Innovations and Protections: Experience of Bangladesh, Detailed available at http://www.unctad.org/trade_env/docs/banglad.pdf
- Fahmida Aktar (2005), Disaster Management in Bangladesh: Role of NGOs, Detailed available at http://drtmc-du.org/userfiles/file/Thesis/Disaster%20Managment%20NGO.pdf
- Flood disasters: Learning from previous relief and recovery operations, Detailed available at http://sheltercentre.org/library/flood-disasters-learning-previous-relief-and-recovery-operations
- Gender Issues in Disaster and Post Conflict Situations (2013), Retrieved from http://www.unhabitat.org/content.asp?typeid=19&catid=286&cid=872
- Government of the People's Republic of Bangladesh Ministry of Food and Disaster Management (2004), Comprehensive Disaster Management Programme, Detailed available at http://reliefweb.int/sites/reliefweb. vint/files/resources/23BEBA005CC4A F394925772-7000773AE-Full_Report.pdf
- Global Platform for Disaster Risk Reduction Bulletin: A Summary Report of the Second Session of the Global Platform for Disaster Risk Reduction, Published by the International Institute for Sustainable Development, Volume 141, Number 2, Monday, 22 June 2009, Detailed

available at http://www.iisd.ca/download/pdf/sd/ymbvol141num2e.pdf

- Holly Sims and Kevin Vogelmann (2002), Popular mobilisation and disaster management in Cuba, Retrieved from http://www.centerforurbanstudies.com/documents/electronic_library/cuba/disaster/disasterpreparation.pdf
- Integrated Floodplain Management: How can we save fish from being over fished in Bangladesh floodplains?(2007), Detailed available at http://www.capri.cgiar.org/pdf/capriwp57.pdf
- Information on Disaster Risk Reduction of the Member Countries (2013), Retrieved from http://www.adrc.asia/nationinformation.php?NationCode=392&Lang..
- Introduction to Disaster Management, Virtual University for the Small States of the Commonwealth (VUSSC), Commonwealth of Learning (COL), Detailed available at http://www.col.org/resources/crsMaterials/VUSSCcrsMat/Pages/default.aspx
- International Forum on Tornado Disaster Risk Reduction for Bangladesh ? To Cope with Neglected Severe Disasters ? 13-14 December 2009, Dhaka, Bangladesh, Detailed available at http://www.preventionweb.net/files/11180_ForumTordanoBangladesh.pdf
- Jeff Dayton-Johnson (2004), Natural Disasters and Adoptive Capacity, Detailed available at http://www.oecd.org/dataoecd/30/63/33845215.pdf
- K. Selvavinayagam, Disaster management practices using ArcGIS, ArcIMS, Detailed available at http://www.articlesbase.com/science-articles/disaster-management-practices-using-arcgis-arcims-arcsde-and-sql-403946.html
- Lisa Schipper and Mark Pelling, Disaster risk, climate change and international development: scope for, and challenges to, integration, Detailed available at http://onlinelibrary.wiley.com/doi/10.1111/j.1467-9523.2006.00304.x/abstract
- Lolita Bildan (2013), Disaster Management in South East Asia - an overview, Retrieved from http://www.icimod.org/?opg=949&q=drr_document&document=1113
- Latin America and the Caribbean (2013), Retrieved from http://www.redcross.org/what-we-do/international-services/where-we-help/latin-america-caribbean
- Mahbub Robbani, Salah Uddit Siddiquee, Sourovi Zaman, and Hiroshi Nakamura (2007), Agriculture in Bangladesh: Recent Trend and Agro environment towards Sustainability, Journal of Faculty of

Agriculture, Shinshu University, Vol. 43, No. 1, Detailed available at http://www. undp.org.bd/projects/proj_detail.php?pid=29

- Md. Safiuddin and Md. Masud Karim, Groundwater Arsenic Contamination in Bangladesh: Causes, Effects and Remediation, Detailed available at http://www.eng-consult.com/pub/ArsenicIEB.pdf
- M. Jahangir Alam Chowdhury (2011), Social Cohesion and Natural Disaster Loss Recovery of Households: Experience from Bangladesh, Detailed available at http://www.oecd.org/dataoecd/59/25/46880436.pdf
- M.V.K. Sivakumar, Natural Disasters and Their Mitigation for Sustainable Agricultural Development, Detailed available at http://www.johannesburgsummit.org/html/documents/backgrounddocs/unisdr%20report.pdf
- Ms. Salma Rahman and Mr. Shahid Mallick, Community, Disability and Response to Disaster Mitigation in Bangladesh, Detailed available at http://www.publicsphereproject.org/events/diac08/proceedings/16.Disaster_Mitigation.Rahman_and_Mallick.pdf
- Madhavi Ariyabandu, Women: the risk managers in natural disasters, Detailed available at http://www.ssri.hawaii.edu/research/GDWwebsite/pdf/Ariyabandu.pdf
- Ministry of Home Affairs, GoI (2013), State level Programmes for strengthening disaster management in India, Retrieved from http://ndmindia.nic.in/DM-Booklet-080211.pdf
- Moving closer to more effective disaster management in Europe. See http://europa.eu/rapid/press-release_MEMO-11-927_en.htm
- Ms. Arjumand Habib, Early Warning System for Severe Thunder Storms in Bangladesh, Detailed available at http://www.iawe.org/WRDRR_Bangladesh/Preprints/S4BMD.pdf
- National Plan for Disaster Management 2008-2015, Detailed available athttp://www.preventionweb.net/files/9472_NationalPlanforDisastermanagement.pdf
- Organisations involved in disaster management (2013), Retrieved from http://www.wcpt.org/node/36994
- Peter Tatham, Karen Spens and Richard Oloruntoba (2009), Cyclones in Bangladesh: A Case Study of a Whole Country Response to Rapid onset Disasters, Detailed Available at http://nova.newcastle.edu.au/vital/access/manager/Repository/uon:9024
- Prabal Barua1, Md. Shah Nawaz Chowdhury and Subrata Sarker, Climate Change and Its risk reduction by mangrove Ecosystem of Bangladesh, Volume 4, Issue 3, pp. 208-225, September - October,

2010, Detailed available at http://www.bdresearchpublications.com/admin/journal/upload/09168/09168.pdf

- Professor M Alimullah Miyan, Cyclone Disaster Mitigation in Bangladesh, Detailed available at http://www.fao.org/forestry/11285-03611be0ad43d80eefb3de4a8ee2e1fd0.pdf
- P.G. Dhar Chakrabarti (2013), Challenges of Disaster Management in India: Implications for the Economic, Political, and Security Environments, Retrieved from http://www.nbr.org/publications/element.aspx?id=549#.UZ8l9VKDH3Y
- Quazi Shahabuddin and Zulfiqar Ali (2006), Natural Disasters, Risks, Vulnerability and Persistence of Poverty: An Analysis of Household Level Data, Detailed available at http://www.chronicpoverty.org/publications/details/natural-disasters-risks-vulnerability-and-persistence-of-poverty-an-analysis-of-household-level-data
- Russia, China to set up regional disaster management center (2008), Retrieved from http://en.rian.ru/russia/20080523/108181773.html
- Risk reduction and emergency preparedness: WHO six-year strategy for the health sector and community capacity development (2007), World Health Organisation, Detailed available at http://www.who.int/hac/techguidance/preparedness/emergency_preparedness_eng.pdf
- Rehabilitation and Reconstruction, Disaster Management Training Programme, Detailed available at http://ocha.unog.ch/drptoolkit/PreparednessTools/Coordination/role%20and%20responsibilities%20of%20UNDMT.pdf
- Risk and Disaster Management: Overview (2013), Retrieved from http://www.unhabitat.org/content.asp?cid=2711&catid=286&typeid=24&subMenuId=0
- Responding to the Earthquake and Tsunami (2013), Retrieved from http://www.redcross.org/what-we-do/international-services/where-we-help/asia/japan
- Sheo Nandan Pandey (2013), The Chinese Disaster Management Mechanism, Retrieved from http://idsa.in/system/files/jds_6_1_NandanPandey.pdf
- Salek M. Seraj, Disaster Management in Metropolitan Dhaka, Detailed available at http://desastres.usac.edu.gt/documentos/pdf/eng/doc5838/doc5838.pdf
- Shardul Agrawala, Tomoko Ota, Ahsan Uddin Ahmed, Joel Smith and Maarten van Aalst (2003), Development and Climate Change in Bangladesh: Focus on Coastal Flooding and The Sundarbans, Detailed available at http://www.oecd.org/dataoecd/46/55/21055658.pdf

- Susmita Dasgupta, Mainul Huq, Zahirul Huq Khan, Manjur Murshed Zahid Ahmed, Nandan Mukherjee, Malik Fida Khan and Kiran Pandey (2010), Vulnerability of Bangladesh to Cyclones in a Changing Climate: Potential Damages and Adaptation Cost, Detailed available at http://papers.ssrn.com/sol3/papers.cfm?abstract_id=1596490
- Suvit Yodmani (2001), Disaster Risk Management and Vulnerability Reduction: Protecting the Poor, Detailed available at http://www.adb.org/poverty/forum/pdf/Yodmani.pdf
- Strategic Priorities of Digital Bangladesh, Section 4.5: Disaster Management, Environment and Climate Change, Detailed available at http://geoportal.icimod.org/symposium2010/PPT/Theme-VI/Shahidul%20Islam.pdf
- Sirajur Rahman Khan, Cyclone Hazard in Bangladesh, Detailed available at http://www.adpc.net/casita/case_studies/coastal%20hazard%20assessment/modelling%20cyclone% 20hazard%20in%20bangladesh/background_information_on_the_ storm_surge_modelling.pdf
- The Hindu (June 30, 2011), Russia for sharing its experience in disaster management, Retrieved from http://www thehindu.com/news/national/russia-for-sharing-its-experience-in-disaster-management/article2148007.ece
- The United Nations Disaster Management Team (UNDMT) India, Retrieved from http://www.un.org.in/_layouts/CMS/undmt.aspx
- The Disaster Management and Resiliency in the Asia Pacific Journalism Fellowship, Retrieved from http://www.eastwestcenter.org/seminars-and-journalism-fellowships/journalism-fellowships/disaster-management-and-resiliency
- Uthpal Kumar, Mohammed Abdul Baten, Abdullah-Al-Masud, Khandakar Showkat Osman, and M. Mizanur Rahman (2010), Cyclone Aila: One Year on Natural Disaster to Human Sufferings, Detailed available at http://www.unnayan.org/reports/climate/ailareport_final.pdf

Index

N